Reader's Notebook
Teacher's Edition

Grade 3

D1210885

HOUGHTON MIFFLIN HARCOURT
School Publishers

Printed in the United States

ISBN   978-0-544-59270-4

7 8 9 10   0690   21 20 19 18 17 16

4500623692   A B C D E F G

Contents

Volume 1

Volume 2

Contents

Name _____ Date _____

Words with Short Vowels

Read each word. Then find and circle it in the Word Find. Words can go across or down. (8 points)

gentle	empty	visit	lily
softly	glance	puppy	tumble

```
s  o  v  t  l  y  u  s  o
p  v  i  s  i  t  s  o  y
u  i  l  o  g  u  f  f  s
p  s  y  f  e  m  p  t  y
p  g  l  a  n  c  e  l  t
y  i  e  t  u  m  y  o
p  u  m  i  l  e  s
t  u  y  p  e  m  y  l  y
b  m  u  t  u  m  b  l  e
```

Write each word in the correct place in the chart below.

Words with Short Vowels

a	e	i	o	u
glance (1)	gentle (1)	visit (1)	softly (1)	puppy (1)
	empty (1)	lily (1)		tumble (1)

Read directions to students.

Phonics

1

Name _____ Date _____

The Predicate of a Simple Sentence

Thinking Question
Which word or words in the sentence tell what the subject does or is?

- Every simple sentence has two parts— the subject and the predicate.
- The **predicate** is the part of a sentence that tells what the subject does or is.
- The predicate can be one word or more than one word. The **complete predicate** includes all the words in the predicate.

I lie beside the river.
My body <u>relaxes in the sun.</u>

Write each sentence. Then underline the complete predicate.

1. Relaxing is not as easy as it looks.
   Relaxing <u>is not as easy as it looks.</u> (1 point)

2. I like to watch the clouds above me.
   I like <u>to watch the clouds above me.</u> (1)

3. Gerry enjoys floating in the pool.
   Gerry <u>enjoys floating in the pool.</u> (1)

4. Ernie sits on the back steps with his dog.
   Ernie <u>sits on the back steps with his dog.</u> (1)

5. My cousins swing in tires hung from ropes.
   My cousins <u>swing in tires hung from ropes.</u> (1)

Read directions to students.

Grammar
© Houghton Mifflin Harcourt Publishing Company. All rights reserved.

3

Assessment Tip: Total 5 points
Grade 3, Unit 1

Name _____ Date _____

The Subject of a Simple Sentence

Thinking Question
Whom or what is the sentence about?

- A sentence is a group of words that tells a complete thought. The **subject** of a simple sentence tells whom or what the sentence is about.
- The subject usually comes at the beginning of the sentence. The subject can be one word or more than one word. The **complete subject** includes all the words in the subject.

The weekend is a special time.
<u>My family</u> enjoys the holidays.

Write the complete subject of each simple sentence.

1. Saturday is a fun day. Saturday (1 point)

2. All my friends get together in the park. All my friends (1)

3. Baseball teams play on the fields. Baseball teams (1)

4. My father coaches the teams. My father (1)

5. My mother watches all the games. My mother (1)

6. Our neighbors bring lots of food. Our neighbors (1)

7. We cook outside until it is dark. We (1)

8. The kids sleep on a blanket. The kids (1)

9. Grandma and Grandpa tell stories. Grandma and Grandpa (1)

10. Many of our teachers join us. Many of our teachers (1)

Read directions to students.

Grammar
© Houghton Mifflin Harcourt Publishing Company. All rights reserved.

2

Assessment Tip: Total 10 points
Grade 3, Unit 1

Name _____ Date _____

Focus Trait: Word Choice
Exact Words

Without Exact Words	With Exact Words
Mr. Brown lived in a big house.	Mr. Brown lived in the enormous, old green mansion on the hill, behind Taft Middle School.

A. Read the sentence that does not use exact words. Then choose words and add details to make the description more exact. Possible responses shown.

Without Exact Words	With Exact Words
1. Every day I go to school.	Every _weekday morning_ I _stroll down_ to Watson School, at the end of my street. (1 point)

B. Read each sentence that does not use exact words. Then look at the illustration on pages 26–27 of *A Fine, Fine School*. Rewrite the sentence using exact words.

Pair/Share Work with a partner to brainstorm exact words to use. Possible responses shown.

Without Exact Words	With Exact Words
2. The children are staying busy.	The children are carrying piles of books and walking down the hall. (1)
3. Mr. Keene is making a face.	Mr. Keene's eyebrows are raised, and he is frowning. (1)
4. The children are using their lockers.	The children are storing pencils and books in their lockers. (1)

Read directions to students.
Writing
© Houghton Mifflin Harcourt Publishing Company. All rights reserved.

5

Name _____ Date _____

Spelling Word Sort

Write each Basic Word under the correct heading.
One word will go under two different headings.

Spelling Words

Basic
1. crop
2. plan
3. thing
4. smell
5. shut
6. sticky
7. spent
8. lunch
9. pumpkin
10. clock
11. gift
12. class
13. skip
14. swing

Review
next
hug

Challenge
hospital
fantastic

Short *a*	Short *e*
plan (1 point)	smell (1)
class (1)	spent (1)
	Review: next (1)

Short *i*	Short *o*
thing (1)	crop (1)
sticky (1)	clock (1)
pumpkin (1)	

Short *u*
shut (1)
lunch (1)
pumpkin (1)
Review: hug (1)

Short *i*
gift (1)
skip (1)
swing (1)

Review: Add the Review Words to your Word Sort.

Challenge: Which Challenge Word has short vowels *o* and *i*?

hospital (1)

Read directions to students.
Spelling
© Houghton Mifflin Harcourt Publishing Company. All rights reserved.

4

Reader's Guide

A Fine, Fine School

The Fine, Fine School Times

Tillie is writing an article for the school newspaper, *The Fine, Fine School Times*. Her article will tell the real story. Use the text and illustrations to help her write the article.

Read pages 20–23. How do the students and teachers feel about going to school on the weekends and during the summer?

Mr. Keene just announced school will be open every single day of the year. I talked to some students and teachers. The students feel that they will not have time to do anything except go to school. (5 points)

The teachers are worried that they might not have enough to teach and that they will get tired from teaching so much. (5)

Mr. Keene has a different opinion. He thinks that the teachers and students will love coming to school every day because learning and teaching is all they want to do. (5)

That's all the news for now!

Words with the VCCV Pattern

Write a word from the box to complete each sentence in the story.

basket	happened	suddenly
chipmunk	princess	garden
rabbit	puppet	trumpet
galloped		

1. The blaring _____trumpet (1 point)_____ announced the show would soon begin.

2. Children sat in front of a little stage in the _____garden (1)_____.

3. Everyone was excited to see the _____puppet (1)_____ show.

4. A furry _____chipmunk or rabbit (1)_____ was the first puppet onstage.

5. Next came a little _____chipmunk or rabbit (1)_____ puppet.

6. What _____happened (1)_____ next was a surprise.

7. The rabbit told the chipmunk she was really a beautiful _____princess (1)_____.

8. The chipmunk gave the rabbit a _____basket (1)_____ of flowers.

9. The rabbit _____suddenly (1)_____ disappeared, and a beautiful princess stood in her place.

10. The princess and the chipmunk _____galloped (1)_____ away on a horse.

Name _____ Date _____

Read pages 30–33. Now Mr. Keene has changed his mind about keeping school open every day. Tillie has written another article to share the news.

The big news in school today is that school will be closed on weekends and during the summer. Mr. Keene said that the main reason for the change was that kids and teachers were not getting a chance to learn anything outside of school. (5)

I talked to some students about the change. One student told me that she liked the days off because she could do things with her family. (5)

Another student told me that now when he was not in school he could learn other things, like (Accept all reasonable responses.) (5)

The teachers and students are all pleased with Mr. Keene's decision. That is all the news for now from *The Fine, Fine School Times.*

Name _____ Date _____

Sentence Fragments

Write the complete subject of each simple sentence. Then underline the complete predicate.

1. Ira loves to read books in summer. _____ Ira (2 points)
2. Gina helps her dad all summer. _____ Gina (2)
3. Michaela rides her bike. _____ Michaela (2)
4. Wanda and Jane planted a garden. _____ Wanda and Jane (2)
5. The kids on Roy's block play baseball. _____ The kids on Roy's block (2)

Write a complete simple sentence for each sentence fragment.
Possible answers shown.

6. Tera and her swim team. _____ Tera and her swim team travel on buses. (1)
7. Has games all summer. _____ The baseball team has games all summer. (1)
8. Have frozen treats. _____ We like to have frozen treats. (1)
9. My friend. _____ My friend visits her grandparents. (1)
10. In the car. _____ She rides in the car. (1)

Name _____ Date _____

Context Clues

Read the sentence. Write the meaning of the underlined word as it is used in the sentence. Use a dictionary if you need help.

1. One fine day when the weather was nice, our family went on a picnic.

   very good (1 point)

2. We ate sandwiches and tried a new kind of juice drink.

   type (1)

3. We plan to take another trip to the park soon.

   an outing; a visit (1)

4. Elena was fatigued after the long, busy day.

   tired (1)

5. The immense sign blocked our view of the building.

   huge; very big (1)

6. The winter day is too frigid to go outdoors.

   very cold (1)

7. Jeffrey was so surprised at what he saw, he couldn't stop gaping.

   staring (1)

8. The detective had a crucial piece of information about the theft.

   very important (1)

Read directions to students.
Vocabulary Strategies   **11**
© Houghton Mifflin Harcourt Publishing Company. All rights reserved.

Assessment Tip: Total 8 points
Grade 3, Unit 1

Name _____ Date _____

Short Vowels

Write a Basic Word to finish the second sentence in each pair of sentences.

Spelling Words

Basic
1. crop
2. plan
3. thing
4. smell
5. shut
6. sticky
7. spent
8. lunch
9. pumpkin
10. clock
11. gift
12. class
13. skip
14. swing

Review
next
hug

Challenge
hospital
fantastic

1. Water is wet.

   Glue is   sticky (1 point)

2. You eat breakfast in the morning.

   You eat   lunch (1)   at noon.

3. You use a ruler to measure length.

   You use a   clock (1)   to measure time.

4. You see with your eyes.

   You   smell (1)   with your nose.

5. A writer writes a book.

   A farmer plants a   crop (1)

6. You can earn money by doing a job.

   When your money is gone, it is   spent (1)

7. Watermelons are seen in summer.

   Pumpkins (1)   are seen in fall.

8. A wolf is part of a pack.

   A student is part of a   class (1)

9. A horse learns to prance.

   A child learns to   skip (1)

10. Before you enter, you must open a door.

    When you leave, you   shut (1)   the door.

Challenge: Make up a pair of sentences similar to the ones above. Use a Challenge Word as the answer. Answers will vary. (2)

Read directions to students.
Spelling   **10**
© Houghton Mifflin Harcourt Publishing Company. All rights reserved.

Assessment Tip: Total 12 points
Grade 3, Unit 1

Name _____ Date _____

Proofreading for Spelling

Read the following invitation. Find and circle the misspelled words. (10 points)

You're Invited!

Please (plen) to attend Mr. Hay's (class) next Monday.

We have (spint) three weeks learning about autumn. We want to share some of the (thangs) we learned with you.

We will begin when the (cluck) strikes ten. We will (shet) the doors at that time. We will teach you about some (crups) farmers grow in our area in the fall. Then we will discuss interesting facts about the sun and Earth at this time of year. Finally, we will eat. You will be hungry from the delicious (smill) of (pompken) pie! It will be our (gaft) to you.

Write the misspelled words correctly on the lines below.

1. _____ plan (1)   6. _____ shut (1)
2. _____ class (1)   7. _____ crops (1)
3. _____ spent (1)   8. _____ smell (1)
4. _____ things (1)   9. _____ pumpkin (1)
5. _____ clock (1)   10. _____ gift (1)

Read directions to students.
Spelling
© Houghton Mifflin Harcourt Publishing Company. All rights reserved.

13

Spelling Words

Basic
1. crop
2. plan
3. thing
4. smell
5. shut
6. sticky
7. spent
8. lunch
9. pumpkin
10. clock
11. gift
12. class
13. skip
14. swing

Review
next
hug

Challenge
hospital
fantastic

Name _____ Date _____

Capitalization and Punctuation

- Correct **capitalization** includes capitalizing the first letter of sentences.
- Every sentence has end **punctuation**, such as a period.

My pencil needs to be sharpened.
Now my writing will be easy to read.

Write each sentence using correct capitalization and punctuation.

1. our school principal visited our class today (2 points)

Our school principal visited our class today

2. all students will take the test next week (2)

All students will take the test next week.

3. the math teacher surprised all of us (2)

The math teacher surprised all of us. (2)

4. that is my favorite book (2)

That is my favorite book. (2)

5. today is a holiday

Today is a holiday. (2)

6. i saw Mr. Clarke yesterday

I saw Mr. Clarke yesterday. (2)

Read directions to students.
Grammar
© Houghton Mifflin Harcourt Publishing Company. All rights reserved.

12

Words with Long Vowels

Lesson 2
READER'S NOTEBOOK

The Trial of
Cardigan Jones
Phonics:
Long Vowels a, e, i, o, u

Read each clue. Write two rhyming words from the Word Bank to answer the clue.

base	rage	globe	joke
home	shade	skate	lime
broke	chase	plate	tone
robe	chrome	slime	phone
cage	shake	snake	trade

1. If you chase your friend around the bases on a field, you play a game of _____ base (1 point) _____ chase (1)

2. If a joke wasn't funny, the _____ joke (1) _____ broke (1)

3. If a lime rots, you will have _____ lime (1) _____ slime (1)

4. A snake that is cold does a _____ snake (1) _____ shake (1)

5. An angry bird in a cage may get _____ cage (1) _____ rage (1)

6. If you put paper plates under your feet, you can go for a _____ plate (1) _____ skate (1)

7. If you put on a bathrobe with a round map of the world on it, you are wearing a _____ globe (1) _____ robe (1)

8. If you switch shady spots, you do a _____ shade (1) _____ trade (1)

9. When you pick up a telephone, you hear a sound called a _____ phone (1) _____ tone (1)

10. A shiny, silver house is a _____ chrome (1) _____ home (1)

Connect to Writing

Sometimes a sentence does not include a complete thought. It is a **fragment**. Correct fragments by adding the missing subject or predicate. This will make your writing easier to understand.

Fragments	Complete Simple Sentences
Taught our cat to fetch. Raul taught.	Raul taught our cat to fetch.
My sister. Showed the puppy tricks.	My sister showed the puppy tricks.

Correct the fragments by combining the subjects and predicates to form complete simple sentences. Write the sentence on the line.

1. Our dog. Loves bones.

    Our dog loves bones. (1 point)

2. Grandpa a trick. Taught him a trick.

    Grandpa taught him a trick. (1)

3. Dogs attention. Love attention.

    Dogs love attention. (1)

4. Danny taught. Our dog to sit.

    Danny taught our dog to sit. (1)

5. The dog to come. Begged us to come.

    The dog begged us to come. (1)

Lesson 2
READER'S NOTEBOOK

The Trial of
Cardigan Jones
Grammar:
Kinds of Sentences

Name _____ Date _____

Commands and Exclamations

- Two kinds of sentences are statements and questions. Two other kinds of sentences are **commands** and **exclamations.**
- A **command** is a sentence that tells someone to do something. It ends with a period. It is also called an **imperative** sentence.
- An **exclamation** is a sentence that shows strong feeling, such as excitement, surprise, or fear. It ends with an exclamation point. It is also called an **exclamatory** sentence.
- All kinds of sentences should begin with a capital letter and end with proper punctuation.

Command/Imperative   Get a chair, please.
Exclamation/Exclamatory   I'm excited!

> **Thinking Question**
> *Is the sentence a command or an exclamation, and what punctuation does it end with?*

Write *command* if the sentence tells someone to do something.
Write *exclamation* if the sentence shows strong feeling.

1. That is the funniest joke! ____exclamation (2 points)__

2. Tell another joke. ____command (2)__

3. I am so happy! ____exclamation (2)__

4. Bring everyone in to hear these. ____command (2)__

5. How my sides hurt from laughing! ____exclamation (2)__

6. Pull out those chairs and sit down. ____command (2)__

7. Please repeat that joke. ____command (2)__

Assessment Tip: Total 14 points

17   Grade 3, Unit 1

Lesson 2
READER'S NOTEBOOK

The Trial of
Cardigan Jones
Grammar:
Kinds of Sentences

Name _____ Date _____

Statements and Questions

- Every sentence begins with a capital letter. There are four kinds of sentences. Statements and questions are two of them.
- A sentence that tells something is a **statement.** It ends with a period. It is also called a **declarative** sentence.
- A sentence that asks something is a **question.** It ends with a question mark. It is also called an **interrogative** sentence.

Statement/Declarative
I wear comfortable clothes.
Question/Interrogative
What do you like to wear?

> **Thinking Question**
> *Is the sentence a statement or a question, and how do I know?*

Write *statement* if the sentence tells something. Write *question* if the sentence asks something.

1. I wear old shirts around the house. ____statement (1 point)__

2. Why don't you go and change your clothes? ____question (1)__

3. Who is coming to visit? ____question (1)__

4. I dress up for company. ____statement (1)__

5. Why do my old clothes feel so good? ____question (1)__

6. Old cotton shirts are very soft. ____statement (1)__

7. A new dress can feel strange. ____statement (1)__

8. My pet moves around the house. ____statement (1)__

Assessment Tip: Total 8 points

16   Grade 3, Unit 1

Name _____ Date _____

Focus Trait: Conventions
Sentence Types

Without a Variety of Sentence Types	With a Variety of Sentence Types
The milkman told the judge what he saw.	"Judge, I'm sure I saw the moose tiptoe up to the window. He put his face right into the pie!" said the milkman.

A. Read the sentence below. Rewrite it as a paragraph using a variety of sentence types. Possible response shown.

Without a Variety of Sentence Types	With a Variety of Sentence Types
1. The moose was clumsy.	"Karen told me about the time that Cardigan broke a statue!" exclaimed Pat. "He also knocked over the judge by accident and broke Mrs. Brown's vase." (2 points)

B. Read each sentence below. Rewrite the sentences, adding a variety of sentence types that will bring your story to life for the reader.

Pair/Share Work with a partner to add a variety of sentence types. Possible responses shown.

Without a Variety of Sentence Types	With a Variety of Sentence Types
2. Page 54: Mrs. Brown didn't know what happened to her pie.	"Please help! I've just seen a moose near my window. Where did he go?" shouted Mrs. Brown. (2)
3. Page 66: The judge found the missing pie.	"Everyone, look!" said the judge. "The smelly pie is right here in the bushes." (2)

Read directions to students.
Writing

Assessment Tip: Total 6 points
Grade 3, Unit 1

19

Lesson 2
READER'S NOTEBOOK

The Trial of
Cardigan Jones
Spelling:
VCe Spellings

Name _____ Date _____

Spelling Word Sort

Write each Basic Word under the correct heading.

Spelling Words

Basic
1. spoke
2. mile
3. save
4. excuse
5. cone
6. invite
7. cube
8. price
9. erase
10. ripe
11. broke
12. flame
13. life
14. rule

Review
these
those

Challenge
surprise
decide

Long a	Long i
1. save (1 point)	4. mile (1)
2. erase (1)	5. invite (1)
3. flame (1)	6. price (1)
	7. ripe (1)
	8. life (1)

Long o	Long u
9. spoke (1)	12. excuse (1)
10. cone (1)	13. cube (1)
11. broke (1)	14. rule (1)

Review: What long vowel sound does the Review Word *these* have? _____ long e (1) _____ What long vowel sound does the Review Word *those* have? _____ long o (1) _____

Challenge: In which column do the two Challenge Words belong? _____ long i (2) _____

Read directions to students.
Spelling

Assessment Tip: Total 18 points
Grade 3, Unit 1

18

Name _____ Date _____

Lesson 2
READER'S NOTEBOOK

The Trial of
Cardigan Jones
Independent Reading

The Trial of Cardigan Jones

Reader's Guide

Questions for the Milkman

What would you say if you were the milkman? Right now, the judge is asking you questions about Cardigan Jones. Use the text and illustrations to explain exactly what you saw that day.

> **What were you doing right before Mrs. Brown's pie was stolen?**

Read page 53.

I was driving my milk truck past Mrs. Brown's house. (5 points)

> **Now tell me exactly what you saw when you looked out of your truck.**

I saw a moose smelling a pie that was sitting on Mrs. Brown's window. I had never seen the moose before. (5)

> **In your own words, tell me why you think Cardigan Jones stole the pie.**

Read pages 60–61.

I saw him smelling Mrs. Brown's pie. After that, the pie was missing. (5)

Read directions to students.
Independent Reading
© Houghton Mifflin Harcourt Publishing Company. All rights reserved.

21   Assessment Tip: 15 Points
Grade 3, Unit 1

Name _____ Date _____

Lesson 2
READER'S NOTEBOOK

The Trial of
Cardigan Jones
Phonics:
Words with the VCe Pattern

Words with the VCe Pattern

Read each word. Draw a line to match the word to its meaning. (10 points)

Column 1	Column 2
1. awake	a. clothes worn to make somebody look like somebody or something else
2. costume	b. to free oneself or get away from
3. divide	c. to bring things together
4. escape	d. an error
5. exercise	e. not asleep
6. microphone	f. a paved path where people can walk alongside a street
7. mistake	g. to separate
8. refuse	h. to say no
9. sidewalk	i. to work out or do a physical activity
10. unite	j. a device to make someone's voice louder

Write each word from Column 1 in the correct place in the chart below. Look at the part of the word with the VCe pattern.

Long *a*	Long *i*	Long *o*	Long *u*
awake (1) escape (1) mistake (1)	divide (1) exercise (1) sidewalk (1) unite (1)	microphone (1)	costume (1) refuse (1)

Read directions to students.
Phonics
© Houghton Mifflin Harcourt Publishing Company. All rights reserved.

20   Assessment Tip: Total 20 points
Grade 3, Unit 1

Lesson 2
READER'S NOTEBOOK

The Trial of
Cardigan Jones
Grammar:
Kinds of Sentences

Name _____ Date _____

Statements, Questions, Commands, and Exclamations

Write *statement* if the sentence tells something. Write *question* if the sentence asks something.

1. I like basketball. ___statement (1 point)___

2. I would not want to climb a mountain. ___statement (1)___

3. Where do you row your boat? ___question (1)___

4. Do you like to play tennis? ___question (1)___

5. What do you know about judo? ___question (1)___

Write *command* if the sentence tells someone to do something. Write *exclamation* if the sentence shows strong feeling.

6. Pick up the tennis racket. ___command (1)___

7. Tennis is a great sport! ___exclamation (1)___

8. Please join me in a game. ___command (1)___

9. Ask him to play tennis with us. ___command (1)___

10. I will not ask him! ___exclamation (1)___

Name _____ Date _____

Read page 62.

> What have you observed about Cardigan Jones in this courtroom?

He is very clumsy. He is always knocking things over. (5)

Read page 67.

> So now we know what really happened to the pie. Tell me, Milkman, how do you feel?

I feel bad because I thought Cardigan Jones stole the pie.

He only knocked it over. (5)

Read page 69.

> How would you describe Cardigan Jones now that you know him better?

He is nice and friendly, but he is also very clumsy. (5)

Lesson 2
READER'S NOTEBOOK

The Trial of
Cardigan Jones
Spelling:
VCe Spellings

Name _____ Date _____

VCe Spellings

Write the Basic Word that belongs in each group.

Spelling Words

Basic
1. spoke
2. mile
3. save
4. excuse
5. cone
6. invite
7. cube
8. price
9. erase
10. ripe
11. broke
12. flame
13. life
14. rule

Review
these
those

Challenge
surprise
decide

1. sphere, pyramid, _____ cone (1 point) _____ cube (1)
2. fire, smoke, _____ flame (1)
3. inch, yard, _____ mile (1)
4. ask, call, _____ invite (1)
5. ready, full-grown, _____ ripe (1)
6. whispered, yelled, _____ spoke (1)
7. law, principle, _____ rule (1)
8. change, wipe away, _____ erase (1)
9. rescue, free, _____ save (1)
10. amount, cost, _____ price (1)

Challenge: Which Challenge Word belongs in a group called *Things That Are Unexpected?* _____ surprise (1)

Lesson 2
READER'S NOTEBOOK

The Trial of
Cardigan Jones
Vocabulary Strategies:
Dictionary/Glossary

Name _____ Date _____

Dictionary/Glossary

Read each word. Find each word in a dictionary or glossary. Complete the chart.

Word	Part(s) of Speech	Word with Endings
1. gavel	noun (1 point)	gavels (1)
2. pilfer	verb (1)	pilfered, pilfering, pilfers (1)
3. declare	verb (1)	declared, declaring, declares (1)
4. testify	verb (1)	testified, testifies, testifying (1)
5. fine	adjective, adverb, noun, verb (1)	fined, finer, finest, fining (1)

Now write one sentence of your own that could be an example sentence for one meaning of each word. Possible responses shown.

1. The judge banged his gavel to get the court's attention. (1)
2. He was accused of pilfering the wallet. (1)
3. Jim was declared the best player. (1)
4. Mrs. Lopez testified about the strange man she saw. (1)
5. The judge fined him $500. (1)

Lesson 2
READER'S NOTEBOOK

The Trial of
Cardigan Jones
Spelling:
VCe Spellings

Name _____ Date _____

Proofreading for Spelling

Read the following passage. Find and circle the misspelled words. (10 points)

Do you sometimes wish there was no such thing as a (roole)? Let's think about how (lief) would be different without rules. You may (surpris) yourself and be thankful for rules!

Let's say you have an ice cream (con). I see it and (decid) I want it. I take your ice cream. I do not say (excoose) me. I eat it all, even though you paid the (prise) for it.

(Thos) actions would make you mad, wouldn't they? But since there are no rules, the only thing I (brok) was your pride. I did not break a rule. Rules (saav) us from situations like these. Rules help us all get along.

Write the misspelled words correctly on the lines below.

1. _____ rule (1)
2. _____ life (1)
3. _____ surprise (1)
4. _____ cone (1)
5. _____ decide (1)
6. _____ excuse (1)
7. _____ price (1)
8. _____ Those (1)
9. _____ broke (1)
10. _____ save (1)

27

Spelling Words

Basic

1. spoke
2. mile
3. save
4. excuse
5. cone
6. invite
7. cube
8. price
9. erase
10. ripe
11. broke
12. flame
13. life
14. rule

Review

these
those

Challenge

surprise
decide

Lesson 2
READER'S NOTEBOOK

The Trial of
Cardigan Jones
Grammar:
Spiral Review

Name _____ Date _____

Writing Subjects and Predicates

- The **subject** of a sentence tells whom or what the sentence is about. The main word in a sentence is often a **noun**. It is called the **simple subject**.
- The **predicate** of a sentence tells what the subject is or was, or what the subject does or did. The main word in the predicate is a **verb**. It is called the **simple predicate**.

The complete subject of each sentence is underlined. Write the simple subject.

1. The room for the dance was large. _____ room (1 point)
2. The band's first song had a fast tempo. _____ song (1)
3. The twins said they would dance to every song. _____ twins (1)
4. The girl in the yellow dress danced happily. _____ girl (1)

The complete predicate of each sentence is underlined. Write the simple predicate.

5. The teachers put drinks and snacks on the tables. _____ put (1)
6. I looked for my cousin on the dance floor. _____ looked (1)
7. Everyone danced to the last song. _____ danced (1)
8. The tired dancers walked home happy. _____ walked (1)

26

Name _____ Date _____

Common Vowel Pairs
ai, ay, ee, ea

Write the word from the Word Bank that best completes each sentence.

always	easel	stain	steam
bait	greedy	players	sweeten
breeze	rain	queen	trail
chain	layers	seasons	

1. Of all the ___seasons (1 point)___, fall is my favorite.

2. When you boil water, the ___steam (1)___ you see is the water vapor.

3. Take your umbrella because it will ___rain (1)___.

4. The door is secured with a lock and strong ___chain (1)___.

5. I knew it was the ___queen (1)___ because of her crown.

6. The hikers walked along the marked ___trail (1)___.

7. The artist paints at his ___easel (1)___.

8. To be safe, I ___always (1)___ look both ways at a stop sign.

9. I will use honey to ___sweeten (1)___ the iced tea.

10. The cake has three different ___layers (1)___.

11. The spilled juice left a ___stain (1)___ on the carpet.

12. On a hot day, a ___breeze (1)___ is welcome.

13. Remember to take the ___bait (1)___ with you when you go fishing.

14. Four ___players (1)___ can play the game at the same time.

15. If you do not share, people may think you are ___greedy (1)___.

Lesson 2
READER'S NOTEBOOK

The Trial of
Cardigan Jones
Grammar:
Connect to Writing

Name _____ Date _____

Connect to Writing

Sentences can be statements, questions, commands, or exclamations. Using all four kinds of sentences in a paragraph makes writing more lively and varied.

Paragraph with One Kind of Sentence	Paragraph with Four Kinds of Sentences
Rowing a boat can be lots of fun. You should try it. You find a boat. You will laugh a lot.	Rowing a boat can be lots of fun. Why don't you try it? Find a boat. You will not stop laughing!

Change each sentence to another type of sentence. The word in parentheses tells you the type of sentence to write. Write the new sentence on the line. Possible responses shown.

1. We won the boat race. (exclamation)

   We won the boat race! (1 point)

2. Do you row the boats there? (statement)

   You row the boats there. (1)

3. Can we put this boat in the water? (command)

   Put this boat in the water. (1)

4. We should watch the boat race. (question)

   Should we watch the boat race? (1)

5. Will you let me ride in the boat? (statement)

   You will let me ride in the boat. (1)

Lesson 3
READER'S NOTEBOOK

Destiny's Gift
Grammar:
Compound Sentences

Simple and Compound Sentences

- A **simple sentence** tells a complete thought.
- A **compound sentence** is made up of two simple sentences joined by the word *and, but, or,* or *so.*

We stood in the front yard. Our neighbors stayed indoors.

We stood in the front yard, but our neighbors stayed indoors.

Thinking Question
Does the sentence tell one complete thought, or does it tell two complete thoughts?

Determine whether each sentence is simple or compound. Write *simple* or *compound* on the line.

1. Young students and their friends met at the bookstore.

    simple (2 points)

2. The children handed out flyers, and their parents carried signs.

    compound (2)

3. A large group of people shouted, but they were not angry.

    compound (2)

4. They shouted to get people to come to the bookstore.

    simple (2)

5. Many old customers came, and some customers gave speeches.

    compound (2)

6. People could buy books, or they could donate money.

    compound (2)

Read directions to students.

Grammar   30

Assessment Tip: Total 12 points

Grade 3, Unit 1

Lesson 3
READER'S NOTEBOOK

Destiny's Gift
Grammar:
Compound Sentences

Coordinating Conjunctions

- A **compound sentence** is made up of two simple sentences joined by a conjunction.
- The words *and, but, or,* and *so* are **conjunctions.** A comma comes before the conjunction.

    And joins two similar ideas.
    But joins two different ideas.
    Or joins two possible ideas.
    So shows that the second idea happens because of the first.

Thinking Question
Which kinds of ideas are being joined into one sentence?

Write the conjunction that best joins the simple sentences. Then write the compound sentence.

1. Dora called Lisa. She called Erin.

    and; Dora called Lisa, and she called Erin. (2 points)

2. Erin was at home. Lisa was not at home.

    but; Erin was at home, but Lisa was not at home. (2)

3. Erin did not have plans. She could visit Dora.

    so; Erin did not have plans, so she could visit Dora. (2)

4. Erin could bring a game. She could bring a movie.

    or; Erin could bring a game, or she could bring a movie. (2)

Read directions to students.

Grammar   31

Assessment Tip: Total 8 points

Grade 3, Unit 1

Name _____ Date _____

Spelling Word Sort

Write each Basic Word under the correct heading.

Long a Spelled ay	Long a Spelled ai
lay (1 point)	trail (1)
today (1)	afraid (1)
	bait (1)
Challenge: yesterday (1)	Review: paint (1)
	Challenge: explain (1)

Long e Spelled ee	Long e Spelled ea
sweet (1)	real (1)
seem (1)	dream (1)
screen (1)	tea (1)
speed (1)	treat (1)
	leave (1)
	Review: please (1)

Review: Add the Review Words to your Word Sort.

Challenge: Add the Challenge Words to your Word Sort.

Read directions to students.
Spelling
© Houghton Mifflin Harcourt Publishing Company. All rights reserved.

32

Assessment Tip: Total 18 points
Grade 3, Unit 1

Spelling Words

Basic
1. lay
2. real
3. trail
4. sweet
5. today
6. dream
7. seem
8. tea
9. treat
10. afraid
11. leave
12. bait
13. cheer
14. speed

Review
paint
please

Challenge
yesterday
explain

Name _____ Date _____

Focus Trait: Development
Express Thoughts and Feelings

These thoughts and feelings…	…help you understand this.
Destiny remembers how much she enjoyed talking with writers. She describes how they shared her love of words.	They show how Destiny feels about talking to authors, and they explain why Destiny wants to become a writer.

A. Read the event from *Destiny's Gift*. Underline the words that show Destiny's thoughts and feelings. Then explain what they help you understand about Destiny. Possible response shown.

These thoughts and feelings…	…help you understand this.
1. Destiny can't stop crying after she finds out about Mrs. Wade's store.	They show how upset Destiny is at the thought of the store closing. (1 point)

B. Read each sentence that tells an event from *Destiny's Gift*. Look at the page listed. Write a sentence that tells about Destiny's or Mrs. Wade's thoughts and feelings.

Pair/Share Work with a partner before you write. Possible responses shown.

Event	Sentence with Thoughts and Feelings
2. Page 88: Destiny says she likes Mrs. Wade's bookstore.	Mrs. Wade's bookstore is Destiny's favorite place in the world, where she feels completely at home. (2)
3. Page 104: Destiny writes something for Mrs. Wade.	Destiny thinks that Mrs. Wade will be very pleased with what she writes for her. (2)

Read directions to students.
Writing
Copyright © Houghton Mifflin Harcourt Publishing Company. All rights reserved.

33

Assessment Tip: Total 5 points
Grade 3, Unit 1

Name _____ Date _____

Reader's Guide

Destiny's Gift

What's the Word?

You see the big, thick dictionary Mrs. Wade keeps on a pedestal in her bookstore. You flip open the dictionary and see the word *content*. You read:

> **content** *adjective*: satisfied with what one is or has

Read page 92. How does the word *content* help describe Destiny and Mrs. Wade? Destiny and Mrs. Wade felt content drinking tea together while

Destiny read to Mrs. Wade from her notebook. **(2 points)**

Next, you flip the dictionary to another page and see the word *worried*. You read:

> **worried** *adjective*: concerned, filled with worry

Read page 96. How does the word *worried* help describe Mrs. Wade? Mrs. Wade was worried that her bookstore would have to close. **(2)**

Finally, you flip through the dictionary to another page and see the word *inspired*. You read:

> **inspired** *adjective*: filled with the spirit to do something

Read page 104. How does the word *inspired* help describe Destiny? Destiny was inspired to write everything she loved about the

bookstore. **(2)**

Read directions to students.
Independent Reading
© Houghton Mifflin Harcourt Publishing Company. All rights reserved.

35   Assessment Tip: 6 Points
Grade 3, Unit 1

Name _____ Date _____

Cumulative Review

Read the grocery list. Write each item in the chart below.

Grocery List

artichokes   grapes   peaches
beans   lemonade   peanuts
beef   limes   pineapple
cheese   grains   prunes
coffee   oatmeal   crayfish

		Long a	Long e	Long i spelled VC*e*	Long o spelled VC*e*	Long u spelled VC*e*
VC*e*		grapes (1 point) lemonade (1)		limes (1) pineapple (1)	artichokes (1)	prunes (1)
ai		grains (1)				
ee			cheese (1) beef (1) coffee (1)			
ay		crayfish (1)				
ea			peaches (1) beans (1) peanuts (1) oatmeal (1)			

Write a recipe on another sheet of paper. Use at least three words on the list. You can use other ingredients, too. **(5 points)**

Read directions to students.
Phonics
© Houghton Mifflin Harcourt Publishing Company. All rights reserved.

34   Assessment Tip: Total 20 points
Grade 3, Unit 1

Name _____ Date _____

Run-On Sentences

- Two or more simple sentences that run together are called **run-on** sentences.
- A run-on sentence may be corrected by forming a **compound sentence**. The conjunctions *and*, *but*, *or*, and *so* are used to form compound sentences.

Thinking Question
Can I use a conjunction to join these sentences and form a compound sentence?

Rita does not like moose Gwen does.
Rita does not like moose, but Gwen does.

Correct each run-on sentence by forming a compound sentence. Write the conjunction and then write the compound sentence.

1. Moose are a kind of deer they are part of the deer family.

so; Moose are the largest kind of deer, so they are part of the

deer family. (2 points)

2. Adult males have large antlers female moose do not.

but; Adult male moose have large antlers, but female moose

do not. (2)

3. Moose are good swimmers they are fast runners.

and; Moose are good swimmers, and they are fast runners. (2)

4. The moose might bellow the moose might grunt.

or; The moose might bellow, or the moose might grunt. (2)

Name _____ Date _____

Destiny has used many interesting words in her notebook called "Mrs. Wade's Bookstore."

Read pages 104–107. Finish writing this page in Destiny's notebook. Tell how she feels about what is happening to the store. Use the dictionary words and any other words you might need.

Mrs. Wade's bookstore might close! There are so many

reasons I love that bookstore and so many reasons I will be

sad if it closes.

(Answers should describe the reasons that Destiny

loves the bookstore, such as looking up words

and learning all there is to know about them,

drinking tea, and reading with Mrs. Wade. Answers

should also describe why Destiny will be sad if the

bookstore closes. For example, she won't have a

place to read anymore, she won't get to spend time

with Mrs. Wade, and Mrs. Wade will be very unhappy

too.) (10)

Name _____ Date _____

Antonyms

lower	all	left
after	take	last

**Read each word below. Write the antonym from the box above.
Then write a sentence using both words.** Possible responses shown.

1. none _____ all (1 point)

   We ate all the popcorn, so there was none left. (1)

2. first _____ last (1)

   Write your last name first. (1)

3. raise _____ lower (1)

   During PE, we had to raise and lower our legs to do leg lifts. (1)

4. right _____ left (1)

   My baby brother does not know his left hand from his right hand. (1)

5. before _____ after (1)

   We will have dinner after school, but before the soccer game. (1)

6. give _____ take (1)

   I will take the cookie and give my sister half. (1)

Read directions to students.
Vocabulary Strategies
© Houghton Mifflin Harcourt Publishing Company. All rights reserved.

Name _____ Date _____

Long *a* and Long *e* Spellings

Spelling Words

Basic
1. lay
2. real
3. trail
4. sweet
5. today
6. dream
7. seem
8. tea
9. treat
10. afraid
11. leave
12. bait
13. screen
14. speed

Review
paint
please

Challenge
yesterday
explain

**Write a Basic Word to answer each clue. Then use letters in
the word to answer the second clue. The letters may not be
in the correct order.**

1. what helps you catch fish b _a_ _i_ t (1 point)

   what you swing in baseball b _a_ t (1)

2. how fast you go s _p_ _e_ _e_ d (1)

   not shallow d _e_ _e_ p (1)

3. something you do when you sleep d _r_ _e_ _a_ m (1)

   what you do with a book r _e_ _a_ d (1)

4. candy has this taste s _w_ _e_ _e_ t (1)

   a direction on a map w _e_ _s_ t (1)

5. a reward for a good dog t _r_ _e_ _a_ t (1)

   what you do with food e _a_ t (1)

6. to go away l _e_ _a_ _v_ e (1)

   a snake-like fish e _e_ l (1)

7. to look or appear to be true s _e_ _e_ m (1)

   your eyes do this for you s _e_ e (1)

8. something you might walk on in the woods t _r_ _a_ i _l_ (1)

   a rodent with a long tail r _a_ t (1)

Read directions to students.
Spelling
© Houghton Mifflin Harcourt Publishing Company. All rights reserved.

Name _____ Date _____

Proofreading for Spelling

Read each sign. Find and circle the misspelled words. (9 points)

1. (Plees) do not feed
   the bears.

2. (Spead) Limit
   55
   Miles per Hour

3. Stay on the (traiyl).

4. Sweet (tee) $1.00
   Peanuts $.50

5. The zoo will close
   (today) at 4 PM.

6. (Leeve) your
   shoes outside.

7. Stay out!
   Wet (paynt).

8. Do not be (afrad)
   to try new things.

Write the misspelled words correctly on the lines below.

1. Please (1)   5. today (1)

2. Speed (1)   6. Leave (1)

3. trail (1)   7. paint (1)

4. Sweet, tea (2)   8. afraid (1)

<blockquote>
Spelling Words

Basic
1. lay
2. real
3. trail
4. sweet
5. today
6. dream
7. seem
8. tea
9. treat
10. afraid
11. leave
12. bait
13. screen
14. speed

Review
paint
please

Challenge
yesterday
explain
</blockquote>

Name _____ Date _____

Kinds of Sentences

- There are four kinds of sentences.

Mom is home.   **Declarative** (statement)
Did you study?   **Interrogative** (question)
Pick up that mess.   **Imperative** (command)
What a great job!   **Exclamatory** (exclamation)

Write *statement* if the sentence tells something. **Write *question*** if
the sentence asks something.

1. John brought his lunch to the picnic. ___ statement (1 point)

2. Are you going to the picnic? ___ question (1)

3. Will you bring a friend? ___ question (1)

Write *command* if the sentence tells someone to do something.
Write *exclamation* if the sentence shows strong feeling.

4. The picnic is really going to be fun! ___ exclamation (1)

5. Hand me that plate. ___ command (1)

6. Wait for me over there. ___ command (1)

Name _____ Date _____

Long o Spelled oa, ow

Each word in the Word Bank is in the puzzle. Find and circle each word in the puzzle. Words can be across or down. (10 points)

arrow	floating	undertow
below	goal	upload
blown	slow	
coach	throwing	

On a separate sheet of paper, use each word in the Word Bank in a sentence. Read your sentences aloud. (10)

Assessment Tip: Total 20 points
Grade 3, Unit 1

Name _____ Date _____

Connect to Writing

Too many short sentences make writing sound choppy. Sometimes you can combine two short sentences to make one longer compound sentence. Use a comma (,) and the conjunction *and*, *but*, or *or* to form compound sentences.

Short Sentences	Compound Sentence
Libby owns many books. She hasn't read them all.	Libby owns many books, but she hasn't read them all.

Use a conjunction to form compound sentences.

1. Victoria came to our book party. She brought ten books.

   Victoria came to our book party, and she brought ten

   books. (1 point)

2. We could hike on Saturday. We could wait until Sunday.

   We could hike on Saturday, or we could wait until Sunday. (1)

Correct these run-ons by using a conjunction to form compound sentences.

3. People could bring books they could bring magazines.

   People could bring books, or they could bring

   magazines. (1)

4. These books are very interesting they are hard to understand.

   These books are very interesting, but they are hard to

   understand. (1)

Assessment Tip: Total 4 points
Grade 3, Unit 1

Name _____ Date _____

Identifying Nouns and Subjects

- A word that names a person, a place, or a thing is a **noun**. The noun that is doing something in a sentence is the subject.

  My **mom** helped to build the new road.

  The **work** lasted one year.

Thinking Questions
Is the word naming a person, a place, or a thing? Which noun tells who or what is doing something?

Write the two nouns in each sentence. Circle the subject of each sentence.

1. (Workers) brought in tables. _____ Workers, tables (3 points)

2. High (winds) knocked down the tents. _____ winds, tents (3)

3. The (sand) blew into the food. _____ sand, food (3)

4. The (moon) was beautiful at night. _____ moon, night (3)

5. My (family) did some work. _____ family, work (3)

6. My (cousin) showed the workers where to go. _____ cousin, workers (3)

7. My (brother) played some music. _____ brother, music (3)

8. My (uncle) put up the signs. _____ uncle, signs (3)

9. Her (mother) brought food sometimes. _____ mother, food (3)

10. The (mayor) visited when the road was done. _____ mayor, road (3)

Assessment Tip: Total 30 points
Grade 3, Unit 1

Grammar
© Houghton Mifflin Harcourt Publishing Company. All rights reserved.
Read directions to students.

Name _____ Date _____

Capitalizing Nouns

- A word that names a person, place, or thing is a noun.
- **Common nouns** name any person, place, or thing. **Proper nouns** name a particular person, place, or thing.
- Proper nouns begin with capital letters and may have more than one word. People's titles and important words in titles of books are capitalized.

  His daughter Audrey visited him at his job in England.

Thinking Question
Does the noun name any person, place, or thing, or does it name a particular person, place, or thing?

Write *common* or *proper* for each underlined noun.

1. Outside of Atlanta, Jessie's father works in an office. _____ proper (1 point)

2. Bennie came to his father's bicycle shop. _____ common (1)

3. Many parents invite their children to the places they work. _____ common (1)

4. Mike went to New York City with his mother. _____ proper (1)

5. They saw a parade and ate great food. _____ common (1)

6. Gary's father took him to an Ice Age display at the museum. _____ proper (1)

Assessment Tip: Total 6 points
Grade 3, Unit 1

Grammar
© Houghton Mifflin Harcourt Publishing Company. All rights reserved.
Read directions to students.

Name _____ Date _____

Focus Trait: Development
Important and Interesting Details

Good writers use interesting details to develop their ideas.

For example:

The girl rode her bike.

The above sentence would be much more interesting with important details added:

The small redheaded girl proudly rode her shiny new yellow bike to school.

Read each sentence and look at the illustration from "Pop's Bridge" on the page listed. **Add interesting details to each sentence.** Possible responses shown.

1. Page 134: The family looked at the bridge.

   Robert and his parents stood at the edge of the water and

   looked at the bridge under the moon. (1 point)

2. Page 137: The boy shouted on the street.

   The boy called out to try to sell newspapers to people passing

   on the busy street. (1)

3. Page 143: Robert was happy.

   Robert grinned as he and thousands of other people walked

   across the bridge. (1)

4. Page 144: He cut the puzzle piece.

   He carefully cut the puzzle piece into two pieces with a pair

   of scissors. (1)

Read directions to students.

Writing
Copyright © Houghton Mifflin Harcourt Publishing Company. All rights reserved.

Assessment Tip: Total 4 points
Grade 3, Unit 1

47

Name _____ Date _____

Spelling Word Sort

Write each Basic Word under the correct heading.

Spelling Words

Basic
1. load
2. opening
3. told
4. yellow
5. soak
6. shadow
7. foam
8. follow
9. glow
10. sold
11. window
12. coach
13. almost
14. throat

Review
cold
most

Challenge
tomorrow
sailboats

Long o Spelled o	Long o Spelled ow
open (1 point)	yellow (1)
told (1)	shadow (1)
sold (1)	follow (1)
almost (1)	glow (1)
Review: cold, most (2)	window (1)
	Challenge: tomorrow (1)

Long o Spelled oa

load (1)

soak (1)

foam (1)

coach (1)

throat (1)

Challenge: sailboats (1)

Review: Add the Review Words to your Word Sort.

Challenge: Add the Challenge Words to your Word Sort.

Read directions to students.

Spelling
© Houghton Mifflin Harcourt Publishing Company. All rights reserved.

Assessment Tip: Total 18 points
Grade 3, Unit 1

46

Reader's Guide

Pop's Bridge

More Views from the Bridge

Mr. Shu, Charlie's dad, is writing a letter to his family in China about what it is like to work on the Golden Gate Bridge. Use the text and illustrations to help you write the letter.

Read page 130. What was it like to be a painter on the Golden Gate Bridge?

Dear Family,

I am working as a painter on the Golden Gate Bridge! You would not believe how big it is! Guess what I do?

Every morning I climb up on the bridge and get out my paint and start painting. (2 points)

It is hard work to be a painter because I have to hang in the air on a support and paint high up. (2)

Sometimes I am afraid that I will fall off the support that holds me up. (2)

I really like being a painter on the bridge. It is exciting work. I will tell you more when the bridge is finally done.

Love to everyone,

Chang Shu

Assessment Tip: 6 Points
Grade 3, Unit 1

Cumulative Review

Read each clue. Unscramble the letters and write the word that answers the clue. Read the words you made.

1. This is a food. Many people eat it in the morning.   mtoeala   oatmeal (1 point)

2. You might do this if you do not want to do something.   anlcopmi   complain (1)

3. Cars drive fast on these kinds of roads. They have two or more lanes.   whgysiha   highways (1)

4. This is a way to heat bread.   tasot   toast (1)

5. This can take you across the sea, when it's windy.   alitabos   sailboat (1)

6. This number is the answer to these math problems: 5 X 3 and 5 + 5 + 5.   efnietf   fifteen (1)

7. There are four of these. They are winter, spring, summer, and fall.   eosnsas   seasons (1)

8. This is the color of a lemon.   lelwyo   yellow (1)

9. This describes something that never moves very quickly.   wols   slow (1)

10. This can help you find your way when you are driving.   pdraaom   roadmap (1)

Assessment Tip: Total 10 points
Grade 3, Unit 1

Name _____ Date _____

Common and Proper Nouns

Write the two nouns in each sentence. Circle the noun that is the subject of the sentence.

1. The (boys) watched the hotel being taken down. _____ boys, hotel (2 points)

2. A large (ball) knocked down the old walls. _____ ball, walls (2)

3. A new (building) would go up in that space. _____ building, space (2)

4. Soon, a huge (hole) was in the ground. _____ hole, ground (2)

Write *common* or *proper* for each underlined noun.

5. We learned about the Rocky Mountains in school. _____ proper (1)

6. My aunt came all the way from Canada. _____ proper (1)

7. The crowd rode horses. _____ common (1)

8. It was an exciting day. _____ common (1)

Write the sentences correctly. Capitalize the appropriate underlined words.

9. We went with mrs. benitez to the museum of natural history.

_____ We went with Mrs. Benitez to the Museum of Natural History. (1)

10. We bought a book called animals in the wild.

_____ We bought a book called Animals in the Wild. (1)

Name _____ Date _____

Charlie Shu has just been to the party at Robert's house to celebrate the opening day of the bridge. He is writing a journal entry about it.

Read pages 144–147. What was the party like for Charlie?

Today was opening day at the bridge! It was so thrilling. After we walked across the bridge, there was a big party at Robert's house.

There were a lot of people and food at the party. I felt excited because the bridge was finally done, and I got to celebrate with everyone. (5)

Remember that puzzle we were doing? Robert had the missing piece all along! My dad and Robert's dad put the piece in together. This made me feel happy because our dads finished the real bridge together and now they had finished the puzzle of the bridge together. (5)

For awhile I thought Robert believed his dad was better than mine. But now I know that he thinks our dads are the same. They both worked hard on the bridge. (5)

It was a really good day for a lot of reasons!

Name _____ Date _____

Word Families

Read each sentence. Use your understanding of the base word to figure out the meaning of the underlined word. Write the base word and the meaning of the underlined word.

1. The window display did not look good, so the crew had to <u>rethink</u> where to put the items.

   think; to think over or consider again (2 points)

2. The children were <u>clinging</u> to each other because of the cold wind.

   cling; sticking closely together (2)

3. The excitement over the team's win caused a <u>celebration</u> that lasted hours.

   celebrate; an activity that makes something special (2)

4. They <u>stretched</u> the rope across the yard.

   stretch; extended or reached from one end to the other (2)

5. As the day became <u>foggier</u>, it became impossible to see the mountains.

   fog; more covered in a cloud of water drops (2)

6. The player was balancing the basketball on one finger, spinning it <u>faster</u> and faster.

   fast; with more speed (2)

7. After another sock disappears, Dad buys a new package of <u>socks</u>.

   sock; more than one covering for the foot (2)

8. It was <u>unbelievable</u> how close the water came during the high tide.

   believe; not able to accept something as true (2)

Name _____ Date _____

Long *o* Spellings

In the spaces below, write a Spelling Word to complete each newspaper ad.

Spelling Words

Basic
1. load
2. open
3. told
4. yellow
5. soak
6. shadow
7. foam
8. follow
9. glow
10. sold
11. window
12. coach
13. almost
14. throat

Review
cold
most

Challenge
tomorrow
sailboats

1. The Shoe Store is _____ ! Come in and try on a pair of our great shoes.

2. _____ Washers We'll clean your glass!

3. Enjoy the _____ of a warm fire! Buy a _____ of our firewood.

4. Do you like baseball? Baseball _____ needed to work with children. Apply in person.

5. Garage Sale today and _____ . _____ the signs to our house.

6. Store Closing Sale We cannot close until everything is _____ .

1. open (1 point)
2. Window (1)
3. glow (1) , load (1)
4. coach (1)
5. tomorrow (1) , Follow (1)
6. sold (1)

Name _____ Date _____

Compound Sentences

- A **compound sentence** is made up of two **simple sentences** joined by a comma followed by a **conjunction**.
- The words *and*, *but*, *or*, and *so* are conjunctions.
- Two simple sentences that run together without using a comma and a conjunction are called a **run-on** sentence.

Simple sentences: Nina will go to the concert. She will go to the movies.

Run-on sentence: Nina will go to the concert she will go to the movies.

Compound sentence: Nina will go to the concert, or she will go to the movies.

Write the conjunction that best joins the two simple sentences into one compound sentence. Then write the compound sentence.

1. Roy wears his helmet. He wears his kneepads.

and; Roy wears his helmet, and he wears his kneepads. (1 point)

2. Betsy will use her gloves. She will borrow a pair.

or; Betsy will use her gloves, or she will borrow a pair. (1)

Correct the run-on sentence by using a comma and a conjunction to form a compound sentence.

3. Riding is fun I like hiking better.

Riding is fun, but I like hiking better. (1)

4. We can ride today we can hike tomorrow.

We can ride today, and we can hike tomorrow. (1)

Read directions to students.
Grammar
© Houghton Mifflin Harcourt Publishing Company. All rights reserved.

54

Assessment Tip: Total 4 points
Grade 3, Unit 1

Spelling Words

Basic
1. load
2. open
3. told
4. yellow
5. soak
6. shadow
7. foam
8. follow
9. glow
10. sold
11. window
12. coach
13. almost
14. throat

Review
cold
most

Challenge
tomorrow
sailboats

Name _____ Date _____

Proofreading for Spelling

Read the following newspaper article. Find and circle the misspelled words. (10 points)

Yelloaw Jackets Win First Game

The stadium was owpen for the game. Coch Smith and her players were ready. The game was sould out. Not even the coald weather kept people away. The crowd cheered as the team entered the stadium.

The first batter scored a run almowst right away. During the game, nine more players folloawed her lead. The Yellow Jackets left the other team in the shados.

A player towld me after the game that they intend to win every game this season. They will be put to the test tomorroaw when they play the Colts.

Write the misspelled words correctly on the lines below.

1. Yellow (1)
2. open (1)
3. Coach (1)
4. sold (1)
5. cold (1)
6. almost (1)
7. followed (1)
8. shadows (1)
9. told (1)
10. tomorrow (1)

Read directions to students.
Spelling
© Houghton Mifflin Harcourt Publishing Company. All rights reserved.

55

Assessment Tip: Total 20 points
Grade 3, Unit 1

Name _____ Date _____

Long *i* Spelled *i, ie, igh*

Read each sentence. Choose the missing word from the box. Write the word in the blank.

find	climb	fried
sights	wild	lie
sigh	untied	
tried	midnight	

1. I did not _____ find (1 point) _____ the book I was looking for.

2. The clock strikes twelve at _____ midnight (1) _____ .

3. Jasmine and her family went into the city to see the

_____ sights (1) _____ .

4. The _____ wild (1) _____ animal ran through the forest.

5. I would like to _____ climb (1) _____ a mountain some day.

6. I tripped over my shoelaces because they were

_____ untied (1) _____ .

7. The best dish at this restaurant is _____ fried (1) _____

chicken.

8. "I wish it would stop raining," Marty said with a

_____ sigh (1) _____ .

9. The police officer _____ tried (1) _____ to direct traffic.

10. George Washington once said, "I cannot tell a

_____ lie (1) _____

"

Read directions to students.

Phonics

Assessment Tip: Total 10 points

Grade 3, Unit 1

57

Name _____ Date _____

Connect to Writing

Using exact nouns helps make your writing clearer and more interesting.

Less-Exact Noun	More-Exact Noun
road	superhighway
area	valley

Replace each underlined noun in the sentences with a more exact noun. Use the nouns in the word box.

ranch	coyotes	ponies
thunderstorms	city	cowboys

1. Ernie saw two men through his binoculars. _____ cowboys (1 point)

2. They were rounding up some animals. _____ ponies (1)

3. Off to one side, some wild animals were hard to see. _____ coyotes (1)

4. Faraway, the sky was filled with rain. _____ thunderstorms (1)

5. They worked hard to get people back to their home. _____ ranch (1)

Correctly capitalize the proper noun, personal title, and book title.

6. (proper noun) new mexico _____ New Mexico (1)

7. (personal title) mrs. lopez _____ Mrs. Lopez (1)

8. (book title) amazing bridges from around the world

_____ Amazing Bridges from Around the World (1)

Read directions to students.

Grammar

Assessment Tip: Total 8 points

Grade 3, Unit 1

56

Name _____ Date _____

Identifying Singular and Plural Nouns

- A noun that names only one person, place, or thing is a **singular noun**. A noun that names more than one person, place, or thing is a **plural noun**.

- Add -s to most singular nouns to form the plural.

  The children played a ball game.
  The children played ball games.

  They ran from place to place.
  They ran to different places.

Write singular or plural for each underlined noun.

1. Many kids played ball games long ago. _____ plural (1 point)

2. The ball was made of cloth. _____ singular (1)

3. One player ran between two stones. _____ plural (1)

4. They would throw the ball at a runner. _____ singular (1)

Write the plural form of the noun in parentheses to complete the sentence.

5. Later, teams drew _____ lines (1) _____ on the field. (line)

6. Teams built _____ walls (1) _____ for another edge of the field. (wall)

7. Some _____ pitchers (1) _____ would throw the ball underhand. (pitcher)

8. Some games would last twelve _____ hours (1) _____. (hour)

Read directions to students.
Grammar 58
© Houghton Mifflin Harcourt Publishing Company. All rights reserved.

Assessment Tip: Total 8 points
Grade 3, Unit 1

Name _____ Date _____

Plural Nouns with -s

- Add -s to most nouns to form the plural.
  Singular: team   cap   bat
  Plural: teams   caps   bats

Write the plural form of the underlined noun.

1. They put a new stain on the floor.

   They tested two different _____ stains (1 point) _____ to see which would be darker.

2. Portia slipped and fell with a loud bang.

   A few minutes later, there were two louder _____ bangs (1)

3. The basketball player wore high-top sneakers.

   More _____ players (1) _____ started wearing them after the first game.

4. The light came on when he fell into the switch.

   After three people fell, more _____ lights (1) _____ came on.

5. They put a sign on the ground to warn people not to slip.

   At the end of the day, there were a dozen _____ signs (1) _____ in that area.

Read directions to students.
Grammar 59
© Houghton Mifflin Harcourt Publishing Company. All rights reserved.

Assessment Tip: Total 5 points
Grade 3, Unit 1

Name _____ Date _____

Focus Trait: Organization
Time-Order Words

Writers use transition words, or time-order words, to organize their writing, and to show when events happen. For example:

After they won the championship game, all the boys on Pedro's soccer team cheered and high-fived each other. Next, they went out for pizza to celebrate.

Read the following paragraph. In each blank, fill in the phrase from the box that fits best. Possible responses shown: (1 point each)

Then	Yesterday morning
Afterwards	During the game
Before I left the house	When I got to the field

1. __Yesterday morning__, I woke up with butterflies in my stomach. It was the day of my first softball game! Immediately, I jumped out of bed. 2. __Then__ I put on my new uniform and ran downstairs for breakfast. 3. __Before I left the house__, I reminded my mother to take the camera to the game. 4. __When I got to the field__, my teammates were there practicing. 5. __During the game__, I got two hits and one run! In the end, we won the game by one point. 6. __Afterwards__, my mother took me out for ice cream.

Assessment Tip: Total 6 points
Grade 3, Unit 1
Read directions to students.

Name _____ Date _____

Spelling Word Sort

Write each Basic Word under the correct heading.

Spelling Words

Basic
1. slight
2. mild
3. sight
4. pie
5. mind
6. tie
7. pilot
8. might
9. lie
10. tight
11. blind
12. fight
13. dies
14. midnight

Review
find
night

Challenge
silent
frightening

Long *i* Spelled *i*	Long *i* Spelled *ie*
mild (1 point)	pie (1)
mind (1)	tie (1)
pilot (1)	lie (1)
blind (1)	die (1)
Review: find (1)	

Long *i* Spelled *igh*

slight (1)	fight (1)
sight (1)	midnight (1)
might (1)	Review: night (1)
tight (1)	

Review: Add the Review Words to your Word Sort.

Challenge: What letter or letters form the long *i* sound in the two Challenge Words?

silent: *i* (1) ; frightening: *igh* (1)

Read directions to students.
Assessment Tip: Total 18 points
Grade 3, Unit 1

Name _____ Date _____

Cumulative Review

Write a word from the box to complete each sentence.

most	lightning	flowed
slimy	toast	railroad
tries	knights	
glowing	title	

1. Lava ___flowed (1 point)___ down the sides of the volcano and into the sea.

2. A bolt of ___lightning (1)___ suddenly flashed across the sky.

3. What is the ___title (1)___ of your favorite book?

4. For breakfast, Karl likes to eat ___toast (1)___ with peanut butter.

5. I love to watch the fireflies ___glowing (1)___ in the dark summer sky.

6. King Arthur and his ___knights (1)___ sat at a huge round table.

7. The worm felt ___slimy (1)___ when I touched it.

8. Always stop, look, and listen before crossing a ___railroad (1)___ track.

9. The athlete finally jumped over the bar after three ___tries (1)___.

10. Lee knew ___most (1)___ of the answers on the test, but not all of them.

Read directions to students.
Phonics
© Houghton Mifflin Harcourt Publishing Company. All rights reserved.

Assessment Tip: Total 10 points
Grade 3, Unit 1

Name _____ Date _____

Reader's Guide

Roberto Clemente

1960 World Series Program

The Pittsburgh Pirates are going to play the New York Yankees. Use examples from the text to fill out each section of the program for famous hitter Roberto Clemente.

Read page 170. Use the information on this page to tell how Clemente started out playing baseball.

1960 World Series
Pittsburgh Pirate Roberto Clemente

How Roberto Clemente Got Started

Roberto Clemente made his own baseball bat and glove and started playing on a field crowded with palm trees. (5 points)
_____
_____
_____

Read page 172. Use what you read to write about how Clemente ended up in Pittsburgh. What was it like for him?

Why Roberto Clemente Came to Pittsburgh

Roberto Clemente received an invitation to play baseball for the Pittsburgh Pirates. Everything was new and strange to him. (5)
_____
_____
_____

Read directions to students.
Independent Reading
© Houghton Mifflin Harcourt Publishing Company. All rights reserved.

Assessment Tip: 10 Points
Grade 3, Unit 1

Lesson 5
READER'S NOTEBOOK

Roberto Clemente
Independent Reading

Name _____ Date _____

Read pages 173–174. Why was Clemente's first game with the Pirates so important?

Roberto Clemente's First Game with the Pirates

At his first game, Roberto Clemente smacked the first pitch. He ran so fast and impressed the fans. (5)

_____

Read pages 175–176. Why did so many children love Roberto Clemente?

Roberto Clemente Has Many Fans

Children loved Roberto Clemente because they thought he had style. They copied everything he did. (5)

_____

Read page 177. How do you think Roberto Clemente felt right before the World Series? Why do you think he felt that way? Imagine you are Roberto Clemente and tell fans how you feel about playing in the World Series.

Roberto Clemente in His Own Words

Hi, baseball fans! I'm Roberto Clemente. The World Series is just about to begin. It's my first World Series! I am nervous to play in such important games. I am also very excited because I know people all over the world will be watching. I am going to work hard to play my best. (10)

Lesson 5
READER'S NOTEBOOK

Roberto Clemente
Grammar:
Plural Nouns with -s and -es

Name _____ Date _____

Plural Nouns with -s and -es

Write *singular* or *plural* for each underlined noun.

1. The fans went to find their <u>seats</u>. plural (1 point)

2. The popcorn seller brought them two <u>boxes</u>. plural (1)

3. Other fans passed a giant <u>ball</u> around. singular (1)

4. A foul ball sailed up into the stands from the <u>field</u>. singular (1)

5. Some fans had special <u>passes</u> that let them go onto the field. plural (1)

Write the plural form of the noun in parentheses to complete the sentence.

6. Two ___fences (1)___ had wire mesh that stopped foul balls. (fence)

7. People stood in the ___aisles (1)___ instead of sitting in their seats. (aisle)

8. The fans clapped for a series of great ___catches (1)___ of hard-hit balls. (catch)

9. The scoreboard could not show any ___sixes (1)___, because that number was broken. (six)

10. There were ___stacks (1)___ of programs to hand out to the fans. (stack)

Name _____ Date _____

Long i Spellings

Write a Basic Word to answer each question.

1. If you were eating a round dessert with a flaky crust, what would you be eating? **pie** (1 point)

2. What is the opposite of loose? **tight** (1)

3. What is the time when one day ends and another begins? **midnight** (1)

4. What would a man wear around his neck if he was getting dressed up? **tie** (1)

5. If you did not tell the truth, what did you tell? **lie** (1)

6. Who flies a plane? **pilot** (1)

7. What do you think with? **mind** (1)

8. What does a boxer have to do? **fight** (1)

Spelling Words

Basic
1. slight
2. mild
3. sight
4. pie
5. mind
6. tie
7. pilot
8. might
9. lie
10. tight
11. blind
12. fight
13. die
14. midnight

Review
find
night

Challenge
silent
frightening

Name _____ Date _____

Prefix mis-

Read the letter. Notice the underlined words. Write a reply to this letter. Use at least four of the underlined words in your letter. Possible response shown. (10 points)

Dear Friend,

I did not mean to misbehave or to mistreat you. I thought it was funny when someone mispronounced your name. I didn't think it would upset you, but I can see that I miscalculated that. If someone said I did not want to be your friend, then they are misinformed. Can we please forget about this misunderstanding?

Your friend

_____
_____

Dear Friend,

Thank you for your note. You are right. I do not like it when people mispronounce my name. I hope that you will not misbehave like this again. If you agree not to, then we can end this misunderstanding.

I promise not to mistreat you, either.

Your friend

_____
_____
_____
_____

Proofreading for Spelling

Lesson 5
READER'S NOTEBOOK

Roberto Clemente

Spelling:
Long i Spellings

Find the misspelled words and circle them. (10 points)

Plane Has Narrow Escape

A brave (pilot) saved the lives of her passengers yesterday when she saved an airplane from crashing.

Captain Jo Ann Foster was flying at 35,000 feet at (midnite) when her plane began to rock. There was only a (sliet) wind, so she knew her plane was in trouble. An engine was out, and the plane was sinking. Not only that, but thick fog made her have to fly (blighnd). She was in a (tite) spot.

Captain Foster quickly thought of things she (mite) do. Different ideas went through her (miend). She would have to (fite) to guide her plane to safety.

"I felt some (miled) fear," she said later, "but I was mainly thinking of how to save the plane and the passengers."

She found the nearest airport on the map and steered toward it. Finally, the airport came in (siet). Captain Foster made a perfect landing, and 147 passengers were safe.

Write the misspelled words correctly on the lines below.

1.	_____ pilot (1)	6.	_____ might (1)
2.	_____ midnight (1)	7.	_____ mind (1)
3.	_____ slight (1)	8.	_____ fight (1)
4.	_____ blind (1)	9.	_____ mild (1)
5.	_____ tight (1)	10.	_____ sight (1)

Read directions to students.
Spelling **69**
© Houghton Mifflin Harcourt Publishing Company. All rights reserved.

Assessment Tip: Total 20 points
Grade 3, Unit 1

Spelling Words

Basic
1. slight
2. mild
3. sight
4. pie
5. mind
6. tie
7. pilot
8. might
9. lie
10. tight
11. blind
12. fight
13. die
14. midnight

Review
find
night

Challenge
silent
frightening

Commas in Sentences

Lesson 5
READER'S NOTEBOOK

Roberto Clemente

Grammar:
Spiral Review

- **Commas** are used in a date or when listing city and state in a sentence.
- Commas are also used when combining sentences and when using nouns or verbs in a series.

On June 3, 1973, in Chicago, Illinois, they played baseball, football, and soccer.

Rewrite each sentence with a comma where it belongs in a date or a place.

1. They loaded the plane bringing supplies on December 29 1972. (2 points)

   They loaded the plane bringing supplies on December 29, 1972.

2. It was headed for Managua Nicaragua. (2)

   It was headed for Managua, Nicaragua.

Combine each group of sentences. Put the nouns or verbs in a series with commas. Write the new sentence.

3. The plane carried food. The plane carried water. The plane carried supplies. (2)

   The plane carried food, water, and supplies. (2)

4. A pilot was onboard. A baseball star was onboard. A helper was onboard. (2)

   A pilot, a baseball star, and a helper were onboard. (2)

Read directions to students.
Grammar **68**
© Houghton Mifflin Harcourt Publishing Company. All rights reserved.

Assessment Tip: Total 8 points
Grade 3, Unit 1

Name _____ Date _____

VCV Words with Long and Short Vowels

**Read each sentence. Choose the missing word from the box.
Write the word. Then reread the complete sentence.**

visit	robot	flavor
tiny	limit	shiver
report	decide	gravel

1. We took a bumpy ride down a ___gravel (1 point)___ road in the country.

2. Chocolate is my favorite ___flavor (1)___ of ice cream.

3. I ___limit (1)___ the amount of sweets that I eat.

4. My sister has a collection of ___tiny (1)___ glass animals.

5. I need to pick a topic for my ___report (1)___ .

6. It was hard to ___decide (1)___ which movie to watch.

7. The icy rain made me ___shiver (1)___ .

8. Steve hopes to ___visit (1)___ the Space Museum someday.

9. That interesting machine is called a ___robot (1)___ .

Read directions to students.
Phonics
© Houghton Mifflin Harcourt Publishing Company. All rights reserved.

71

Name _____ Date _____

Connect to Writing

Using the correct spelling of plural nouns makes your writing clearer and easier to understand. Add -s to form the plural of most singular nouns. Add -es to form the plural of a singular noun that ends with s, sh, ch, or x.

Sentences With Singular Nouns That Should be Plural Nouns	Sentences with Correct Plural Nouns
The baseball player tried two bat before choosing one.	The baseball player tried two bats before choosing one.
The teams sat on two bench.	The team sat on two benches.

**Circle the singular noun that should be plural in each sentence.
Then write the sentence using the plural spelling of the noun.**

1. The fans rode to the baseball game in ten (bus.) (1 point)
   The fans rode to the baseball game in ten buses. (1)

2. Most of the fans have already been to a few (game) this year. (1)
   Most of the fans have already been to a few games this year. (1)

3. Juan and Mary took their baseball (glove) to the game. (1)
   Juan and Mary took their baseball gloves to the game. (1)

4. The pitcher made two great (catch.) (1)
   The pitcher made two great catches. (1)

5. Another player made two good (toss) to first base. (1)
   Another player made two good tosses to first base. (1)

Read directions to students.
Grammar
© Houghton Mifflin Harcourt Publishing Company. All rights reserved.

70

Action Verbs

A word that tells what people or things do is a **verb**.
Words that show action, or something that is
done, are **action verbs**.

The owl **blinked** its eyes.

It **slept** in a hollow tree.

Thinking Question
What is the subject doing?

Each sentence has one action verb. Write the action verb on the line.

1. Some animals sleep during the day. _____ sleep (1 point)

2. They look for food at night. _____ look (1)

3. Owls see well in the dark. _____ see (1)

4. The owl spread its wings wide. _____ spread (1)

5. Then it flew from the tree. _____ flew (1)

6. It beat its wings quietly. _____ beat (1)

7. The owl spotted a small mouse. _____ spotted (1)

8. It swooped down for the mouse. _____ swooped (1)

9. The mouse hid in a hollow log. _____ hid (1)

10. The owl returned to its tree. _____ returned (1)

Read directions to students.

Grammar

Assessment Tip: Total 10 points

Grade 3, Unit 2

72

Being Verbs

Some verbs do not show action. The verbs *am, is, are,
was,* and *were* are examples of **being verbs**. They are
forms of the verb *be*. They tell what someone
or something is or was.

I *am* interested in bats.
I *was* proud of my knowledge of bats.
They *are* amazing flyers.
You *were* last at the zoo.
He *is* skilled at identifying bats.
We *were* excited at the zoo.

Am, is, and *are* show present tense. *Was* and *were*
show past tense.

Thinking Question
What does the sentence tell me about what the subject is or was?

Write the being verb on the line. Write *present* or *past* for each verb.

1. My father was nice to my class. _____ was, past (1 point)

2. He is kind and gives us his zoo passes. _____ is, present (1)

3. We were thankful. _____ were, past (1)

4. The boys are upset when they cannot go. _____ are, present (1)

5. You are good to help us. _____ are, present (1)

6. Most people are happy with the idea. _____ are, present (1)

7. They were surprised when we asked. _____ were, past (1)

8. They are annoyed sometimes but not often. _____ are, present (1)

9. I am careful to ask nicely. _____ am, present (1)

10. I was friendly to everyone. _____ was, past (1)

Read directions to students.

Grammar   73

Assessment Tip: Total 10 points

Grade 3, Unit 2

Name _____ Date _____

Spelling Word Sort

Write each Basic Word in the box where it belongs. You will
write words with two vowel sounds in more than one box.

Spelling Words

Basic
1. math
2. toast
3. easy
4. socks
5. Friday
6. stuff
7. paid
8. cheese
9. June
10. elbow
11. program
12. shiny
13. piles
14. sticky

Review
each
both

Challenge
comb
holiday

Vowel sound in *rope*	Vowel sound in *meet*
toast (1 point)	easy (1)
elbow (1)	cheese (1)
program (1)	shiny (1)
(challenge) comb (1)	sticky (1)

Vowel sound in *came*	Vowel sound in *bite*
Friday (1)	Friday (1)
paid (1)	shiny (1)
(challenge) holiday (1)	piles (1)

Vowel sound in *blue*	Vowel sound in *flat*
June (1)	math (1)
	program (1)

Vowel sound in *cup*	Vowel sound in *dress*
stuff (1)	elbow (1)

Vowel sound in *skip*	Vowel sound in *add*
sticky (1)	socks (1)
(challenge) holiday (1)	(challenge) holiday (1)

Challenge: Add the Challenge Words to your Word Sort.

Read directions to students.
Spelling

Assessment Tip: Total 23 points
Grade 3, Unit 2

74

Name _____ Date _____

Focus Trait: Evidence
Details and Examples

Writer's Idea	Details and Examples
Bats hang upside down.	Bats' toes are shaped like hooks, so it's no effort for a bat to hang upside down.

**A. Read each of the writer's ideas. Find the details and
examples from *Bat Loves the Night* that help explain the idea.
Complete the sentences.** Possible responses shown. (1 point each)

Writer's Idea	Details and Examples
1. Bats use their wings like we use our arms and hands.	A bat's wing is its arm and hand. Four extra-long fingers support the skin of the wing.
2. Bats use sound to locate things in the dark.	She beams her voice around her like a flashlight , and the echoes come singing back. They carry a sound picture of all her voice has touched.

**B. Read the writer's idea. Look at the pages from *Bat Loves the
Night*. Write details and examples that help explain the idea.**

Pair/Share Work with a partner to find sentences in the story
that include details and examples that support the writer's idea.

Writer's Idea	Details and Examples
3. Baby bats mature quickly.	Baby bats drink their mother's milk until they learn to fly at a few weeks old. Then they can leave the roost at night to find their own food. (2)

Possible response
shown.

Read directions to students.
Writing

Assessment Tip: Total 8 points
Grade 3, Unit 2

75

Cumulative Review

Write a word from the box to complete each sentence. Then read the complete sentence.

pilot	tiger
second	bacon
flavor	planet
	visit
	finish
	cabins

1. Can we play outside after we ___ finish (1 point) ___ our homework?

2. My cousins came to ___ visit (1) ___ us last summer.

3. As we were leaving the plane, the ___ pilot (1) ___ shook my hand.

4. The scouts stayed in small ___ cabins (1) ___ near the lake.

5. Chocolate is the ___ flavor (1) ___ of ice cream that I like best.

6. Would you like ___ bacon (1) ___ with your eggs?

7. Look! That reddish light in the sky is the ___ planet (1) ___ Mars!

8. Brad came in ___ second (1) ___ in the race, right behind Jay.

9. We watched a ___ tiger (1) ___ sleep under the tree.

Reader's Guide

Bat Loves the Night

File a Missing Bat Report

One night you were looking out of your window with your binoculars when you saw a bat flying through the sky. Scientists who are tracking the bat want some information, and you have that information. Fill out this missing bat report using information from the text.

Read pages 212–214. What was the first thing you saw the bat do when you looked out the window?

I saw the bat fly out into the garden from under the broken tile. (2 points)

_____

Read pages 215–217. Someone reported the bat was swooping and gliding through the sky. What do you think she was doing?

I think the bat was using sounds and echoes to find food. (2)

_____

Read pages 218–219. We have evidence that a moth showed up at some point. Did you see what happened? Tell us, step by step.

First, the moth flew below the bat. The bat grabs the moth. (2)

Then, the moth slithered out of the bat's mouth. (2)

Finally, the bat scooped the moth up again and ate it. (2)

Lesson 6
READER'S NOTEBOOK

Bat Loves the Night
Grammar:
What Is a Verb?

Action Verbs and Being Verbs

There is one action verb in each sentence. Write the verb on the line.

1. Randy looked for a book about bats. ___looked (1 point)___

2. He found one in the back shelf. ___found (1)___

3. He searched for new facts. ___searched (1)___

4. He learned that bats do not live in Antarctica. ___learned (1)___

5. He borrowed the book. ___borrowed (1)___

Write the being verb on the line. Then write *present* or *past.*

6. We are interested in nature. ___are, present (1)___

7. You were thoughtful to bring the binoculars. ___were, past (1)___

8. I am able to see through the binoculars. ___am, present (1)___

9. We are tired of walking in the heat. ___are, present (1)___

10. The bats were hidden in the caves. ___were, past (1)___

Read directions to students.
Grammar
© Houghton Mifflin Harcourt Publishing Company. All rights reserved.

Assessment Tip: Total 10 points
Grade 3, Unit 2

79

Lesson 6
READER'S NOTEBOOK

Bat Loves the Night
Independent Reading

Read pages 220–221. You are the only one to see where the bat went next. Describe what happened.

The bat flew back to the roof of the barn and swooped back

in under the tile. (2) _____

Read pages 222–224. We suspect that there are baby bats living in the barn. Tell us everything you know about the babies.

Yes, there are. The bat went inside and the baby bat

snuggled up with her. (2) _____

Read page 225. Now we think we know where the bat is. What do you think the bat is doing? When can we see this bat again?

The bat is sleeping now, but she will come out again

when it is dark outside. (2) _____

Read directions to students.
Independent Reading
© Houghton Mifflin Harcourt Publishing Company. All rights reserved.

Assessment Tip: 6 Points
Grade 3, Unit 2

78

Name _____ Date _____

Suffixes -able, -ible

Write a sentence using the words provided. Make sure the sentence helps the reader understand the meaning of the word.
Possible responses shown.

1. agreeable

Travis was agreeable to petting the friendly dog. (1 point)

2. valuable

Her collection of paintings is more valuable than her car. (1)

3. reversible

The hat is reversible, red on one side and grey on the other. (1)

4. comfortable

My most comfortable shirt is a soft t-shirt. (1)

5. breakable

Jenny hoped the plate was not easily breakable. (1)

6. sensible

Because of the clouds, he thought it was sensible to take an umbrella. (1)

7. spreadable

The soft cheese is spreadable. (1)

8. flexible

The flexible straw bends easily. (1)

Read directions to students.
Vocabulary Strategies
© Houghton Mifflin Harcourt Publishing Company. All rights reserved.

Assessment Tip: Total 8 points
Grade 3, Unit 2

Name _____ Date _____

More Short and Long Vowels

Write the Basic Words that match each heading.

Spelling Words

Basic
1. math
2. toast
3. easy
4. socks
5. Friday
6. stuff
7. paid
8. cheese
9. June
10. elbow
11. program
12. shiny
13. piles
14. sticky

Review
each
both

Challenge
comb
holiday

Proper Nouns

1. Friday (1 point)

2. June (1)

Common Nouns

3. math (1)   7. cheese (1)

4. toast (1)   8. elbow (1)

5. socks (1)   9. program (1)

6. stuff (1)   10. piles (1)

Describing Words

11. easy (1)

12. shiny (1)

13. sticky (1)

Verb

14. paid (1)

On the line below, write a sentence using one word from each group above. Possible response shown.

15. On Friday, my mother paid for piles of shiny stuff. (2)

_____

Read directions to students.
Spelling
© Houghton Mifflin Harcourt Publishing Company. All rights reserved.

Assessment Tip: Total 16 points
Grade 3, Unit 2

Lesson 6
READER'S NOTEBOOK

Bat Loves the Night
Spelling:
More Short and Long Vowels

Spelling Words

Basic
1. math
2. toast
3. easy
4. socks
5. Friday
6. stuff
7. paid
8. cheese
9. June
10. elbow
11. program
12. shiny
13. piles
14. sticky

Review
each
both

Challenge
comb
holiday

Proofreading for Spelling

Find the misspelled words and circle them. (10 points)

(Jun)1: This was a great day! It started out like any other (Frieday.) I did all the usual (stufe.) I got dressed, put on my shoes and (soks,) and ate some (tost) and jam. But as I started to (coamb) my hair, I heard kids playing outside. For a minute, I thought it might be a (holliday.) Then suddenly I remembered that school is out. This is the first day of summer vacation! There are no more (mathe)tests, no more (pils) of homework, and no more long days of sitting still.

The rest of the day was perfect. I played kickball with my friends, rode my bike, and went to the pool. It was so much fun that I think I'll do it all again tomorrow. Or maybe I'll just read a book and take it (eazy.) I love summer!

Write the misspelled words correctly on the lines below.

1. _____ June (1)
2. _____ Friday (1)
3. _____ stuff (1)
4. _____ socks (1)
5. _____ toast (1)

6. _____ comb (1)
7. _____ holiday (1)
8. _____ math (1)
9. _____ piles (1)
10. _____ easy (1)

Read directions to students.
Spelling
© Houghton Mifflin Harcourt Publishing Company. All rights reserved.

Assessment Tip: Total 20 points
Grade 3, Unit 2

83

Lesson 6
READER'S NOTEBOOK

Bat Loves the Night
Grammar: Spiral Review

Complete Subjects and Predicates

- A sentence is a group of words that tells a complete thought and has a complete subject and a complete predicate.
- The **subject** tells whom or what the sentence is about and usually comes at the beginning of the sentence.
- The **predicate** tells what the subject does or is, and it can be one word or more than one word.

Many different words tell about the same idea.

Subject	Predicate

Write the subject or the predicate of each sentence.

1. Tommy cut pictures from the magazine. (subject) _____ Tommy (1 point)

2. He and his friends glued them to a poster. (predicate) _____ glued them to a poster (1)

Combine each pair of sentences. Use a conjunction to form a compound subject in each new sentence. Write the new sentence on the line.

3. My friends gathered magazines about animals. The teachers gathered magazines about animals. (1 point)

My friends and the teachers gathered magazines about animals.

4. The kids carried the magazines. The teachers carried the magazines. (1)

The kids and teachers carried the magazines.

Read directions to students.
Grammar
© Houghton Mifflin Harcourt Publishing Company. All rights reserved.

Assessment Tip: Total 4 points
Grade 3, Unit 2

82

Name _____ Date _____

Connect to Writing

If the subject you are writing about is doing more than one action, you can tell about it in one sentence. You can combine more than one simple predicate to form a compound predicate. This can help make your sentences longer and less choppy.

Short Sentences with Simple Predicates	Longer, Smoother Sentence with Compound Predicate
Bat opens her eyes. Bat twitches her ears.	Bat opens her eyes and twitches her ears.
My father saw a bat. My father took a picture of it.	My father saw a bat and took a picture of it.

Combine each pair of sentences. Use a compound predicate in each new sentence. Write the new sentence on the line.

1. I like to read about bats. I like to write stories about them.

   I like to read about bats and write stories about them. (2 points)

2. The bat flew by the streetlight. The bat soared toward the pond.

   The bat flew by the streetlight and soared toward the pond. (2)

3. My brother drew a picture of a bat. My brother gave it to me.

   My brother drew a picture of a bat and gave it to me. (2)

4. I found a book about bats in the library. I brought it home.

   I found a book about bats in the library and brought it home. (2)

Name _____ Date _____

Three-Letter Clusters

Read each question and choose an answer from the box. Write the word.

screwdriver	springtime	strongest
throne	scrubbing	unscramble
sprinkler	thrilling	streetlight

1. What do you call the person who can lift the heaviest load? _____ strongest (1 point)

2. What lights the neighborhood on nights when there is no moon in the sky? _____ streetlight (1)

3. How would it feel to have an audience stand and applaud for you? _____ thrilling (1)

4. When do most trees grow new leaves? _____ springtime (1)

5. What helps grass grow when there is no rain? _____ sprinkler (1)

6. What is kept in a toolbox and can help put things together? _____ screwdriver (1)

7. What is the best way to get dirty hands clean? _____ scrubbing (1)

8. What is a queen's chair called? _____ throne (1)

9. How can you make a word from a set of mixed-up letters? _____ unscramble (1)

Name _____ Date _____

Present, Past, and Future Tense

Thinking Question
In what tense does the action of the verb occur, and what ending does the verb have?

Many verbs in the **present tense** with singular subjects use an *-s* ending. Verbs in the present tense with plural subjects do not use an ending.
Many verbs in the **past tense** use an *-ed* ending.
Verbs in the **future tense** use the helping verb *will*.

The artist paints a curving line.	present
The artists paint a curving line.	present
The artist painted a curving line.	past
The artist will paint a curving line.	future

Write *present* if the underlined verb shows present tense. Write *past* if the underlined verb shows past tense. Write *future* if the underlined verb shows future tense.

1. My friends and I <u>walked</u> to the library. _____ past (1 point)
2. We will <u>search</u> for interesting picture books. _____ future (1)
3. Lora <u>flips</u> through many books. _____ present (1)
4. Kitty <u>stacked</u> the books that we liked. _____ past (1)
5. Roberto and Vera <u>look</u> for the best ones. _____ present (1)
6. Quentin will <u>place</u> a marker at the colorful ones. _____ future (1)
7. Tory <u>loves</u> art with bright colors. _____ present (1)
8. Walt <u>prefers</u> art drawn with colored pencils. _____ present (1)

Read directions to students.
Assessment Tip: Total 8 points
Grammar 87 Grade 3, Unit 2
© Houghton Mifflin Harcourt Publishing Company. All rights reserved.

Name _____ Date _____

Present and Past Tense

Thinking Question
In what tense does the action of the verb occur, and what ending does the verb have?

Many verbs in the **present tense** have an *-s* ending with a singular subject. Many verbs in the present tense do not have an *-s* ending with a plural subject. Most verbs in the **past tense** have an *-ed* ending.

An artist paints paintings.	present
Artists paint paintings.	present
An artist painted paintings yesterday.	past

Write *present* if the underlined verb shows the present tense.
Write *past* if the underlined verb shows the past tense.

1. Our class <u>gathers</u> pages for a book. _____ present (1 point)
2. We <u>combined</u> them into a small book. _____ past (1)
3. We <u>fold</u> some pages in two. _____ present (1)
4. Other students <u>traced</u> lines for borders. _____ past (1)
5. Carmen <u>cuts</u> the rough edges. _____ present (1)
6. Walt and John <u>iron</u> the pages flat. _____ present (1)
7. Some older kids <u>poked</u> holes in the page. _____ past (1)
8. One group ties <u>string</u> through the holes. _____ present (1)
9. The string <u>pulled</u> the pages together. _____ past (1)
10. In the last step, we <u>cover</u> it with thick paper. _____ present (1)

Read directions to students.
Assessment Tip: Total 10 points
Grammar 86 Grade 3, Unit 2
© Houghton Mifflin Harcourt Publishing Company. All rights reserved.

Name _____ Date _____

Focus Trait: Purpose
Topic Sentence

Good writers of opinion paragraphs include a topic sentence that states an opinion. The topic sentence helps readers understand the writer's purpose for writing. This makes an opinion stronger and more convincing. Compare the following sentences.

Weak Topic Sentence: Illustrators work on drawings.
Strong Topic Sentence: Illustrators often do very interesting work.

Read each paragraph. Revise the topic sentence in each paragraph to state an opinion. Possible responses shown.

1. Have you thought about composting leaves in the fall? That means you put the leaves in a pile instead of in the trash. The leaves eventually break down and can be added to gardening beds.

   It's a good idea to compost leaves in the fall. (2 points)
   _____

2. Many people exercise. Exercise helps people maintain a healthy weight. It also gives people more energy throughout the day.

   Everyone should exercise regularly for better health. (2)
   _____

Assessment Tip: Total 4 points
Grade 3, Unit 2

89

Name _____ Date _____

Spelling Word Sort

Write each Basic Word in the box where it belongs.

Spelling Words

Basic
1. three
2. scrap
3. street
4. spring
5. thrill
6. scream
7. strange
8. throw
9. string
10. scrape
11. spray
12. threw
13. strong
14. scratch

Review
think
they

Challenge
straight
scramble

scr	spr
scrap (1 point)	spring (1)
scream (1)	spray (1)
scrape (1)	
scratch (1)	
(challenge) scramble (1)	

str	thr
street (1)	three (1)
strange (1)	thrill (1)
string (1)	throw (1)
strong (1)	threw (1)
(challenge) straight (1)	

Challenge: Add the Challenge Words to your Word Sort.

Assessment Tip: Total 16 points
Grade 3, Unit 2

88

Name _____ Date _____

What Do Illustrators Do?

A Comic Book Guide to Illustrated Books

Now that you know what illustrators do, you can write about it in your own comic. Use examples from the text to help explain how an illustrated book is made.

Create a comic using the cat and the dog that watched as the illustrations were created.

Draw and write what illustrators do. Use details from page 246 for Step 1 and page 247 for Step 2.

First, an illustrator makes a plan and a dummy of the book. (Students should include a drawing using the cat and the dog.) (5 points)

Then, the illustrator makes sketches. (Students should include an illustration using the cat and the dog.) (5)

Step 1

Step 2

Assessment Tip: 10 Points
Grade 3, Unit 2

Name _____ Date _____

Cumulative Review

Write words from the box to complete each paragraph.

threw	scratched	strong
screen	through	described
stretched	screamed	strange

Ray couldn't find the key to his house. He __scratched (1 point)__ his head
                                                                    1
and tried to remember where he had seen it last. He went to the school
office and __described (1)__ his lost key chain. The clerk looked
                    2
__through (1)__ the Lost and Found box and found the key chain.
         3
Ray was grateful that someone had turned in his key!

***

Emily shivered as she looked out the window into the dark, foggy night.
Suddenly she heard a __strange (1)__ noise coming from the back yard!
                                4
She tiptoed to the back of the house and pushed open the __screen (1)__
                                                                         5
door. She heard someone pound on the house and say, "Boo!" Emily
__screamed (1)__. Then her brother stepped into the light and they both
        6
laughed.

***

There was once a troll so mean and so tough that no one in the village
was __strong (1)__ enough to fight him. The villagers __stretched (1)__
          7   8
out a huge net on the ground and hid next to their houses. When the troll
came to town and stepped onto the net, the people wrapped him up, carried
him out of town, and __threw (1)__ him into a big mud puddle. The
                                9
troll never came back!

Assessment Tip: Total 9 points
Grade 3, Unit 2

Name _____ Date _____

Present, Past, and Future Tense

Write *present* if the underlined verb shows present tense.
Write *past* if the underlined verb shows past tense.

1. Bill, the artist, selects a wall for art. ___present___ (1 point)

2. He looked everywhere for a good wall. ___past___ (1)

3. Some kids live near this wall. ___present___ (1)

4. The owner allowed us to paint it. ___past___ (1)

5. Bill climbs on a tall ladder. ___present___ (1)

Write *present* if the underlined verb shows present tense. Write
past if the underlined verb shows past tense. Write *future* if the
underlined verb shows future tense.

6. The artist will measure the wall first. ___future___ (1)

7. The colors drip down the wall. ___present___ (1)

8. Someone else painted this wall long ago. ___past___ (1)

9. When it is done, people will enjoy the wall. ___future___ (1)

10. The new art stretches high into the sky. ___present___ (1)

Read directions to students.
Grammar
Assessment Tip: Total 10 points
Grade 3, Unit 2

Name _____ Date _____

Read page 251. What do illustrators do to help them
draw faces? Use what you learned to have the dog tell
the cat two details from page 251 about drawing faces.

| She looks at her expressions in the mirror. (Students should include an illustration of the dog talking to the cat.) (5) | Sometimes illustrators get another person to model for them. (Students should include an illustration of the dog talking to the cat.) (5) |

How Illustrators Draw Faces

Read page 258. In this comic, draw the cat talking about what
she learned from the cover of *Jacqueline & the Magic Bean*. What
does this cover tell you about the story?

In this book, a girl instead of a boy is going to climb the
beanstalk. (Students should include an illustration using
the cat.) (5)

Jacqueline & the Magic Bean

Read directions to students.
Independent Reading
Assessment Tip: 15 Points
Grade 3, Unit 2

Name _____ Date _____

Three-Letter Clusters

Write the Basic Word that is an antonym of the underlined word in each sentence.

1. Why did you choose such a common costume?

2. My uncle helped me learn how to catch a ball.

3. The fall is my favorite time of year.

4. Please spread the mud from your boots before coming in.

5. The surprise party was a big bore for me!

6. Are you weak enough to lift this heavy box?

7. Don't whisper in the library.

8. Everyone caught confetti to celebrate the new year.

1. strange (1 point)   5. _____ thrill (1)

2. _____ throw (1)   6. _____ strong (1)

3. _____ spring (1)   7. _____ scream (1)

4. _____ scrape (1)   8. _____ threw (1)

Challenge: Write a word that means the opposite of each Challenge Word. Possible responses shown.

9. _____ bent, curved, round, crooked, curly (1)

10. _____ unscramble (1)

Use one of the Challenge Words and its antonym in a sentence.

11. My hair is straight, but my sister's hair is curly. (1)

Spelling Words

Basic
1. three
2. scrap
3. street
4. spring
5. thrill
6. scream
7. strange
8. throw
9. string
10. scrape
11. spray
12. threw
13. strong
14. scratch

Review
think
they

Challenge
straight
scramble

Name _____ Date _____

Synonyms

sketch	large	see
view	show	illustrate
polite	pleasant	enormous
		exhibit

Read each word below. Write the two synonyms from above that have almost the same meaning as the word.

1. display

   show, exhibit (2 points)

2. huge

   large, enormous (2)

3. nice

   pleasant, polite (2)

4. observe

   view, see (2)

5. draw

   illustrate, sketch (2)

Choose one set of synonyms. Write a sentence or two for each word to show the difference in the shades of meaning. Possible response shown.

6. I sketched my idea quickly. Later, I will use the sketch to

   illustrate my poem. (2)

   _____

   _____

Name _____ Date _____

Kinds of Sentences

- There are four kinds of sentences.

The art is wonderful.	**Declarative** (statement)
Who made that piece?	**Interrogative** (question)
Pick up the mess you made.	**Imperative** (command)
What a bold color she used!	**Exclamatory** (exclamation)

Write *statement* if the sentence tells something. Write *question* if the sentence asks something.

1. We walked outside to paint. ___statement (1 point)___

2. Who is going to come with us? ___question (1)___

3. Why are we going outside? ___question (1)___

Write *command* if the sentence tells someone to do something.
Write *exclamation* if the sentence shows strong feeling.

4. Painting outside is fun! ___exclamation (1)___

5. Do not spill paint out here. ___command (1)___

6. Create a painting with bold colors. ___command (1)___

Read directions to students.
Assessment Tip: Total 6 points
Grammar
Grade 3, Unit 2
© Houghton Mifflin Harcourt Publishing Company. All rights reserved.

Name _____ Date _____

Proofreading for Spelling

Find the misspelled words and circle them. (10 points)

Coming Soon!

War of the Giants

In the (sterange) world of the future, giant animals roam the earth. But what happens when the beasts come together in the last city on Earth? See these (thse) monsters clash in the biggest battle of all time!

Birdzilla This giant bird has claws (srong) enough to (scratch) through solid rock. It is headed (steraight) for the city!

The Ape King When angry, this towering ape can lift a car off the (steet) and (thow) it into the air. People (skream) and run. But can they get away?

The Night Croc This huge crocodile waits at the edge of town. When you least expect it, he will (sping) out of the dark and attack. This movie is filled with (thills) and surprises.

Don't Miss It!

Write the misspelled words correctly on the lines below.

1. ___strange (1)___
2. ___three (1)___
3. ___strong (1)___
4. ___scratch (1)___
5. ___straight (1)___
6. ___street (1)___
7. ___throw (1)___
8. ___scream (1)___
9. ___spring (1)___
10. ___thrills (1)___

Read directions to students.
Assessment Tip: Total 20 points
Spelling
Grade 3, Unit 2
© Houghton Mifflin Harcourt Publishing Company. All rights reserved.

Spelling Words

Basic
1. three
2. scrap
3. street
4. spring
5. thrill
6. scream
7. strange
8. throw
9. string
10. scrape
11. spray
12. threw
13. strong
14. scratch

Review
think
they

Challenge
straight
scramble

Name _____ Date _____

Silent Letters *kn*, *wr*

Read each line of the poem. Choose the missing word from the box. Write the word.

wring	wrists	knight
wrapped	knot	wrong
kneel	wrinkles	knee

Handy Things to Remember

To keep a gift a secret, keep it __wrapped (1 point)__ and out of sight.
1

To fight a pesky dragon, call a strong and fearless __knight (1)__ !
2

If one string isn't long enough, get two and make a __knot (1)__ .
3

To get the answers right, not __wrong (1)__ , remember what you're
4
taught.

To make a wet sponge dry, you need to __wring (1)__ it out.
5

Hold it tightly with both hands and twist your __wrists (1)__ about.
6

Wear __knee (1)__ pads when you're skating to keep from getting hurt.
7

To look your best, make sure there are no __wrinkles (1)__ in your shirt.
8

If you __kneel (1)__ in an anthill, stand up as quickly as you can.
9

If you forget these handy tips, just read them all again!

Read directions to students.
Phonics
© Houghton Mifflin Harcourt Publishing Company. All rights reserved.

99

Name _____ Date _____

Connect to Writing

If all of the action in a paragraph happens during the same time, keep the verbs in the same tense.

Incorrect Paragraph

Next year, I will take an art class. Other students and I paint pictures of one another. We will study drawing and painting.

Correct Paragraph

Next year, I will take an art class. Other students and I will paint pictures of one another. We will study drawing and painting.

Read this paragraph. Change each underlined verb to make it match the tense of the other verbs. Write the new sentences on the lines below.

Maybe twenty years from now, cars will be very different than they are now. Drivers <u>enter</u> an address into a computer. The car will go to that place, and the driver will be able to read or take a nap! Cars <u>serve</u> drinks and snacks. Cars slow down automatically when there is a stop sign ahead. All cars run on energy from the sun. Cars of the future <u>have</u> exciting features!

1. Drivers will enter an address into a computer. (2 points)
   _____

2. Cars will serve drinks and snacks. (2)
   _____

3. Cars will slow down automatically when there is a stop sign ahead. (2)
   _____

4. All cars will run on energy from the sun. (2)
   _____

5. Cars of the future will have exciting features! (2)
   _____

Read directions to students.
Grammar
© Houghton Mifflin Harcourt Publishing Company. All rights reserved.

98

Lesson 8
READER'S NOTEBOOK

The Harvest Birds
Grammar:
Using Commas

Commas in a Series of Verbs

Thinking Question
Are there three or more words listed in the sentence?

A **series** is a list of three or more words used in a sentence. Use commas to separate three or more verbs included in a series. Commas tell readers when to pause.

Juan planted, watered, and harvested vegetables.

Write each sentence correctly. Add commas where they are needed. If no commas are needed, write *No Commas* on the line.

1. I plan write and correct my folktale.

I plan, write, and correct my folktale. (1 point)

2. The animals in my story walk talk and snore.

The animals in my story walk, talk, and snore. (1)

3. My friends listened laughed and clapped as I read my story.

My friends listened, laughed, and clapped as I read my story. (1)

4. A snake trapped and tried to eat a frog in Ron's folktale.

No Commas (1)

5. The frog danced jumped and ran away from the snake.

The frog danced, jumped, and ran away from the snake. (1)

Read directions to students.
Assessment Tip: Total 5 points
Grade 3, Unit 2

Lesson 8
READER'S NOTEBOOK

The Harvest Birds
Grammar:
Using Commas

Commas in a Series of Nouns

Thinking Question
Are there three or more words listed together in the sentence?

A series is a list of three or more words used in a sentence. Use **commas** to separate three or more nouns included in a series. Commas tell readers when to pause.

Juan grew beans, corn, and tomatoes.

Write each sentence correctly. Add commas where they are needed.

1. Jamal Tina and Ed want to write their own folktales.

Jamal, Tina, and Ed want to write their own folktales. (1 point)

2. Their class is having a contest for plays poems and folktales.

Their class is having a contest for plays, poems, and folktales. (1)

3. The friends read stories on Monday Tuesday and Wednesday.

The friends read stories on Monday, Tuesday, and Wednesday. (1)

4. Jamal read folktales about crows fish and cats.

Jamal read folktales about crows, fish, and cats. (1)

5. Tina likes the folktales of England Spain and Mexico.

Tina likes the folktales of England, Spain, and Mexico. (1)

6. Folktales can take place in deserts jungles and cities.

Folktales can take place in deserts, jungles, and cities. (1)

Read directions to students.
Assessment Tip: Total 6 points
Grade 3, Unit 2

Name _____ Date _____

Focus Trait: Elaboration
Using Linking Words

Linking words and phrases can connect supporting reasons to opinions in a paragraph. This makes the author's ideas easier to understand.

Linking Words

because	since
therefore	for example

Rewrite each passage so a linking word or phrase connects the reason to the opinion. Possible responses shown.

1. The male peacock is the most beautiful bird. It has shimmering purple and green feathers.

   The male peacock is the most beautiful bird because it has shimmering purple and green feathers. (1 point)

2. Our zoo has animals from many places. It has rare orangutans, pandas, and polar bears.

   Our zoo is very unique. For example, it has rare orangutans, pandas, and polar bears. (1)

3. The garden in our back yard is unusual. We built it on a hill.

   The garden in our back yard is unusual, since we built it on a hill. (1)

4. Our pumpkin was the best in the fair. It won first place.

   Our pumpkin was the best in the fair. Therefore, it won first place. (1)

Read directions to students.

Writing 103

Assessment Tip: Total 4 points

Grade 3, Unit 2

Name _____ Date _____

Spelling Word Sort

Spelling Words

Basic
1. itch
2. wreck
3. knee
4. patch
5. wrap
6. knot
7. watch
8. knife
9. stretch
10. write
11. knew
12. knock
13. match
14. wrong

Review
know
catch

Challenge
wrinkle
knuckle

Write each Basic Word in the web where it belongs.

wr: wreck (1 point), wrap (1), (challenge) wrinkle (1), write (1), wrong (1)

kn: (challenge) knuckle (1), knee (1), knot (1), knife (1), knock (1), knew (1)

tch: itch (1), patch (1), watch (1), match (1), stretch (1)

Challenge: Add the Challenge Words to your Word Sort. Write each one near the correct group, and draw a line to connect it to the web.

Read directions to students.

Spelling 102

Assessment Tip: Total 16 points

Grade 3, Unit 2

Name _____ Date _____

Reader's Guide

The Harvest Birds

A Radio Interview

The harvest birds have come in for a special radio interview. They saw everything that happened to Juan Zanate, and they are ready to tell his story. Use details from the text to answer the interviewer's questions.

Read pages 285–292.

Interviewer: Juan Zanate was looking for land for a long time. Finally, Grandpa Chon agreed to give him some. You were there and saw what happened next. Please explain what happened.

Harvest Birds: None of the townspeople believed that Juan Zanate could grow anything, and they all laughed at him. We helped him because he was so kind to us. (5 points)
_____
_____

Interviewer: Why did the farmers laugh at Juan Zanate?

Harvest Birds: The farmers laughed because they thought planting weeds on the border of the field was a crazy idea. (5)
_____

Assessment Tip: 10 Points

105

Grade 3, Unit 2

Name _____ Date _____

Cumulative Review

Write words from the box to complete the lines of the play.

know	wrong	wrote
threw	knees	through
knickknacks	wrap	knocked

Granny and the Rascal

Granny Gopher: Who _knocked_ (1 point) over my beautiful vase?

Rascal Raccoon: Why are you so upset about a silly old vase? You have plenty of other _knickknacks_ (1) sitting around.

Granny Gopher: That vase was special. Great-Granny Gopher gave it to me. Now, is there something you'd like to confess?

Rascal Raccoon: I _know_ (1) that you think I broke that vase, but I never went near it.

Granny Gopher: That's what you said after you _threw_ (1) a baseball _through_ (1) my window.

Rascal Raccoon: You were _wrong_ (1) about that, too.

Granny Gopher: There were witnesses to that crime. Skunk and Rabbit _wrote_ (1) me a note saying they *saw* you break the window.

Rascal Raccoon: You can't trust what those tattle-tales say!

Granny Gopher: You can at least clean up this broken glass. It's hard for me to get down on my sore old _knees_ (1) to do a job like this.

Rascal Raccoon: Uh, sure, Granny Gopher. I have to _wrap_ (1) a present for Rabbit's birthday party right now. But I'll stop by and help you later. *I promise!*

Assessment Tip: Total 9 points

104

Grade 3, Unit 2

Name _____ Date _____

Read pages 293–297.

Interviewer: Juan had a great harvest at the end of the summer. How did people react to this?

Harvest Birds: Everyone was amazed. They wanted to learn the secret to his great harvest. (5)

Interviewer: Now just between us, what is your secret?

Harvest Birds: We told him to plant the weeds around the border because plants need to grow together. They should never be separated. (5)

Interviewer: Well, thank you, harvest birds! I think we have a better understanding of Juan Zanate now. Is there anything you would like to add?

Harvest Birds: (Accept any reasonable responses that relate to the birds and the story.) (5)

Read directions to students.
Independent Reading
© Houghton Mifflin Harcourt Publishing Company. All rights reserved.

106

Assessment Tip: 15 Points
Grade 3, Unit 2

Name _____ Date _____

Commas in Addresses

- Use a comma to separate each part of an address.

  Susan Henley, 29 Wylie Lane, Ocoee, Florida

Write each address correctly. Add commas where they are needed.

1. Tammy Ruiz 14 Silver Brook Road Dallas Texas

   Tammy Ruiz, 14 Silver Brook Road, Dallas, Texas. (1 point)

2. Wayne Thomas 1170 South Pleasant Street Belding Michigan

   Wayne Thomas, 1170 South Pleasant Street, Belding, Michigan. (1)

3. The package is going to Dave Layler 73 Bent Road Remsen New York.

   The package is going to Dave Layler, 73 Bent Road, Remsen, New York. (1)

4. My friend lives at 87 Moore Avenue Glendale California.

   My friend lives at 87 Moore Avenue, Glendale, California. (1)

5. We are moving to 60 Myrtle Street Addis Louisiana.

   We are moving to 60 Myrtle Street, Addis, Louisiana. (1)

6. The letter is from Lucy Rawly 170 Adobe Way Albuquerque New Mexico.

   The letter is from Lucy Rawly, 170 Adobe Way, Albuquerque, New Mexico. (1)

Read directions to students.
Grammar
© Houghton Mifflin Harcourt Publishing Company. All rights reserved.

107

Assessment Tip: Total 6 points
Grade 3, Unit 2

Name _____ Date _____

Context Clues

Read each sentence. Use context clues to figure out the meaning of the underlined word. Use a dictionary to check that your meanings are correct. Possible responses shown.

1. Did you <u>note</u> our meeting on your calendar?

   write down (2 points)

2. We needed another <u>yard</u> of yarn to finish the sewing project.

   36 inches, or 3 feet (2)

3. I didn't win, but I didn't feel <u>bitter</u> about it.

   angry or having a hard time accepting something (2)

4. She always hangs up her coat, so it was odd that she <u>misplaced</u> it.

   lost; put in the wrong place (2)

5. The <u>shallow</u> bowl only held a little bit of water.

   not very deep (2)

6. Tina was <u>mortified</u> when she fell in front of the school.

   embarrassed (2)

Assessment Tip: Total 12 points
Grade 3, Unit 2

Name _____ Date _____

Unexpected Consonant Spellings

Write the Basic Word that best completes each sentence.

Spelling Words

Basic
1. itch
2. wreck
3. knee
4. patch
5. wrap
6. knot
7. watch
8. knife
9. stretch
10. write
11. knew
12. knock
13. match
14. wrong

Review
know
catch

Challenge
wrinkle
knuckle

1. Your elbow and your ___knee (1 point)___ are both body parts that can bend.

2. A pair of scissors and a ___knife (1)___ are both tools for cutting.

3. To share a story, you can tell it to someone or ___write (1)___ it down.

4. Two things that can have a flame are a candle and a ___match (1)___ .

5. To tell the time, you can look at a clock or check your ___watch (1)___ .

6. To let someone know you're at the door, ring the bell or ___knock (1)___ .

7. You can tie a bow or just tie a ___knot (1)___ .

8. A rubber band and bubble gum are both things that can ___stretch (1)___ .

Challenge: Name something that is similar to a knuckle. Then write to tell how the two things are alike. Possible responses shown.

9. ___a knee (1)___

10. ___A knuckle is where your finger bends. A knee is where your leg bends. (1)___

Assessment Tip: Total 10 points
Grade 3, Unit 2

Sentence Fragments

- A **sentence** is a group of words that tells a complete thought. It tells who or what, and it tells an action or state of being.

  A man planted seeds in his garden.

Write the group of words that will complete each sentence.

lives in the tree   on the fence

1. A bird _____ lives in the tree (1 point)

2. Rabbits _____ like to eat garden vegetables

soft and cute   like to eat garden vegetables

    Rabbits (1) _____ like to eat garden vegetables (1)

3. _____ are vegetable eaters.

Rabbits   Usually

    Rabbits (1)

4. _____ ate the whole garden of flowers.

A herd of goats (1)

Broke through a fence   A herd of goats

For each item, combine the two fragments to write a complete sentence.

5. A bird is. a clever but shy animal.

    A bird is a clever but shy animal. (1)

6. A garden needs. a fence that can keep animals out.

    A garden needs a fence that can keep animals out. (1)

Read directions to students.

Grammar
© Houghton Mifflin Harcourt Publishing Company. All rights reserved.

110

Assessment Tip: Total 6 points

Grade 3, Unit 2

Proofreading for Spelling

Spelling Words

1. itch
2. wreck
3. knee
4. patch
5. wrap
6. knot
7. watch
8. knife
9. stretch
10. write
11. knew
12. knock
13. match
14. wrong

Review
know
catch

Challenge
wrinkle
knuckle

Find the misspelled words and circle them. (10 points)

Lost Hiker Rescued on Big Pine Trail

Thanks to her own quick thinking, 10-year-old Rosa Gomez was rescued along Big Pine Trail on Saturday. The girl had stopped to (wach) a group of deer and lost her hiking group. She tried to catch up but took the (rong) trail. Rosa (new) she was lost and wanted to leave clues to help someone find her. She decided to (rite) her name in the dirt with a stick each time she took a turn. The girl had to stop after she fell on a rocky area. Her (nuckles) were scraped and her (nee) was badly cut. To stop the bleeding, Rosa used her pocket (nife) to cut a strip from her sweatshirt. She used the cloth to (rap) the injury and tie a (not) just as she had learned to do in first-aid training. The minutes began to (strech) into hours, but Rosa stayed calm. Rescuers found her just before dark.

Write the misspelled words correctly on the lines below.

1. watch (1)
2. wrong (1)
3. knew (1)
4. write (1)
5. knuckles (1)
6. knee (1)
7. knife (1)
8. wrap (1)
9. knot (1)
10. stretch (1)

Read directions to students.

Spelling
© Houghton Mifflin Harcourt Publishing Company. All rights reserved.

111

Assessment Tip: Total 20 points

Grade 3, Unit 2

Name _____ Date _____

Vowel Diphthongs *ow* and *ou*

**Read each sentence. Choose the missing word from the box.
Write the word.**

crowded	rowdy	outdoors
found	showers	sunflower
howling	doghouse	shouted

1. As soon as the rain stopped, the children hurried
   __outdoors (1 point)__ to play.

2. When a wolf is __howling (1)__ , you can hear it from
   far away.

3. Our poodle Fifi sleeps in her __doghouse (1)__ , where it
   is warm and dry.

4. When the birthday girl came in, everyone jumped up and
   __shouted (1)__ , "Surprise!"

5. Will it be sunny today, or will we have __showers (1)__ ?

6. The __sunflower (1)__ seeds that we planted grew into
   tall plants with bright yellow blooms.

7. Carl still hasn't __found (1)__ the jacket that he lost
   last month.

8. The bus was so __crowded (1)__ that a lot of riders
   had to stand up.

9. If the children get too __rowdy (1)__ , they might
   wake the baby.

Assessment Tip: Total 9 points
Grade 3, Unit 2

Name _____ Date _____

Connect to Writing

You can combine short, choppy sentences to make your writing
smoother. You can combine sentences by **joining single words
in a series.** You use commas to separate the nouns or verbs in a
series. Remember to add *and* after the last comma.

Short, Choppy Sentences	Longer, Smoother Sentence
Carla watched crows. Carla watched gulls. Carla watched pigeons.	Carla watched crows, gulls, and pigeons.

**Combine three short, choppy sentences by joining nouns or verbs
in a series. Write the new sentence on the line.**

1. | The crows in the story walked. | The crows in the story laughed. | The crows in the story talked. |
|---|---|---|

The crows in the story walked, laughed, and talked. (2 points)

2. | Carla told Ramon about the crows. | Carla told Ed about the crows. | Carla told Lisa about the crows. |
|---|---|---|

Carla told Ramon, Ed, and Lisa about the crows. (2)

3. | The crows perched on branches. | The crows perched on wires. | The crows perched on rooftops. |
|---|---|---|

The crows perched on branches, wires, and rooftops. (2)

4. | Ramon played with the birds. | Ramon laughed with the birds. | Ramon sang with the birds. |
|---|---|---|

Ramon played, laughed, and sang with the birds. (2)

Assessment Tip: Total 8 points
Grade 3, Unit 2

Name _____ Date _____

Abstract Nouns

Thinking Question
Does the noun name an idea, a feeling, or a quality?

A noun that names an idea, a feeling, or a quality is an **abstract noun**. You cannot see, hear, taste, smell, or touch an abstract noun.

The couple did not have much <u>wealth</u>.

Their <u>joy</u> was obvious for everyone to see.

The word in parentheses tells whether the abstract noun in the sentence names an idea, a feeling, or a quality. Write the noun.

1. He took delight in keeping the audience in suspense.

(feeling) _____ delight (1 point)

2. He told the story with complete honesty.

(quality) _____ honesty (1)

Write a sentence for each abstract noun.   Possible answers shown.

3. beauty

_____ There is beauty in the dancer's movements. (1)

4. childhood

_____ He spent his childhood in Japan. (1)

Assessment Tip: Total 4 points
Grade 3, Unit 2

Name _____ Date _____

Abstract Nouns

Thinking Questions
Does the noun name an idea, a feeling, or a quality?

• A **noun** can name a person, place, or thing. This kind of noun is a **concrete noun**.

• A noun can also name an idea, a feeling, or a quality. This is called an **abstract noun**. You cannot see, hear, taste, smell, or touch an abstract noun.

He listened in the <u>hope</u> of hearing a new story.

It was just <u>luck</u> that he arrived in time.

A noun in each sentence is underlined. Write *abstract* if the noun names an idea, a feeling, or a quality. Write *concrete* if it is a noun you can see, hear, taste, smell, or touch.

1. The younger men enjoyed the older man's <u>friendship</u>.

_____ abstract (1 point)

2. The old man found <u>strength</u> in being among friends.

_____ abstract (1)

3. The friends took <u>delight</u> in listening to the old man's stories.

_____ abstract (1)

4. One story was about a silly <u>king</u>. _____ concrete (1)

5. The crowd's <u>laughter</u> pleased the old man. _____ abstract (1)

6. It gave him <u>energy</u> to tell another story.

_____ abstract (1)

Assessment Tip: Total 6 points
Grade 3, Unit 2

Name _____ Date _____

Focus Trait: Organization
Order of Reasons

When you provide an opinion, be sure to begin your answer by stating your opinion clearly. Use words from the question in your opinion statement. Then provide reasons in order. List the strongest reason first.

EXAMPLE:

Question: In *Kamishibai Man*, why do you think the old man and his wife call each other "Grandma" and "Grandpa" although they have no children of their own?

Strong Opening and Reasons: I think the old man and his wife call each other "Grandma" and "Grandpa" because they wish they had children and grandchildren. They are also older in age.

Read each question about *Kamishibai Man*. **Write a strong opening sentence that clearly states your opinion. Then provide reasons in order. List the strongest reason first.** Possible responses shown.

1. **Question:** Why do you think the children were always happy to see the kamishibai man?

   Opinion Statement and Reasons: I think the children were always happy to see the kamishibai man because he told them good stories and sold tasty candy. (2 points)

2. **Question:** Why do you think the little boy ran away from the kamishibai man?

   Opinion Statement and Reasons: I think the little boy ran away from the kamishibai man because he didn't have any money and was ashamed. (2)

Read directions to students.
Writing

Assessment Tip: Total 4 points
Grade 3, Unit 2

Name _____ Date _____

Spelling Word Sort

Write each Basic Word in the correct list.

Spelling Words

Basic
1. clown
2. round
3. bow
4. cloud
5. power
6. crown
7. thousand
8. crowd
9. sound
10. count
11. powder
12. blouse
13. frown
14. pound

Review
house
found

Challenge
mountain
coward

mouth	down
round (1 point)	clown (1)
cloud (1)	bow (1)
thousand (1)	power (1)
sound (1)	crown (1)
count (1)	crowd (1)
blouse (1)	powder (1)
pound (1)	frown (1)
(challenge) mountain (1)	(challenge) coward (1)

Challenge: Add the Challenge Words to your Word Sort.

Read directions to students.
Spelling

Assessment Tip: Total 16 points
Grade 3, Unit 2

Name _____ Date _____

Cumulative Review

Write a word from the box to complete each rhyme.

| clown | cow | kneel | pout | wreck |
| count | crown | knight | powder | write |

1. You're going to have to ___kneel (1 point)___ to change that wheel.

2. A princess wears a gown with her ___crown (1)___.

3. Please add some chili ___powder (1)___ to the chowder.

4. Why would you paint a frown on a ___clown (1)___?

5. You won't see that ___knight (1)___ lose a fight.

6. When you're dressed as a scout, do not ___pout (1)___.

7. The lady hurt her neck in the ___wreck (1)___.

8. Be careful with that plow around the ___cow (1)___.

9. You should get this amount when you ___count (1)___.

10. Before you start to ___write (1)___, turn on a light.

Read directions to students.
Phonics
© Houghton Mifflin Harcourt Publishing Company. All rights reserved.
Assessment Tip: Total 10 points
Grade 3, Unit 2
118

Name _____ Date _____

Reader's Guide

Kamishibai Man

A New Point of View:
The Boy Who Didn't Like Candy

When I was a boy, I listened to the stories of the kamishibai man every day. Help me tell his story with details from the text and illustrations.

Read pages 324–326. Why was the old man surprised?

The kamishibai man came to the city, and he was very

surprised because everything looked different. There

were a lot of cars and tall buildings. People had cut

down trees to make shops and restaurants.   (5 points)

Read pages 328–330. Why was the old man happy?

The old man remembered all of us as children

listening to his stories. He remembered how happy

and excited we had been.   (5)

Read directions to students.
Independent Reading
© Houghton Mifflin Harcourt Publishing Company. All rights reserved.
Assessment Tip: 10 Points
Grade 3, Unit 2
119

Name _____ Date _____

Lesson 9
READER'S NOTEBOOK

Kamishibai Man
Grammar:
Abstract Nouns

Abstract Nouns

- The subject of a sentence is a noun. It can be concrete or abstract.
- A noun that names an idea, a feeling, or a quality is an **abstract noun.**

In the story, the girls formed a friendship.

Two nouns in each sentence are underlined. Circle the subject of the sentence. Write the abstract noun.

1. The story begins with memories of a missing locket.

   memories (2 points)

2. A letter had information about the locket.

   information (2)

3. The girls had confidence in themselves.

   confidence (2)

4. After several hours, Annette had success and found the

   locket. success (2)

Choose two abstract nouns from above and write a sentence with them. Possible answer shown.

5. I had success getting the information I needed from the

   Internet. (2)

Read page 332. Why did I run away from the kamishibai man when I was a little boy?

I said I did not like candies, but I really ran away because

I had no money to buy candies. (5)

Read page 333–334. How did television change things?

The other children stopped listening to the

kamishibai man because they wanted to watch

television instead. (5)

Read page 338. What happened when the large crowd gathered?

Everyone still loved the kamishibai man! We had

grown up, but we wanted to hear his stories again.

We still remembered how much we loved them. (5)

Name _____ Date _____

Vowel Sound in *town*

Write the Basic Word that best replaces the underlined word or words in each sentence.

1. The man wears a ring of gold and jewels on his head to show he is king.

2. The actress waved to the large group of people as she walked by.

3. The angry bees made a loud buzzing noise.

4. Her brother's teasing made Marta put an unhappy look on her face.

5. Let's say the numbers in order as Justin jumps the rope.

6. A performer in a silly costume gave out balloons to all the children.

7. That gray puffy shape in the sky looks like it might bring rain.

8. For my birthday, I had a circle-shaped cake decorated to look like a soccer ball.

1. crown (1 point)	5. count (1)
2. crowd (1)	6. clown (1)
3. sound (1)	7. cloud (1)
4. frown (1)	8. round (1)

Challenge: On another sheet of paper, write a one-paragraph story using both Challenge Words and one or more Basic Words. Responses will vary. (2)

Spelling Words

Basic
1. clown
2. round
3. bow
4. cloud
5. power
6. crown
7. thousand
8. crowd
9. sound
10. count
11. powder
12. blouse
13. frown
14. pound

Review
house
found

Challenge
mountain
coward

Read directions to students.
Spelling
© Houghton Mifflin Harcourt Publishing Company. All rights reserved.

122

Assessment Tip: Total 10 points
Grade 3, Unit 2

Name _____ Date _____

Dictionary/Glossary

Read each word. Find each word in a print or digital dictionary. Complete the chart.

Word	Part(s) of Speech	Word with Endings
1. jewel	noun (1 point)	jewels (1)
2. rickety	adjective (1)	ricketier, ricketiest (1)
3. blast	noun, verb (1)	blasts, blasting, blasted (1)
4. sharp	adjective, adverb, noun (1)	sharps, sharper, sharpest (1)
5. blur	noun, verb (1)	blurs, blurred, blurring (1)

Now write one sentence of your own that could be an example sentence for one meaning of each word. Possible responses shown.

1. Did you notice the jewels she was wearing around her neck? (1)

2. The stairs looked too rickety to climb. (1)

3. Music blasted from the radio. (1)

4. A knife is a sharp object that can cut things. (1)

5. I couldn't tell who was in the photo because it was blurred. (1)

Read directions to students.
Vocabulary Strategies
© Houghton Mifflin Harcourt Publishing Company. All rights reserved.

123

Assessment Tip: Total 20 points
Grade 3, Unit 2

Proofreading for Spelling

Find the misspelled words and circle them. (10 points)

Dear Uncle Tony,

Thanks for the circus tickets that you sent.
I can always (cownt) on you to make my birthday
a lot of fun! I really enjoyed the elephant act. The
biggest one must have weighed a (thausand) (pownds).
The acrobat show was great, too. No one made
a (sownd) while one acrobat carried his partner over
the tightrope. When they came down, they leaped
through a (rownd) hoop that was on fire. The (crawd)
went crazy! Then, a (cloun) pretended he was going
to do the same thing, but he was too scared. His
buddies laughed at him as if he was a big (couward).
Finally, he jumped through the hoop and his pants
caught fire. When he took his (bouw), he saw the
(clowd) of smoke behind him. It was really funny.
I hope that next time you come to town, we can
all go to the circus together!

Love,
Gina

Write the misspelled words correctly on the lines below.

1. count (1)
2. thousand (1)
3. pounds (1)
4. sound (1)
5. round (1)
6. crowd (1)
7. clown (1)
8. coward (1)
9. bow (1)
10. cloud (1)

125

Assessment Tip: Total 20 points   Grade 3, Unit 2

Spelling Words

Basic

1. clown
2. round
3. bow
4. cloud
5. power
6. crown
7. thousand
8. crowd
9. sound
10. count
11. powder
12. blouse
13. frown
14. pound

Review
house
found

Challenge
mountain
coward

Writing Titles and Addresses

- Begin the first, last, and each important word in a book or story title with a capital letter. Example: Reptiles on the Road
- Capitalize a person's title when it is in front of his or her name. Example: Detective Ruiz
- Use a comma to separate each part of an address. Example: Ken Lopez, 530 Sandy Lane, Hialeah, Florida

Capitalize each title correctly.

1. I checked out swimming with the dolphins from the library. (1 point)

   I checked out Swimming with the Dolphins from the library. (1 point)

2. He listened to coach Taylor speak.

   He listened to Coach Taylor speak. (1)

3. Her story is called "never listen to a gerbil."

   Her story is called "Never Listen to a Gerbil!" (1)

4. The book a great leader is about president Washington.

   The book A Great Leader is about President Washington. (1)

Write each address correctly. Add commas where they are needed.

5. Sam Johnson 22 Meadowlark Avenue Houston Texas

   Sam Johnson, 22 Meadowlark Avenue, Houston, Texas (1)

6. She moved to 749 South Lake Road Spokane Washington.

   She moved to 749 South Lake Road, Spokane, Washington. (1)

124

Assessment Tip: Total 6 points   Grade 3, Unit 2

Name _____ Date _____

Words with *au, aw, al,* and *o*

Read each sentence and choose an answer from the box. Write the word. Then read the sentence aloud.

tablecloth	yawning	offered
sauce	faucet	bossy
false	awesome	mall

1. To save water, be sure to fix a leaky _____ faucet (1 point) as soon as possible.

2. We went shopping at the _____ mall (1) and had lunch at the Food Court.

3. My _____ bossy (1) cousin Cindy makes her brothers do everything her way.

4. Pete had homemade yogurt with raspberry _____ sauce (1) on top.

5. On our test, we had to tell whether each statement was true or _____ false (1)

6. The desert sunset was an _____ awesome (1) sight!

7. Coach Simms _____ offered (1) to help me work on my pitch.

8. The gravy spilled and stained our best _____ tablecloth (1)

9. Are the girls _____ yawning (1) because they are tired or because they are bored?

Assessment Tip: Total 9 points
Grade 3, Unit 2

Name _____ Date _____

Connect to Writing

Exact nouns are used to make your writing clearer and more interesting.

Noun	Exact Noun
The story filled Linda with happiness.	The story filled Linda with delight.
His actions showed his kindness.	His actions showed his compassion.

Replace each underlined noun in the sentences with a more exact noun. Use the nouns in the word box.

joy	doubt
panic	bravery

1. Jen felt uncertainty about telling her story to strangers.
_____ doubt (1 point)

2. Her fear grew as more people arrived. _____ panic (1)

3. Seeing her best friend in the audience gave her courage.
_____ bravery (1)

4. In the story, the characters felt happiness about the coming circus. _____ joy (1)

Assessment Tip: Total 4 points
Grade 3, Unit 2

Subject Pronouns

Name _____ Date _____

A **pronoun** is a word that can take the place of one or more nouns in a sentence. The pronouns *I, you, he, she, it, we,* and *they* are **subject pronouns**. Pronouns can be singular or plural. A noun and the subject pronoun that replaces it must match each other in singular and plural forms.

Thinking Question
What pronoun can replace and match a noun or nouns in a sentence?

The telegraph was important.   It was important.
Samuel Morse invented it.   He invented it.
Our class learned this.   We learned this.

Write each sentence. Replace the underlined word or words with a subject pronoun.

1. Samuel Morse was born in Massachusetts. (1 point)

   He was born in Massachusetts.

2. Lucretia Walker became his wife.

   She became his wife. (1)

3. The couple had two children.

   They had two children. (1)

4. Painting was another thing Morse did well.

   It was another thing Morse did well. (1)

5. The students and I enjoyed learning about him.

   We enjoyed learning about him. (1)

Object Pronouns

Name _____ Date _____

The **pronouns** *me, you, him, her, it, us,* and *them* are called **object pronouns**. Object pronouns follow action verbs and words like *to, for, at, of,* and *with*. A noun and the object pronoun, or **antecedent**, that replaces it must match each other in singular and plural forms.

- The pronouns *it* and *you* are both **subject pronouns** and object pronouns.

Thinking Question
What pronoun replaces and matches one or more nouns that are the objects in a sentence?

Nikola Tesla helped invent radio.
Nikola Tesla helped invent it.
Others worked with Tesla.
Others worked with him.

Write each sentence. Replace the underlined word or words with an object pronoun.

1. A man named Marconi worked on wireless communication.

   A man named Marconi worked on it. (1 point)

2. He helped make radios popular.

   He helped make them popular. (1)

3. Marconi married Beatrice O'Brien in 1905.

   Marconi married her in 1905. (1)

4. Other people said they had invented the system.

   Other people said they had invented it. (1)

5. People are grateful to Marconi for what he did.

   People are grateful to him for what he did. (1)

Name _____ Date _____

Spelling Word Sort

Write each Basic Word where it belongs in the chart.

soft	paw
cross (1 point)	awful (1)
cloth (1)	law (1)
cost (1)	crawl (1)
(challenge) often (1)	raw (1)
	lawn (1)
	(challenge) strawberry (1)

fall
talk (1)
chalk (1)
also (1)
salt (1)
wall (1)
always (1)

Challenge: Add the Challenge Words to your Word Sort.

Assessment Tip: Total 16 points
Grade 3, Unit 2

130

Spelling Words

Basic
1. talk
2. cross
3. awful
4. law
5. cloth
6. cost
7. crawl
8. chalk
9. also
10. raw
11. salt
12. wall
13. lawn
14. always

Review
soft
small

Challenge
often
strawberry

Name _____ Date _____

Focus Trait: Conventions
Avoiding Redundancy

Good writers introduce a new idea in each sentence. This writer crossed out a sentence that repeats an idea and wrote a new idea.

Thomas Edison loved to read. He would spend the entire day at the library. He wanted to read every book in the library. He would start at the last book on the shelf and work back to the first. ~~Edison wanted to read all of the books there.~~

New idea: *He would dream about his next experiment as he read.*

Read each paragraph. Cross out the sentence that repeats an idea. Write a new idea. Possible responses shown.

1. Thomas Edison was a very creative child. He created a laboratory in the cellar of his home. He would mix chemicals there. ~~He would do this in the cellar.~~ He also asked questions so that he could learn about things.

   New Idea: Sometimes he made up his own experiments. (2 points)

2. Edison's mother was important in his life. She educated him at home. ~~She taught him very well there.~~ She also encouraged him to learn for himself.

   New Idea: When he was older, she gave him advice. (2)

3. Edison invented many helpful things. He invented the carbon transmitter, which made voices sound louder. He invented the light bulb. ~~This invention helped people.~~ He even invented the motion picture.

   New Idea: Edison also invented the phonograph, a machine

   that talked. (2)

Assessment Tip: Total 6 points
Grade 3, Unit 2

131

Name _____ Date _____

Lesson 10
READER'S NOTEBOOK

Young Thomas Edison
Phonics:
Cumulative Review

Cumulative Review

Write words from the box to complete the sentences.

cause	walkie-talkies	squawked
officer	foggy	already
paws	fault	flossing

1. My friend and I used _walkie-talkies (1 point)_ to communicate.

2. Brushing and _flossing (1)_ keep teeth healthy.

3. The chicken _squawked (1)_ loudly and flapped its wings.

4. The police _officer (1)_ directed traffic when the lights were not working.

5. Dr. Ross finally figured out the _cause (1)_ of the baby's fever.

6. When Tasha arrived, the game had _already (1)_ started.

7. It was so _foggy (1)_ that I could barely see my neighbor's house.

8. It was my _fault (1)_ that the library book got torn.

9. The kitten is all black except for its four white _paws (1)_ .

Assessment Tip: Total 9 points
Grade 3, Unit 2

Reader's Guide

Young Thomas Edison

A Tour of the Thomas Edison Museum

Welcome to the Thomas Edison Museum! I am a tour guide for the museum. Help me take our visitors on a tour. We will explore Thomas Edison's early life by looking at some objects.

Read page 362.

This is a bottle from Thomas Edison's childhood. Why is it here in the museum?

When he was a child, Thomas Edison used bottles like this one while doing experiments in his family's cellar.

(5 points)

Read page 366.

Here you can see an old newspaper from when Thomas Edison was twelve years old. Why is it here in the museum?

This newspaper is from a time when Thomas Edison worked as a paper boy. (5)

Assessment Tip: 10 Points
Grade 3, Unit 2

Name _____ Date _____

Pronoun-Antecedent Agreement

- A pronoun can take the place of one or more nouns in a sentence.
- An **antecedent** is the noun or noun phrase to which a pronoun refers. An antecedent usually comes before the pronoun, but it may come after. Pronouns and antecedents must agree in number, person, and gender.

Raul thought about <u>his</u> invention.
Maggie thought about <u>her</u> invention.
Raul and Maggie thought about <u>their</u> inventions.

Complete each sentence by writing the pronoun that agrees with the underlined antecedent. Remember to make sure the pronoun and antecedent match in number, person, and gender.

1. Kevin checked out an invention book because _____ it _____ had a lot of information.

2. <u>I</u> said, "Show _____ me _____ the book."

3. <u>Maggie</u> typed up the notes _____ she _____ wrote about the invention.

4. <u>The students</u> felt _____ they _____ had done a great job.

5. <u>Ms. Jones</u> said _____ she _____ was proud of the students' hard work.

6. After _____ he _____ was done, <u>Raul</u> went home.

Read directions to students.
Grammar   135
© Houghton Mifflin Harcourt Publishing Company. All rights reserved.

Name _____ Date _____

Read page 372.

Here is a photograph of an old locomotive. Why is it in the Thomas Edison museum?

Thomas Edison traveled on trains and worked as a

telegraph operator. (5)

Read page 376.

Here is the last letter Thomas Edison received from his mother in 1869. Why is it here?

His mother was very important to him. He loved to get

letters of advice and encouragement from her. (5)

Read pages 379–381.

Now if you step into the final room of the museum, you will see all of Thomas Edison's famous inventions! Why was he known as "The Wizard"?

He was famous for making many important

inventions. (5)

Thank you for taking a tour of the Thomas Edison Museum. It has been my pleasure to be your guide!

Read directions to students.
Independent Reading
© Houghton Mifflin Harcourt Publishing Company. All rights reserved.

134

Young Thomas Edison
Vocabulary Strategies:
Shades of Meaning

Name _____ Date _____

Shades of Meaning

For each set of related words, write them in order on the arrows to show the shades of meanings of the words. If necessary, look up unfamiliar words in a dictionary before completing the arrows.

1. believe, suspect, think

   suspect → think → believe (3 points)

2. happy, elated, content

   content → happy → elated (3 points)

3. angry, upset, furious, annoyed

   upset → angry → annoyed → furious (4 points)

4. scorching, hot, warm

   warm → hot → scorching (3 points)

5. glance, look, glare, stare

   glance → look → stare → glare (4 points)

6. excited, exhilarated, enthusiastic

   enthusiastic → excited → exhilarated (3 points)

Assessment Tip: Total 20 points
Grade 3, Unit 2

Young Thomas Edison
Spelling:
Vowel Sound in *talk*

Name _____ Date _____

Vowel Sound in *talk*

Read the titles and lists below. Write the Basic Word that belongs in each blank.

Spelling Words
Basic
1. talk
2. cross
3. awful
4. law
5. cloth
6. cost
7. crawl
8. chalk
9. also
10. raw
11. salt
12. wall
13. lawn
14. always
Review
soft
small
Challenge
often
strawberry

1. Things to Look for Before You _____ Cross (1 point) _____ : cars, trucks, bicycles

2. Ways to Communicate: draw a picture, use sign language, _____ talk (1) _____

3. Writing Tools: pencil, pen, _____ chalk (1) _____

4. Things That Are Against the _____ Law (1) _____ : littering, speeding, stealing

5. Spices and Seasonings: garlic, cinnamon, _____ salt (1) _____

6. Things People Eat _____ Raw (1) _____ : apples, lettuce, tomatoes

7. Parts of a Building: staircase, window, _____ wall (1) _____

8. Things Made of _____ Cloth (1) _____ : shirt, scarf, sheet

Challenge: Write two lists similar to those above. Include a Challenge Word in each title or list. Responses will vary. (2)

Assessment Tip: Total 10 points
Grade 3, Unit 2

Name _____ Date _____

Proofreading for Spelling

Find the misspelled words and circle them. (10 points)

This morning was auful. I wanted to sleep late, but my brother kept whining. He was crawss because Mom wouldn't let him go out and play unless I went with him. I olways have to babysit! All I wanted was a little sleep. Since when is that against the lauw? Anyway, I took Ben out to play. I stretched out on the laun to relax, but before long Ben just had to crol over and bug me. He doesn't very well yet, but I know what "jump game" means. Ben auften watches me play hopscotch and thinks it looks funny. I got some chawk and drew a board on the sidewalk. Ben laughed when I hopped on the squares. Then he was bored again. He wanted to swing. He aulso wanted a drink of water. When Ben finally took his nap, I ran to Ana's house. I'm going to sleep over tonight. Maybe I'll get to sleep late at *her* house!

Write the misspelled words correctly on the lines below.

1. _____ awful (1)
2. _____ cross (1)
3. _____ always (1)
4. _____ law (1)
5. _____ lawn (1)
6. _____ crawl (1)
7. _____ talk (1)
8. _____ often (1)
9. _____ chalk (1)
10. _____ also (1)

Read directions to students.

Spelling
© Houghton Mifflin Harcourt Publishing Company. All rights reserved.

Assessment Tip: Total 20 points
Grade 3, Unit 2

139

Spelling Words

Basic
1. talk
2. cross
3. awful
4. law
5. cloth
6. cost
7. crawl
8. chalk
9. also
10. raw
11. salt
12. wall
13. lawn
14. always

Review
soft
small

Challenge
often
strawberry

Name _____ Date _____

Singular and Plural Nouns

- A noun that names only one person, place, or thing is a **singular noun**.
- A noun that names more than one person, place, or thing is a **plural noun**.
- Add *-s* to most singular nouns to form the plural.
- Add *-es* to form the plural of a singular noun that ends in *-s*, *-sh*, *-ch*, or *-x*.

Students have invented things for many of their school classes.

Write singular or plural for each underlined noun.

1. An invention is like a lightbulb lighting up in your head.
   _____ singular (1 point)

2. Before, my thoughts were in the dark. _____ plural (1)

3. I don't know how a new idea comes to me. _____ singular (1)

4. I phoned two friends about my idea. _____ plural (1)

5. I will give them two guesses about what it is.
   _____ plural (1)

Use proofreading marks to change the underlined nouns from singular nouns to plural nouns. (5)

     ideas *boxes*

Thank you for the idea box that you sent. We should meet to talk about
    thoughts   *brothers*
your thought with my brother.
inventions
the invention we are thinking about. I shared

Read directions to students.

Grammar
© Houghton Mifflin Harcourt Publishing Company. All rights reserved.

Assessment Tip: Total 10 points
Grade 3, Unit 2

138

Name _____ Date _____

Reader's Guide

Amos and Boris

Postcard to Pearl

Help Amos send a postcard to his friend, Pearl, telling her about his travel plans. Use the text and illustrations to describe the most important details about Amos and his boat. Then, use this information to write the postcard.

Read pages 3–5. Why did Amos love where he lived?   (2 points)

He loved the ocean. _____

He loved the smell and sound of the ocean.   (2 points)
_____

Why did Amos decide to build a boat?

He wanted to see the faraway places _____

on the other side of the ocean.   (2)
_____

What did Amos do when the boat was finished, before setting sail?

He loaded the boat with all the things he would need, _____

like food and bandages and things to play with.   (2)
_____

How do you think Amos felt before setting sail?

He felt excited to finally be traveling on the ocean.   (2)
_____

Name _____ Date _____

Connect to Writing

Using a pronoun in place of a noun helps to avoid repeating words.

Repeated Nouns	Better Sentences
In 1806, Thomas Young thought of the phonograph. Later, Leon Scott improved the phonograph. Thomas Edison made the phonograph work.	In 1806, Thomas Young thought of the phonograph. Later, Leon Scott improved it. Thomas Edison made it work.

Rewrite each item. Use pronouns in place of repeated nouns.

1. The first phonograph did not play records. The first phonograph put sounds on a tin tube. Sounds entered the first phonograph through a bell. (3 points)

The first phonograph did not play records. It put sounds on

a tin tube. Sounds entered it through a bell. (3)
_____

2. Later, phonographs played records. These records were flat rings of wax. A needle cut sound into the records.

Later, phonographs played records. They were flat rings of

wax. A needle cut sound into them. (3)
_____

3. Bell and Tainter made their phonograph in 1886. Bell and Tainter called their phonograph a gramophone. The government gave its approval to Bell and Tainter.

Bell and Tainter made their phonograph in 1886. They called it a

gramophone. The government gave its approval to them. (3)
_____

Name _____ Date _____

From Amos's Journal

Amos kept a journal during his time on the boat. Use the text and illustrations to help fill out his journal entries.

Read page 6. What was the weather like when Amos started out? How did he feel at first?

September 6

I am starting out on the ocean.

The sea is calm. I am very excited.   (2 points)

Read page 7. How did Amos feel on his first day out at sea?

September 7

This day is very miserable. I feel sick all the time.

I hope I feel better soon.   (2)

How did Amos feel after the first day?

September 8

My seasickness is gone. I feel great today. The weather

is beautiful. I feel so happy on my boat!   (2)

Assessment Tip: 6 Points
Grade 3, Unit 2

Name _____ Date _____

Now, use your answers to write the postcard. On the front, draw a picture of Amos and his boat. On the back, write a note from Amos to Pearl. Describe his plans for the boat and where he wants to go.

(Students should draw a picture of Amos and
his boat.) (5 points)

Front of Postcard

32¢

TO:

Pearl M. Friend
333 Cheddar Street
Cheesetown, USA

Dear Pearl,

I love the ocean so much that

I decided to build a boat. It was

hard work, but it was worth it!

I am going to the other side of

the ocean!   (10)

Love, Amos

Back of Postcard

Assessment Tip: 15 Points
Grade 3, Unit 2

Name _____ Date _____

Message in a Bottle

Imagine that Amos found his pen and paper with him in the water. Quickly, he wrote a message for help and put it in a bottle. First, use the text and illustrations to explain what happened. Then use that information to write Amos's message in a bottle.

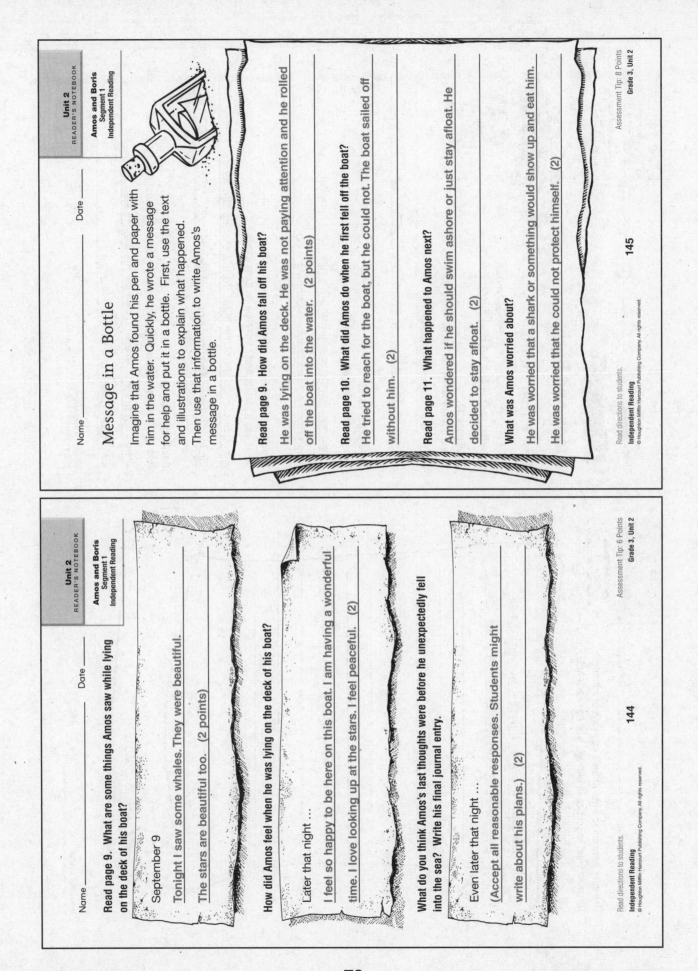

Read page 9. How did Amos fall off his boat?
He was lying on the deck. He was not paying attention and he rolled off the boat into the water. (2 points)

Read page 10. What did Amos do when he first fell off the boat?
He tried to reach for the boat, but he could not. The boat sailed off without him. (2)

Read page 11. What happened to Amos next?
Amos wondered if he should swim ashore or just stay afloat. He decided to stay afloat. (2)

What was Amos worried about?
He was worried that a shark or something would show up and eat him. He was worried that he could not protect himself. (2)

Read directions to students.
Independent Reading
© Houghton Mifflin Harcourt Publishing Company. All rights reserved.
Assessment Tip: 8 Points
Grade 3, Unit 2
145

Name _____ Date _____

Read page 9. What are some things Amos saw while lying on the deck of his boat?
September 9
Tonight I saw some whales. They were beautiful. The stars are beautiful too. (2 points)

How did Amos feel when he was lying on the deck of his boat?
Later that night …
I feel so happy to be here on this boat. I am having a wonderful time. I love looking up at the stars. I feel peaceful. (2)

What do you think Amos's last thoughts were before he unexpectedly fell into the sea? Write his final journal entry.
Even later that night …
(Accept all reasonable responses. Students might write about his plans.) (2)

Read directions to students.
Independent Reading
© Houghton Mifflin Harcourt Publishing Company. All rights reserved.
Assessment Tip: 6 Points
Grade 3, Unit 2
144

Unit 2
READER'S NOTEBOOK

Amos and Boris
Segment 2
Independent Reading

Reader's Guide

Amos and Boris

Best Friend Award

After his adventures with Boris, Amos decided to give Boris a Best Friend Award.

Read page 12.
How did Amos feel before Boris found him?

He thought about drowning.

He was afraid and sad. (2 points)

Read pages 13–15.
How did Amos feel when he first met Boris?

Amos was happy to see Boris. He was even happier

when Boris agreed to take him home. (2)

Read pages 18–19.
What was it like for Amos traveling on Boris's back?

Amos had a lot of fun. He liked Boris's stories about

life in the water. They became best friends. (2)

Read page 20.
How did Amos feel when it was time to say goodbye to Boris?

Amos felt grateful that Boris saved his life. He also felt

sad to say goodbye. (2)

Read directions to students.
Independent Reading   147
© Houghton Mifflin Harcourt Publishing Company. All rights reserved.

Assessment Tip: 8 Points
Grade 3, Unit 2

Unit 2
READER'S NOTEBOOK

Amos and Boris
Segment 1
Independent Reading

Use your answers to write Amos's message in a bottle.
Describe what happened to him and why he needs help.

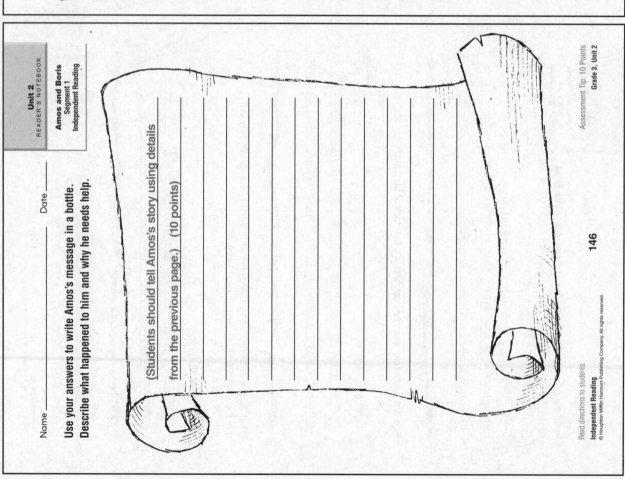

(Students should tell Amos's story using details

from the previous page.) (10 points)

Read directions to students.
Independent Reading   146
© Houghton Mifflin Harcourt Publishing Company. All rights reserved.

Assessment Tip: 10 Points
Grade 3, Unit 2

Design a Best Friend Award for Boris from Amos.
On the award, write why Boris is a good friend.
Use details from the story.

To: Boris

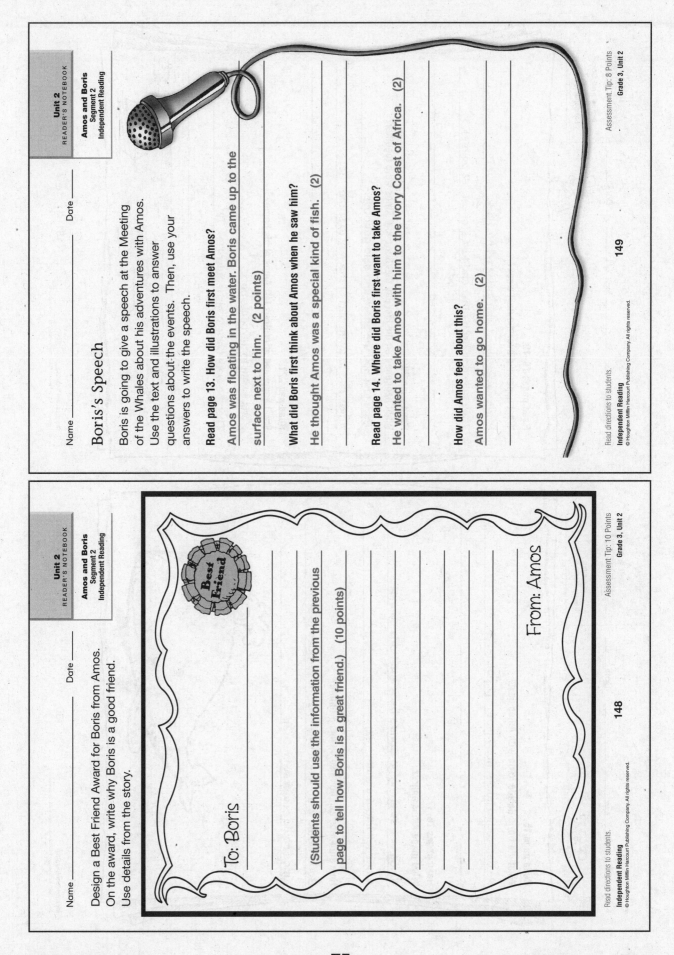

Best Friend

(Students should use the information from the previous
page to tell how Boris is a great friend.) (10 points)

From: Amos

Assessment Tip: 10 Points
Grade 3, Unit 2

Boris's Speech

Boris is going to give a speech at the Meeting
of the Whales about his adventures with Amos.
Use the text and illustrations to answer
questions about the events. Then, use your
answers to write the speech.

Read page 13. How did Boris first meet Amos? (2 points)

Amos was floating in the water. Boris came up to the

surface next to him. (2 points)

What did Boris first think about Amos when he saw him? (2)

He thought Amos was a special kind of fish. (2)

Read page 14. Where did Boris first want to take Amos? (2)

He wanted to take Amos with him to the Ivory Coast of Africa. (2)

How did Amos feel about this?

Amos wanted to go home. (2)

Assessment Tip: 8 Points
Grade 3, Unit 2

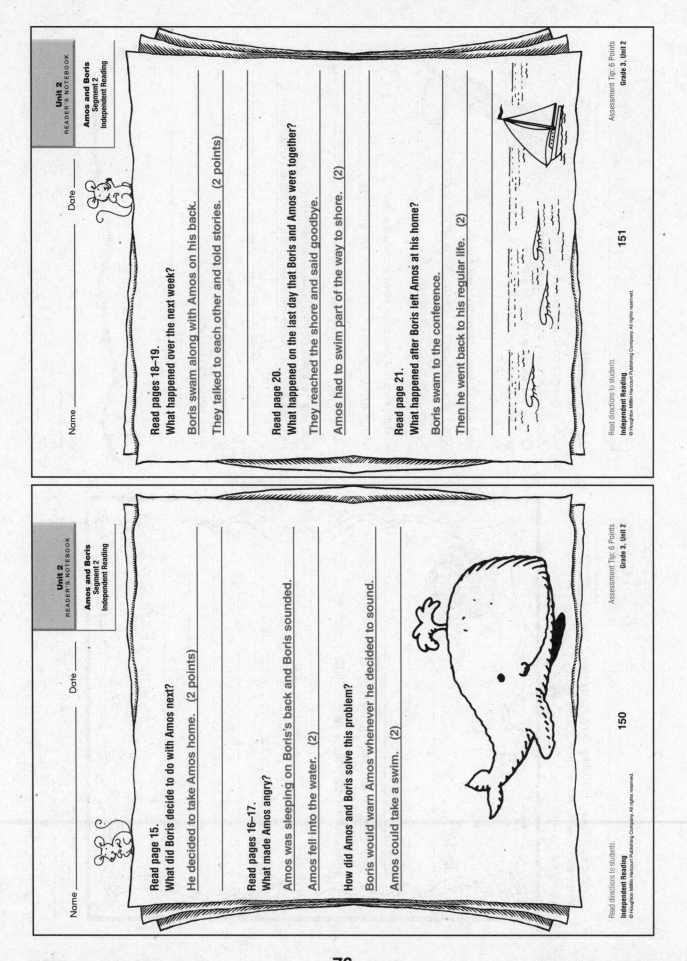

Name _____ Date _____

Unit 2
READER'S NOTEBOOK

Amos and Boris
Segment 2
Independent Reading

Read pages 18–19.
What happened over the next week?

Boris swam along with Amos on his back.

They talked to each other and told stories.   (2 points)

Read page 20.
What happened on the last day that Boris and Amos were together?

They reached the shore and said goodbye.

Amos had to swim part of the way to shore.   (2)

Read page 21.
What happened after Boris left Amos at his home?

Boris swam to the conference.

Then he went back to his regular life.   (2)

Read directions to students.
Independent Reading
© Houghton Mifflin Harcourt Publishing Company. All rights reserved.

151

Assessment Tip: 6 Points
Grade 3, Unit 2

Name _____ Date _____

Unit 2
READER'S NOTEBOOK

Amos and Boris
Segment 2
Independent Reading

Read page 15.
What did Boris decide to do with Amos next?

He decided to take Amos home.   (2 points)

Read pages 16–17.
What made Amos angry?

Amos was sleeping on Boris's back and Boris sounded.

Amos fell into the water.   (2)

How did Amos and Boris solve this problem?

Boris would warn Amos whenever he decided to sound.

Amos could take a swim.   (2)

Read directions to students.
Independent Reading
© Houghton Mifflin Harcourt Publishing Company. All rights reserved.

150

Assessment Tip: 6 Points
Grade 3, Unit 2

Reader's Guide

Amos and Boris

Unit 2
READER'S NOTEBOOK

Amos and Boris
Segment 3
Independent Reading

Interview with the Elephants

Imagine you are one of the elephants from the story and you are being interviewed for a radio program about Boris's rescue.

Read pages 22–23.
Tell me, Elephant, how did it all start?

Hurricane Yetta was one of the worst storms ever. Boris, the whale,

was flung ashore by a tidal wave. (2 points)

_____

Read page 24.
What happened when Amos, the mouse, came down to the beach?

He saw his old friend Boris lying on the beach. (2)

_____

What do you think it was like when Amos and Boris first saw each other again?

I think they were surprised to see each other. They were probably

scared for Boris. Whales need to be in the water. (2)

Unit 2
READER'S NOTEBOOK

Amos and Boris
Segment 2
Independent Reading

Now use your answers to write Boris's speech. The speech should describe the events from Boris's point of view.

Speech for the Meeting of Whales

(Accept all reasonable responses. Students should include

facts they have gathered on the previous pages: things that

happened to Amos and Boris together in the order that

they happened.) (10 points)

_____

_____

_____

_____

_____

_____

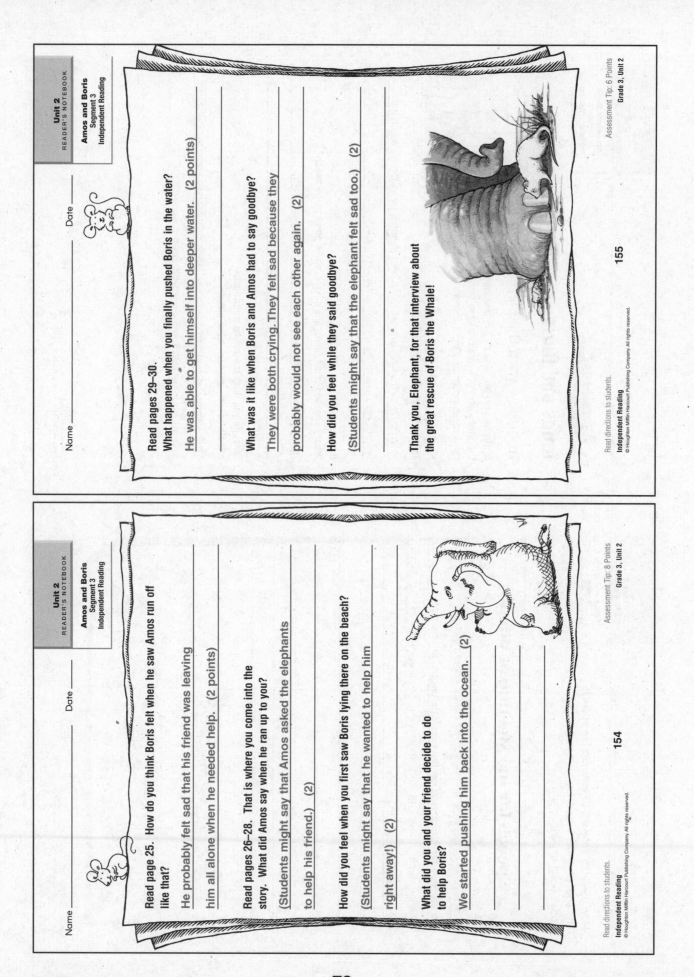

Name _____

Date _____

Read pages 29–30.
What happened when you finally pushed Boris in the water?   (2 points)

He was able to get himself into deeper water.   (2 points)

What was it like when Boris and Amos had to say goodbye?

They were both crying. They felt sad because they

probably would not see each other again.   (2)

How did you feel while they said goodbye?

(Students might say that the elephant felt sad too.)   (2)

Thank you, Elephant, for that interview about
the great rescue of Boris the Whale!

Read directions to students.
Independent Reading
© Houghton Mifflin Harcourt Publishing Company. All rights reserved.
155
Assessment Tip: 6 Points
Grade 3, Unit 2

Name _____

Date _____

Read page 25. How do you think Boris felt when he saw Amos run off
like that?

He probably felt sad that his friend was leaving

him all alone when he needed help.   (2 points)

Read pages 26–28. That is where you come into the
story. What did Amos say when he ran up to you?
(Students might say that Amos asked the elephants

to help his friend.)   (2)

How did you feel when you first saw Boris lying there on the beach?
(Students might say that he wanted to help him

right away!)   (2)

What did you and your friend decide to do
to help Boris?
We started pushing him back into the ocean.   (2)

Read directions to students.
Independent Reading
© Houghton Mifflin Harcourt Publishing Company. All rights reserved.
154
Assessment Tip: 8 Points
Grade 3, Unit 2

Name _____ Date _____

One More Adventure

First, Boris saved Amos. Then, Amos helped save Boris. What if Boris and Amos had one more adventure? Write about what might happen next to the two friends. First, answer these questions about how the story ended.

Read page 30.
How do you think Boris felt at the end of the book?

He felt very sad that he probably would not get to see Amos again.

_____

(2 points)

How do you think Amos felt at the end of the book?

He also felt sad that he would not get to see Boris again. (2)

_____

Do you think they would ever meet again? Why or why not?
(Accept all reasonable answers. Students should

_____

explain why or why not.) (2)

Read directions to students.
Independent Reading
© Houghton Mifflin Harcourt Publishing Company. All rights reserved.

156

Assessment Tip: 6 Points
Grade 3, Unit 2

Name _____ Date _____

Now think of another adventure for Amos and Boris. Plan your story below.

Who are the characters in your story?
(Accept all reasonable answers.) (5 points)

_____

What is the setting?
(Accept all reasonable answers.) (5)

_____

What problem do the characters have? How do they solve it?
(Accept all reasonable answers.) (5)

_____

Read directions to students.
Independent Reading
© Houghton Mifflin Harcourt Publishing Company. All rights reserved.

157

Assessment Tip: 15 Points
Grade 3, Unit 2

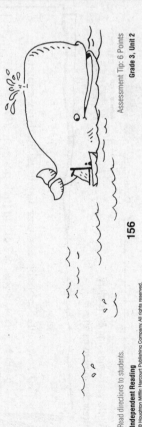

Name _____ Date _____

Vowel Diphthongs *oi, oy*

Read each sentence. Choose the missing word from the box.
Write the word. Then reread the complete sentence.

broiling	ointment	soy
coiled	oyster	disappoint
voyage	avoid	hoist

1. While hiking, Debra saw a snake ___ coiled (1 point) ___ up on the path.

2. Before you can go sailing, you have to ___ hoist (1) ___ the sails.

3. Steve made sure to get his mom a birthday card so that he would not ___ disappoint (1) ___ her.

4. My bike has a flat tire because I could not ___ avoid (1) ___ the broken glass on the sidewalk.

5. Christine cooked the hotdogs by ___ broiling (1) ___ them.

6. My grandmother is making a ___ voyage (1) ___ around the world.

7. I don't like seafood, so I did not eat the ___ oyster (1) ___.

8. Gwen put some ___ ointment (1) ___ on her poison ivy rash.

9. My mom eats burgers that are made with ___ soy (1) ___ instead of meat.

159

Name _____ Date _____

Write your Amos and Boris story.
Draw a picture to go with it.

(Accept all reasonable text and drawings. Students should
include Amos, Boris, or both in their pages.) (10 points)

158

Lesson 11
READER'S NOTEBOOK

Technology Wins
the Game
Grammar:
More Plural Nouns

Changing *y* to *i*

- Add -*s* or -*es* to most singular nouns to form **regular plural nouns.**
- If a noun ends with a consonant and *y*, change the *y* to *i*, and add -*es* to form the plural.

  Singular: *family   party*
  Plural: *families   parties*

Thinking Question
Does the noun end with a consonant and y?

Write the plural form of each singular noun in parentheses. Then write a new sentence using the plural form of the noun. Possible responses shown.

1. My teammates and I play basketball in many _____ cities (1 point) _____ (city)

   I have traveled to many cities. (1)

2. We once played against a team that had _____ ponies (1) _____ on their shirts. (pony)

   The ponies grazed in the field. (1)

3. Another team had two _____ butterflies (1) _____ on their shirts. (butterfly)

   Butterflies landed on the flowers. (1)

4. The teams are not really _____ enemies (1) _____ (enemy)

   They said they were sorry and stopped being enemies. (1)

5. I made _____ copies (1) _____ of the photos I took of the class. (copy)

   The teacher made enough copies for the class. (1) .

Read directions to students.
Grammar
© Houghton Mifflin Harcourt Publishing Company. All rights reserved.
160
Assessment Tip: Total 10 points
Grade 3, Unit 3

Lesson 11
READER'S NOTEBOOK

Technology Wins
the Game
Grammar:
More Plural Nouns

Irregular Plural Nouns

- The spelling of **irregular plural nouns** changes in a special way.

  The woman wanted to be as tall as the other women.

- The spelling of some nouns does not change when they are plural.

  That black sheep is as large as all the other sheep.

- The noun *woman* changes to *women* when it is plural.
- The noun *sheep* remains *sheep* when it is plural.

Thinking Questions
Does the noun add -s or -es to form a plural, or does it change its spelling? Does its spelling not change?

Write the plural form of the noun in parentheses to complete each sentence.

1. Tara grew up to be stronger than most other _____ women (1 point) _____ (woman)

2. She was taller than most of the other _____ children (1) _____ her age. (child)

3. As she grew, she could run faster than most _____ deer (1) _____ . (deer)

4. Every fall she ran through the _____ leaves (1) _____ . (leaf)

5. She ran and won many races against _____ men (1) _____ . (man)

6. She lived on a farm with ducks and _____ geese (1) _____ . (goose)

Read directions to students.
Grammar
© Houghton Mifflin Harcourt Publishing Company. All rights reserved.
161
Assessment Tip: Total 6 points
Grade 3, Unit 3

Name _____ Date _____

Focus Trait: Elaboration
Signal Words

Cause	Effect
Amy practiced every day	won race

Sentence: Because Amy practiced every day, she won the race.

Read each cause and effect. Use a signal word to fill in the blank.
Possible response shown.

	Cause	Effect
1.	bought new running shoes	Cal's feet don't hurt
2.	skier gets lost	sensor sends information

Sentence:

1. Cal bought new running shoes _so (1 point)_ his feet don't hurt.

2. _If (1)_ a skier gets lost, a sensor sends information.

	Cause	Effect
3.	tennis racket lighter	player can hit ball harder
4.	Jana runs on grass	sometimes slips when it rains
5.	water is cold	Max wears bodysuit

Sentence:

3. Because the tennis racket is lighter, a player can hit the ball harder. (2 points)

4. Since Jana runs on grass, she sometimes slips when it rains. (2)

5. The water is cold, so Max wears a bodysuit. (2)

Read directions to students.
Writing
Copyright © Houghton Mifflin Company. All rights reserved.

Assessment Tip: Total 8 points
Grade 3, Unit 3

163

Lesson 11
READER'S NOTEBOOK

Technology Wins
the Game
Spelling:
Vowel Sound in joy

Name _____ Date _____

Vowel Sound in *joy*

Write each Basic Word under the correct heading.

Spelling Words

Basic
1. joy
2. point
3. voice
4. join
5. oil
6. coin
7. noise
8. spoil
9. toy
10. joint
11. boy
12. soil
13. choice
14. boil

Review
come
are

Challenge
poison
destroy

Vowel Sound in *joy* spelled *oi*	Vowel Sound in *joy* spelled *oy*
point (1 point)	joy (1)
voice (1)	toy (1)
join (1)	boy (1)
oil (1)	
coin (1)	Challenge: destroy (1)
noise (1)	
spoil (1)	
joint (1)	
soil (1)	
choice (1)	
boil (1)	
Challenge: poison (1)	

Challenge: Add the Challenge Words to your Word Sort.

Read directions to students.
Spelling
© Houghton Mifflin Harcourt Publishing Company. All rights reserved.

Assessment Tip: Total 16 points
Grade 3, Unit 3

162

Name _____ Date _____

Technology Wins the Game

Reader's Guide

Sports Equipment Instruction Manual

You are writing a step-by-step manual that tells how sports equipment is made using the latest technology. It also explains how technology has changed over the years. Use information from the text to write the manual.

Read page 407. How are tennis balls made?

HOW TO MAKE A TENNIS BALL

Step 1: Join together two matching pieces of rubber. (2 points)

Step 2: Wrap two pieces of felt around the ball. (2)

Step 3: Add a rubber seam to keep the felt cover together. (2)

Step 4: Place tennis balls into a can that is under pressure. (2)

Read page 408. How have vaulting poles changed over time?

THE HISTORY OF VAULTING POLES

First, poles were made of wood. (2)

Next, poles were made of bamboo. (2)

Then, poles were made of aluminum. (2)

Today, poles are made of fiberglass. (2)

It took years to come up with the best technology for vaulting poles. But fiberglass is the best material because the poles are very light and bend easily. (2)

Read directions to students.
Independent Reading
© Houghton Mifflin Harcourt Publishing Company. All rights reserved.

165

Name _____ Date _____

Cumulative Review

Write a word from the box to complete each sentence. Then read the complete sentence.

royal	cowboy	pointy
enjoy	avoid	voyage
oiled	loyal	noisy

1. The men working outside my window were so
_____noisy (1 point)_____ that I could not fall asleep.

2. Theresa is a _____loyal (1)_____ friend, so I know I can
trust her.

3. Marc knew that his trip around the world would be the
_____voyage (1)_____ of a lifetime.

4. The metal lid was rusted shut because no one had
_____oiled (1)_____ it for years.

5. A king and a queen are _____royal (1)_____ rulers.

6. Victor is mad at me, so he is trying to _____avoid (1)_____
talking to me.

7. If you _____enjoy (1)_____ funny movies, you will love
this one!

8. Once I get some fake _____pointy (1)_____ ears, my elf
costume will be complete.

9. Randy loved taking horseback riding lessons because it
made him feel like a _____cowboy (1)_____.

Read directions to students.
Phonics
© Houghton Mifflin Harcourt Publishing Company. All rights reserved.

164

Right worksheet

Lesson 11
READER'S NOTEBOOK

Technology Wins
the Game
Grammar:
More Plural Nouns

Name _____ Date _____

Irregular Plural Nouns

Write the plural form of each singular noun in parentheses.

1. two tiny ___babies (1 point)___ (baby)

2. four long ___stories (1)___ (story)

3. twelve ripe ___cherries (1)___ (cherry)

4. fresh red ___berries (1)___ (berry)

5. eight cute ___puppies (1)___ (puppy)

Write *singular* or *plural* for each underlined noun.

6. Many <u>women</u> play sports. ___plural (1)___

7. Many <u>men</u> take part in sports, too. ___plural (1)___

8. Jack wore a guard to protect his <u>teeth</u>. ___plural (1)___

9. A <u>child</u> can play sports at school. ___singular (1)___

10. <u>Geese</u> do not play sports. ___plural (1)___

Assessment Tip: Total 10 points   Grade 3, Unit 3

Left worksheet

Name _____ Date _____

Read page 410. How have running shoes changed over time? Use the text and the timeline to fill in the manual page.

THE HISTORY OF RUNNING SHOES

First, running shoes were sandals. (2)

Next, running shoes had rubber soles. (2)

Next, running shoes had spikes. (2)

Next, running shoes had extra cushioning in heels and soles. (2)

Today, running shoes are made for every style runner and for any surface. (2)

Read page 412. How have football helmets changed over time?

THE HISTORY OF FOOTBALL HELMETS

First, football helmets were made of leather. (2)

Next, more padding was added to the helmets. (2)

Then, face masks were added to protect the nose and teeth. (2)

Next, the top of the helmet was made more round. (2)

Next, football helmets were made of plastic. (2)

Today, football helmets are made of special plastic that is light and strong. (2)

The newest technology for football helmets is computer chips. These help because if a player hits his head, the chip sends a message to a computer. Scientists hope the chips will be able to send messages to coaches if a player is injured. (4)

Assessment Tip: 26 Points   Grade 3, Unit 3

Lesson 11
READER'S NOTEBOOK

Technology Wins
the Game
Spelling:
Vowel Sound in *joy*

Vowel Sound in *joy*

Spelling Words

Basic
1. joy
2. point
3. voice
4. join
5. oil
6. coin
7. noise
8. spoil
9. toy
10. joint
11. boy
12. soil
13. choice
14. boil

Review
come
are

Challenge
poison
destroy

Use the Basic Words to complete the puzzle. (1 point each)

Across
1. a decision
3. to become a member
5. a sound
7. dirt
8. the tip of a pencil
10. to heat a liquid until it bubbles
11. great happiness

Down
1. a metal piece of money
2. a dark, slippery liquid
3. the place where two bones connect
4. what one uses to speak
6. to go bad
9. something to play with
10. a male child

Read directions to students.
Spelling

168

Lesson 11
READER'S NOTEBOOK

Technology Wins the Game
Vocabulary Strategies:
Suffixes *-less, -ful, -ous*

Suffixes *-less*, *-ful*, *-ous*

In each sentence, circle the word with the suffix *-less*, *-ful*, or *-ous*. Then write the base word, the suffix, and the word meaning. Use context clues in the sentence to help you find the meaning.

1. Uncle Mario is a (skillful) carpenter who can build just about anything out of wood. (1 point)

skill (1)	ful (1)	full of skill (1)
base word	**suffix**	**meaning**

2. Gloria was happy to hear that her trip to the dentist would be (painless). (1)

pain (1)	less (1)	without pain (1)
base word	**suffix**	**meaning**

3. My grandmother is an (adventurous) person who likes to see new places and try new things. (1)

adventure (1)	ous (1)	full of adventure, or liking adventure (1)
base word	**suffix**	**meaning**

4. It is hard to say no to our coach because he is such a (powerful) person. (1)

power (1)	ful (1)	full of power (1)
base word	**suffix**	**meaning**

5. Our dog Red sometimes yelps in his sleep, but he had a (dreamless) nap today. (1)

dream (1)	less (1)	without dreams (1)
base word	**suffix**	**meaning**

Read directions to students.
Vocabulary Strategies

169

Proofread for Spelling

Lesson 11
READER'S NOTEBOOK

Technology Wins
the Game
Spelling:
Vowel Sound in *joy*

Spelling Words

Basic
1. joy
2. point
3. voice
4. join
5. oil
6. coin
7. noise
8. spoil
9. toy
10. joint
11. boy
12. soil
13. choice
14. boil

Review
come
are

Challenge
poison
destroy

Circle the ten misspelled Spelling Words in the following letter. Then write each word correctly. (10 points)

Dear Louise,

I hope that you are doing well. I wish that I could (jion) you this week at camp. Sadly, I've lost my (voic) so Mom says I have to rest. Sitting inside while everyone else has fun definitely wouldn't be my (choyce). (Boiy) am I bored! I did get a cool new (toi), though. It is a tiny robot that makes a weird (noyse) whenever you (poynt) a light at it. I think Dad wants to (destroiy) it already. He thinks playing with it is like (poyson) to my brain and says I should read more books. He's probably right. Oh, I also got a neat old (coyn) from my grandfather. Anyway, write back when you can!

Your friend,

Albert

1. _____ join (1)   6. _____ noise (1)
2. _____ voice (1)   7. _____ point (1)
3. _____ choice (1)   8. _____ destroy (1)
4. _____ boy (1)   9. _____ poison (1)
5. _____ toy (1)   10. _____ coin (1)

Read directions to students.
Spelling
© Houghton Mifflin Harcourt Publishing Company. All rights reserved.

Assessment Tip: Total 20 points
Grade 3, Unit 3

Kinds of Verbs

Lesson 11
READER'S NOTEBOOK

Technology Wins
the Game
Grammar:
Spiral Review

- A word that tells what people or things do is a **verb**. Words that show action are **action verbs**.
- Some verbs do not show action. They are **being verbs**. The verbs *am, is, are, was,* and *were* are forms of the verb *be.* They tell what someone or something is or was.

    The players jump, and they are strong.

Identify the underlined verb in each sentence. Write *action* or *being* on the line.

1. Tammy worked hard for the race. _____ action (1 point)

2. She was a weak runner. _____ being (1)

3. Her coach taught her exercises. _____ action (1)

Combine each pair of sentences. Use both verbs in the new sentence. Write the new sentence on the line.

4. Jena jumped four feet high. Jena landed in the foam pit.
   Jena jumped four feet high and landed in the foam pit. (1)

5. The team ran around the track. The team was soon tired.
   The team ran around the track and was soon tired. (1)

6. The coaches were impressed. The coaches were happy.
   The coaches were impressed and happy. (1)

Read directions to students.
Grammar
© Houghton Mifflin Harcourt Publishing Company. All rights reserved.

Assessment Tip: Total 6 points
Grade 3, Unit 3

Name _____ Date _____

Homophones

Read each sentence. Choose the missing word from the box. Write the word. Then reread the complete sentence.

chews	mail	heal
choose	cent	heel
male	sent	he'll

1. A stallion is a __male (1 point)__ horse.

2. I didn't have a __cent (1)__ in my purse.

3. That wound should __heal (1)__ in a few days.

4. Becky's shoe was worn down at the __heel (1)__.

5. Ernesto always __chews (1)__ his food slowly.

6. Ginger's uncle __sent (1)__ her a birthday present.

7. Watch for an important letter in the __mail (1)__.

8. It is hard to __choose (1)__ between two of your favorite foods.

9. If the cat doesn't like his food, __he'll (1)__ complain.

Read directions to students.
Phonics
© Houghton Mifflin Harcourt Publishing Company. All rights reserved.

Assessment Tip: Total 9 points
Grade 3, Unit 3

173

Name _____ Date _____

Connect to Writing

If a noun ends with a consonant and *y*, change the *y* to *i*, and add *-es* to form the plural.

Sometimes the spelling of a noun changes in a special way.

The spelling of some nouns does not change to form the plural.

Incorrectly Formed Plural	Correctly Formed Plural
cherry, cherrys	cherry, cherries
goose, gooses	goose, geese
deer, deers	deer, deer

Proofread the paragraph. Find five mistakes in the spelling of plural nouns. Write the corrected sentences on the lines below.

The mans on the ski team learned a lot from the women. They showed them how to relax and go faster. They told storys about great women skiers. On top of the mountain, the skiers saw deers. They had to be careful not to run into them. Two women fell on the way down. Their familys were worried. But they were all right. Now they don't have any worrys.

1. The men on the ski team learned a lot from the women. (1 point)

2. They told stories about great women skiers. (1)

3. On top of the mountain, the skiers saw deer. (1)

4. Their families were worried. (1)

5. Now they don't have any worries. (1)

Read directions to students.
Grammar
© Houghton Mifflin Harcourt Publishing Company. All rights reserved.

Assessment Tip: Total 5 points
Grade 3, Unit 3

172

Name _____ Date _____

Capitalizing and Punctuating Quotations

Thinking Questions
What are the first and last words of the speaker? Which end mark is correct for the quotation? Does the quotation begin or end the sentence?

- Always capitalize the first word of the speaker's exact words.
- If the quotation comes first, add a comma, question mark, or exclamation point inside the **quotation marks** at the end of the speaker's words and add a period at the end of the sentence.
- If the quotation comes last, add a comma at the end of the tag and a question mark, exclamation point, or period inside the quotation marks.

Rewrite the sentences with correct capitalization and punctuation.

1. Sherry exclaimed "my flowers are growing so well"

   Sherry exclaimed, "My flowers are growing so well!" (1 point)

2. Marco asked "what did you do to help them grow"

   Marco asked, "What did you do to help them grow?" (1)

3. "my sister and I weeded and watered them every day" replied Sherry

   "My sister and I weeded and watered them every day," replied Sherry. (1)

4. "carrying water is hard work" exclaimed Sherry

   "Carrying water is hard work!" exclaimed Sherry. (1)

Read directions to students.
Grammar
© Houghton Mifflin Harcourt Publishing Company. All rights reserved.
175
Assessment Tip: Total 4 points
Grade 3, Unit 3

Name _____ Date _____

Quotation Marks

Thinking Question
What are the exact words of the speaker?

- **Quotation marks** ("") show dialogue, or the exact words a person or character says.
- Put quotation marks at the beginning and the end of a person or character's exact words.

  at the beginning

  Sherry said, "I am determined to grow flowers in my yard."

  at the end

Rewrite the sentences, adding quotation marks as needed.

1. Sherry said, This summer, I will start a garden.

   Sherry said, "This summer, I will start a garden." (1 point)

2. Cindy asked, What plants will you grow?

   Cindy asked, "What plants will you grow?" (1)

3. Sherry replied, I was thinking of planting sunflower seeds.

   Sherry replied, "I was thinking of planting sunflower seeds." (1)

4. Cindy exclaimed, I love sunflowers!

   Cindy exclaimed, "I love sunflowers!" (1)

Read directions to students.
Grammar
© Houghton Mifflin Harcourt Publishing Company. All rights reserved.
174
Assessment Tip: Total 4 points
Grade 3, Unit 3

Name _____ Date _____

Focus Trait: Evidence
Details to Compare and Contrast

A compare-and-contrast paragraph tells how two or more things are alike and different. Good writers use to help them compare and contrast things.

Without details: Carrots and lettuce are different in color.

With details: Carrots are orange, but lettuce is green.

Use detail words to describe each vegetable. Possible responses shown.

Carrot		Beet
1. long (1 point)	1.	round (1)
2. sweet (1)	2.	sweet (1)

Use detail words from your list above to write one sentence comparing and one sentence contrasting the vegetables.

3. Both carrots and beets taste sweet. (1)

4. Carrots are long, but beets are round. (1)

Pair/Share Work with a partner to describe each vegetable. Then write a sentence comparing them and a sentence contrasting them. Possible responses shown.

Lettuce		Corn
5. green (1)	5.	yellow (1)
6. grows above ground (1)	6.	grows above ground (1)

7. Lettuce is green, but corn is yellow. (1)

8. Neither vegetable grows below the ground. (1)

177

Name _____ Date _____

Homophones

Spelling Words

Basic
1. hole
2. whole
3. its
4. it's
5. hear
6. here
7. won
8. one
9. our
10. hour
11. their
12. there
13. fur
14. fir

Review
road
rode

Challenge
peace
piece

Write Basic Words to answer the following questions.

1. Which two words use the same vowel sound as *air*?

   there (1 point) , their (1)

2. Which two words use the same vowel sound as *ear*?

   here (1) , hear (1)

3. Which two words use the same vowel sound as *burn*?

   fur (1) , fir (1)

4. Which two words use the same vowel sound as *once*?

   won (1) , one (1)

5. Which two words use the same vowel sound as *go*?

   whole (1) , hole (1)

6. Which two words use the same vowel sound as *in*?

   its (1) , it's (1)

7. Which two words use the same vowel sound as *now*?

   our (1) , hour (1)

Challenge: Write two sentences. Use one Challenge Word in each sentence.

1. Responses will vary. (1) _____

2. Responses will vary. (1) _____

176

Right-hand page (179)

Name _____ Date _____

Reader's Guide

Tops and Bottoms

Gardening Journal

Hi, I'm Hare! I am keeping a garden journal to record the planting and harvesting. Help me fill it in with information from the text.

Read page 434. How did I get started?

I had an idea about growing crops! I knew Bear

would like my plan because he could sleep and

I could do all the work.   (5 points)

_____

Read page 435. How did I take care of the land?

My family worked together to water and weed.

That first summer, the land needed a lot

of work.   (5)

_____

Read page 438. Tell about the harvest. What was clever about what I grew?

We harvested carrots, radishes, and beets.

This was clever because we got the bottoms,

and the bottoms are the best parts of these

vegetables.   (5)

_____

Read directions to students.
Independent Reading
Assessment Tip: 15 Points
Grade 3, Unit 3

Left-hand page (178)

Name _____ Date _____

Words Ending in -er, -le

Write a word from the box to complete each sentence in the story. Then read the complete sentence.

bottle	ladle	table
dreamer	longer	teacher
kettle	sweeter	warmer

1. "Wake up, _____dreamer (1 point)_____ !" my mom calls every morning.

2. "Can't I sleep a little _____longer (1)_____ ?" I always ask.

3. Soon I am in the kitchen, where it is _____warmer (1)_____ and full of action.

4. The _____table (1)_____ is already set for breakfast.

5. I get the _____bottle (1)_____ of milk from the refrigerator.

6. In a few minutes the tea _____kettle (1)_____ whistles and the water is ready.

7. I love making Mom's tea for her. "Just a bit more honey, to make it _____sweeter (1)_____ ," I say.

8. Then I watch as Dad puts a _____ladle (1)_____ full of oatmeal in my favorite bowl. Yum!

9. He wraps up a muffin, smiles, and winks. "Give this to your _____teacher (1)_____ before school today."

Read directions to students.
Phonics
Assessment Tip: Total 9 points
Grade 3, Unit 3

Read pages 439–440. What was the next plan?

Bear was not happy about getting only the tops

of the vegetables. So, we decided to give him

the bottoms this time. We went back to work

and planted, watered, and weeded. (5)

Read page 443. Why was Bear angry again?

We grew lettuce, broccoli, and celery this

season. Bear was not happy this time because

we got the best parts of the vegetables again. (5)

Read pages 444–449. How did Bear think he would win this time?

Bear wanted the tops and bottoms this season.

But we had a good idea. This time we would

grow corn. The middle would be the best part. (5)

Read page 450. What did Bear finally do?

Bear decided that he would plant his own crops.

By working hard, he will get some of the good

parts of the vegetables. (5)

Read directions to students.
Independent Reading

Assessment Tip: 20 Points
Grade 3, Unit 3

Capitalizing and Punctuating Quotations

- Capitalize the first word of the speaker's exact words.
- If the quotation comes first, add a comma, question mark, or exclamation point inside the **quotation marks** at the end of the speaker's words and add a period at the end of the sentence.
- If the quotation comes last, add a comma at the end of the tag and a question mark, exclamation point, or period inside the quotation marks.

Write the sentences using correct capitalization and punctuation.

1. Jessie asked "where are they selling their tomatoes" (1 point)

   Jessie asked, "Where are they selling their tomatoes?" (1 point)

2. "They have a roadside stand" replied Manny.

   "They have a roadside stand," replied Manny. (1)

3. "Do they also sell cucumbers" asked Jessie.

   "Do they also sell cucumbers?" asked Jessie. (1)

4. "I'm not sure" Manny said.

   "I'm not sure," Manny said. (1)

5. Manny said "the stand is past this farm"

   Manny said, "The stand is past this farm." (1)

6. "They do have cucumbers" Jessie exclaimed.

   "They do have cucumbers!" Jessie exclaimed. (1)

Read directions to students.
Grammar

Assessment Tip: Total 6 points
Grade 3, Unit 3

Name _____ Date _____

Idioms

Read the web below. Write the meaning of each idiom. (You may find the meanings by looking up *head* in the dictionary.) (2 points each)

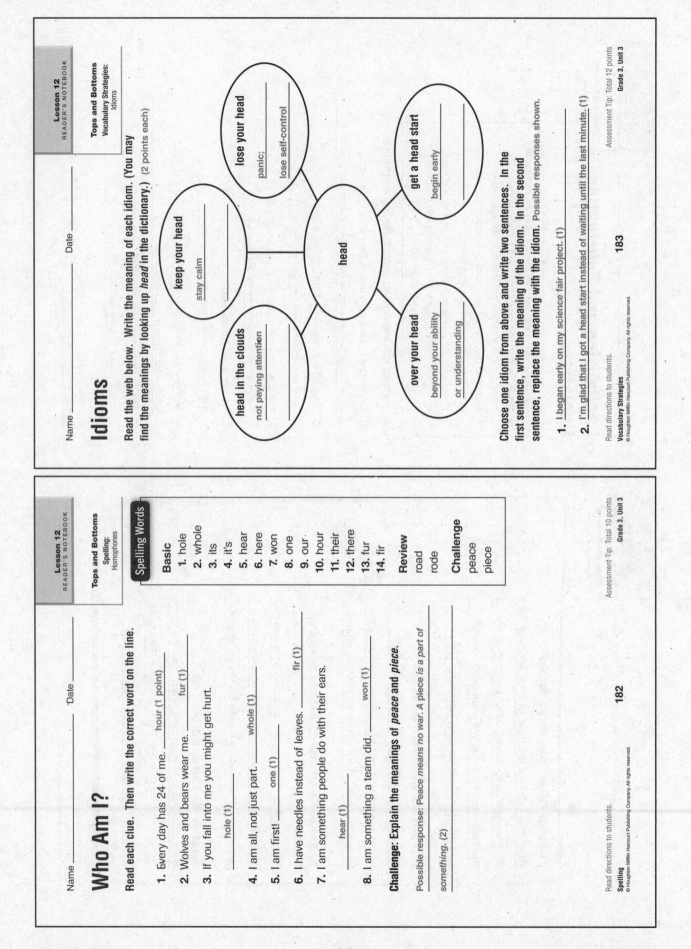

keep your head
stay calm _____

lose your head
panic; _____
lose self-control

head

head in the clouds
not paying attention _____

get a head start
begin early _____

over your head
beyond your ability _____
or understanding

Choose one idiom from above and write two sentences. In the first sentence, write the meaning of the idiom. In the second sentence, replace the meaning with the idiom. Possible responses shown.

1. I began early on my science fair project. (1)

2. I'm glad that I got a head start instead of waiting until the last minute. (1)

Name _____ Date _____

Who Am I?

Read each clue. Then write the correct word on the line.

1. Every day has 24 of me. _____ hour (1 point)

2. Wolves and bears wear me. _____ fur (1)

3. If you fall into me you might get hurt.
_____ hole (1)

4. I am all, not just part. _____ whole (1)

5. I am first! _____ one (1)

6. I have needles instead of leaves. _____ fir (1)

7. I am something people do with their ears.
_____ hear (1)

8. I am something a team did. _____ won (1)

Challenge: Explain the meanings of *peace* and *piece*.

Possible response: Peace means no war. A piece is a part of

_____ something. (2)

Spelling Words

Basic
1. hole
2. whole
3. its
4. it's
5. hear
6. here
7. won
8. one
9. our
10. hour
11. their
12. there
13. fur
14. fir

Review
road
rode

Challenge
peace
piece

Verb Tenses

Lesson 12
READER'S NOTEBOOK

Tops and Bottoms
Grammar:
Spiral Review

- Verbs in the **present tense** tell that the action in the sentence is happening now. Use an *-s* ending for singular subjects and no ending for a plural subject.
- Verbs in the **past tense** tell about action in the sentence that has already happened. Many verbs add *-ed* to show past tense.
- Verbs that tell about an action that is going to happen are in the **future tense.** You use the helping verb *will*.

I plant today. Yesterday, I planted.
I will plant tomorrow.

Write *present, past,* **or** *future* **for the tense each verb shows.**

1. When she was a baby, her family called her Sammy. _____ past (1 point)

2. When she grows up, her friends will call her Sam. _____ future (1)

3. In third grade, they call her Samantha. _____ present (1)

Rewrite sentences with underlined verbs from this paragraph. Change each underlined verb to make it match the tense of the first sentence. Write the new sentences on the lines below.

Our dog, Yappy, ran into the street. My brother calls to him very loudly. Yappy will stop for my brother.

4. My brother called to him very loudly. (1) _____

5. Yappy stopped for my brother. (1) _____

Proofreading for Spelling

Lesson 12
READER'S NOTEBOOK

Tops and Bottoms
Spelling:
Homophones

Find the misspelled words and circle them. Then write each word correctly. (10 points)

Dear Pat,

I'm writing this in the shade of a big (fur) tree. Its soft needles cover the ground like a blanket. (Its) a quiet summer day in the city's biggest park. All around, (their) is a feeling of (piece) and restfulness. My dog, Corvo, lies lazily in the hot sun. I'll bet his (fir) makes him hot on this summer day. I pick up a (peace) of paper that someone has left on the ground. Let's keep the city clean! I've been (hear) an (our) and I could stay all day. I can hardly (here) the traffic. The cars with (there) noise seem far away. I like writing letters, but I wish you were here!

Your friend,
Chris

1. fir (1)	6. piece (1)
2. It's (1)	7. here (1)
3. there (1)	8. hour (1)
4. peace (1)	9. hear (1)
5. fur (1)	10. their (1)

Spelling Words

Basic
1. hole
2. whole
3. its
4. it's
5. hear
6. here
7. won
8. one
9. our
10. hour
11. their
12. there
13. fur
14. fir

Review
road
rode

Challenge
peace
piece

Lesson 13
READER'S NOTEBOOK

Yonder Mountain:
A Cherokee Legend
Phonics: Contractions
with n't, 'd, 've

Name _____ Date _____

Contractions with n't, 'd, 've

**Read each sentence. Choose the missing word
from the box. Write the word. Then reread the complete sentence.**

aren't	couldn't	should've
they'd	you'd	haven't
I've	we've	I'd

1. If I ever had to sleep in the woods, __I'd (1 point)__ bring lots of bug spray.

2. I tried to open the jar, but I __couldn't (1)__ because
the lid was on too tight.

3. If you saw the movie, __you'd (1)__ love it as much
as I did.

4. My parents __aren't (1)__ too strict, but they do
have some rules.

5. Personally, __I've (1)__ always admired Ben
Franklin.

6. We haven't seen the movie, but __we've (1)__
both read the book.

7. "I __should've (1)__ known that you were behind all of
this," said the hero to the villain.

8. Why are you serving us dessert when we __haven't (1)__
eaten dinner yet?

9. If our friends saw us, __they'd (1)__ be really surprised.

Assessment Tip: Total 9 points
Grade 3, Unit 3

Name _____ Date _____

Connect to Writing

Use quotation marks (" ") to show the exact words
someone says. A quotation may come before or after
the tag.

Before the Tag	After the Tag
"I'll help make dinner," Ralph said.	Ralph said, "I'll help make dinner."
"What would you like to eat?" Pete asked.	Pete asked, "What would you like to eat?"

**Rewrite the sentences, adding quotation marks and commas
as needed.**

1. I would like roasted vegetables Ralph replied.

"I would like roasted vegetables," Ralph replied. (1 point)

2. Pete said I have carrots.

Pete said, "I have carrots." (1)

3. Would you like carrots Pete asked.

"Would you like carrots?" Pete asked. (1)

4. I love carrots! Ralph exclaimed.

"I love carrots!" Ralph exclaimed. (1)

5. They are one of my favorites said Pete.

"They are one of my favorites," said Pete. (1)

Assessment Tip: Total 5 points
Grade 3, Unit 3

Lesson 13
READER'S NOTEBOOK

Yonder Mountain:
A Cherokee Legend
Grammar:
Subject-Verb Agreement

Name _____ Date _____

Subject-Verb Agreement

- A **verb** that tells about an action that is happening now is in the present tense. Verbs in the present tense have two forms. The correct form to use depends on the **subject** of the sentence.

- Except for *I*, add *-s* to the verb when the noun in the subject is singular. Do not add *-s* to the verb when the noun in the subject is plural.

> **Thinking Question**
> Is the noun in the subject singular or plural?

> The word *Cherokee* means "people who live in the mountains."
> The Cherokee now live mostly in Oklahoma and North Carolina.

Underline the correct present-tense verb in parentheses. Then write each sentence correctly.

1. People (hear, hears) the Cherokee language.

People hear the Cherokee language. (1 point)

2. Fur trader Abraham Wood (send, sends) two men.

Fur trader Abraham Wood sends two men. (1)

3. The program about the Cherokee (begins, begin) at 7:00.

The program about the Cherokee begins at 7:00. (1)

4. The Cherokee (moves, move) to the west in the 1880s.

The Cherokee move to the west in the 1880s. (1)

Lesson 13
READER'S NOTEBOOK

Yonder Mountain:
A Cherokee Legend
Grammar:
Subject-Verb Agreement

Name _____ Date _____

Subject-Verb Agreement

- Some **verbs** end with *-es* instead of *-s*. Add *-es* to verbs that end with *s*, *sh*, *ch*, or *x* when they are used with a singular noun in the **subject**. Do not add *-es* when the noun in the subject is plural.

- Some verbs end with a consonant and *y*. Change the *y* to *i*, and add *-es* when you use this kind of verb with a singular noun.

> **Thinking Question**
> Does the verb end in *s*, *sh*, *ch*, *x*, or a consonant and *y*?

> The town searches for a new music director.
> A singer worries it will not happen.

- The verb *search* adds *-es*. The verb *worry* changes the *y* to *i* and adds *-es*.

Underline the correct present-tense verb in parentheses. Then write each sentence correctly.

1. A newspaper writer (asks, askes) for a new music director.

A newspaper writer asks for a new music director. (1 point)

2. A town citizen. (watchs, watches) for a new music director.

A town citizen watches for a new music director. (1)

3. A woman who knows music (hurrys, hurries) into town.

A woman who knows music hurries into town. (1)

4. She (trys, tries) to get everyone to sing well together.

She tries to get everyone to sing well together. (1)

Lesson 13
READER'S NOTEBOOK

Yonder Mountain:
A Cherokee Legend
Spelling:
Contractions

Name _____ Date _____

Contractions

Write each Basic Word under the correct heading.

Spelling Words

Basic
1. I'd
2. he's
3. haven't
4. doesn't
5. let's
6. there's
7. wouldn't
8. what's
9. she's
10. aren't
11. hasn't
12. couldn't
13. he'd
14. they're

Review
can't
isn't

Challenge
we're
weren't

Contractions combining a base word and *not*	Contractions combining a base word and *is, us, or has*
haven't (1 point)	he's (1)
doesn't (1)	let's (1)
wouldn't (1)	there's (1)
aren't (1)	what's (1)
hasn't (1)	she's (1)
couldn't (1)	
Challenge: weren't (1)	

Contractions combining a base word and *are*	Contractions combining a base word and *had or would*
they're (1)	I'd (1)
Challenge: we're (1)	he'd (1)

Challenge: Add the Challenge Words to your Word Sort.

Read directions to students.

Assessment Tip: Total 16 points
Grade 3, Unit 3

Name _____ Date _____

Focus Trait: Organization
Group Related Information

An informative paragraph gives facts and details about a topic. When you write an informative paragraph, group related information together.

Read pages 479–480 of *Yonder Mountain*. Write facts and details about Gray Wolf in the web.

Gray Wolf

thinks plants will help people (1 point)

returns to village (1 point)

rests on trail (1 point)

gathers healing plants (1 point)

Pair/Share Work with a partner to write sentences that group the information in the web. Possible response shown. (8 points)

Gray Wolf climbed the mountain. Because the mountain was so steep, he

had to stop and rest along the trail. While resting, he noticed some healing

plants. Gray Wolf began to gather the healing plants because he thought

they would help his people. Once he had gathered the plants, he headed

back down the mountain to the village.

Read directions to students.

Assessment Tip: Total 12 points
Grade 3, Unit 3

Name _____ Date _____

Lesson 13
READER'S NOTEBOOK

Yonder Mountain:
A Cherokee Legend
Phonics:
Cumulative Review

Cumulative Review

Write a word from the box to complete each sentence.
Then read the sentence.

road	they've	we've
you'd	I'd	rode
aren't	hasn't	didn't

1. If you _____ didn't (1 point) _____ leave the door open, who did?

2. We were on the _____ road (1) _____ at six in the morning.

3. This old trunk _____ hasn't (1) _____ been opened in years.

4. Eric and Marc have no idea how to get to the beach
because _____ they've (1) _____ never been there.

5. _____ I'd (1) _____ guess that you are hungry after
working all day.

6. Carla and Shannon _____ aren't (1) _____ old enough to
stay up so late.

7. Dee was excited to tell her friends how she
_____ rode (1) _____ a horse on vacation.

8. If _____ you'd (1) _____ just listen more, and talk less, you
could learn a lot.

9. My cousin pulled me outside, saying, " _____ We've (1) _____
got to leave now!"

Read directions to students.
Phonics
© Houghton Mifflin Harcourt Publishing Company. All rights reserved.

192

Assessment Tip: Total 9 points
Grade 3, Unit 3

Reader's Guide

Yonder Mountain

A Scene from Yonder Mountain

You are going to tell the story of Yonder Mountain as a
play. Fill in the different parts with details from the story.

**Read pages 473–475. Use what you read on these pages to write
a script for Chief Sky. Help him tell the audience how the three
young men are alike. What do they want? What do they do?**

Chief Sky: These three men all want to be the new chief.

They will all climb the mountain and bring something back.

(5 points)

**Read pages 476–480. Use these pages to help Black Bear
and Gray Wolf tell the audience about their adventures.**

Black Bear: I climbed up the mountain. I saw sparkling

stones. I knew my people could trade these stones for food.

I ran back down to the village with some stones. (5)

Gray Wolf: I also climbed up the mountain. I also saw the

sparkling stones, but I didn't pick up the sparkling stones.

I climbed higher. Then I found herbs and roots that could

heal my people. I ran back down to the village. (5)

Read directions to students.
Independent Reading
© Houghton Mifflin Harcourt Publishing Company All rights reserved.

193

Assessment Tip: 15 Points
Grade 3, Unit 3

Lesson 13
READER'S NOTEBOOK

Yonder Mountain:
A Cherokee Legend
Grammar:
Subject-Verb Agreement

Name _____ Date _____

Subject-Verb Agreement

The subject of each sentence is underlined. Write the correct form of the verb in parentheses to complete each sentence.

1. A climber ___searches (1 point)___ for a way to the top. (search)

2. Two strong men ___pull (1)___ themselves up the cliffs. (pull)

3. A woman ___fixes (1)___ her ropes to be safe. (fix)

4. One person ___passes (1)___ another as they climb. (pass)

5. Friends ___help (1)___ someone who is tired. (help)

6. Some boys ___race (1)___ to see who can be first to the top. (race)

7. A bird ___flies (1)___ up to the highest point. (fly)

8. One group ___crosses (1)___ a deep valley on the way. (cross)

9. One tired person ___slips (1)___ on the way up. (slip)

10. I ___reach (1)___ the top of the mountain first. (reach)

Read directions to students.
Grammar
195
© Houghton Mifflin Harcourt Publishing Company. All rights reserved.
Assessment Tip: Total 10 points
Grade 3, Unit 3

Name _____ Date _____

Read pages 481–484. Use what you read on these pages to write the script for Soaring Eagle. He will tell the audience about his journey up the mountain.

Soaring Eagle: I climbed the mountain too. I saw the sparkling stones, and I saw the herbs. But the chief said to go to the top of the mountain. So I did. I brought back a story of smoke signals. People need our help. (5)

Read pages 485–487. Why did Chief Sky choose Soaring Eagle to be the new chief? Write a script for Chief Sky. He will tell the audience why he chose Soaring Eagle.

Chief Sky: Soaring Eagle will be our next chief because he wanted to help not just his own people, but other people who were in need. This meant that he would be a great leader. (5)

Read directions to students.
Independent Reading
194
© Houghton Mifflin Harcourt Publishing Company. All rights reserved.
Assessment Tip: 10 Points
Grade 3, Unit 3

Name _____ Date _____

Lesson 13
READER'S NOTEBOOK

Yonder Mountain:
A Cherokee Legend
Spelling:
Contractions

Contractions

Write the Spelling Word that is a contraction of each word pair below.

Spelling Words

Basic
1. I'd
2. he's
3. haven't
4. doesn't
5. let's
6. there's
7. wouldn't
8. what's
9. she's
10. aren't
11. hasn't
12. couldn't
13. he'd
14. they're

Review
can't
isn't

Challenge
we're
weren't

1. have not ___haven't___ (1 point)

2. what is ___what's___ (1)

3. let us ___let's___ (1)

4. he had ___he'd___ (1)

5. could not ___couldn't___ (1)

6. there is ___there's___ (1)

7. are not ___aren't___ (1)

8. she is ___she's___ (1)

9. they are ___they're___ (1)

10. does not ___doesn't___ (1)

11. I had ___I'd___ (1)

12. would not ___wouldn't___ (1)

13. he is ___he's___ (1)

14. has not ___hasn't___ (1)

Name _____ Date _____

Lesson 13
READER'S NOTEBOOK

Yonder Mountain
Vocabulary Strategies:
Homophones and Homographs

Homophones and Homographs

Read the following paragraph. Proofread it to find mistakes with homophones. Write the wrong homophone and the correct homophone on the lines.

My grandmother and I walked to the park. On our weigh, we passed a fruit stand.

"Mind if we peak at your selection?" my grandmother asked.

"Go ahead!" the fruit vendor said. "I have all kinds of fresh fruits write here! Here, have this red pare," he added. "It's perfectly ripe."

"Thanks," my grandmother said. "I almost mist that one!"

1. weigh, way (2 points) _____

2. peak, peek (2) _____

3. write, right (2) _____

4. pare, pear (2) _____

5. mist, missed (2) _____

Choose a pair of homophones. Write a sentence that shows the meaning of each word. Possible response shown.

My Aunt Gloria climbed to the peak of Mount Washington.
_____

I would like to peek into the window of that house. (2)
_____

Lesson 13
READER'S NOTEBOOK

Yonder Mountain:
A Cherokee Legend
Grammar:
Spiral Review

Name _____ Date _____

Writing Quotations

- Show dialogue by putting quotation marks (" ") at the beginning and the end of a speaker's exact words.
  She asked, "Are you climbing?"
- Place a comma after *said* or *asked*. Use a capital letter for the first word of the quotation and an end mark inside the quotation marks.
  He said, "Give it to me."
  "We're finally home!" Kim shouted.

Write each sentence correctly by adding quotation marks.

1. The teacher said, Hillary climbed the tallest mountain.
   The teacher said, "Hillary climbed the tallest mountain." (1 point)

2. She asked, What is the tallest mountain called?
   She asked, "What is the tallest mountain called?" (1)

3. He said, It is named Mount Everest.
   He said, "It is named Mount Everest." (1)

Write each sentence correctly. Use quotation marks, correct capitalization, end marks, and punctuation.

4. The teacher asked would you like to climb a mountain
   The teacher asked, "Would you like to climb a mountain?" (1)

5. The girl said climbing Mount Everest would be exciting
   The girl said, "Climbing Mount Everest would be exciting." (1)

Read directions to students.
Grammar
© Houghton Mifflin Harcourt Publishing Company. All rights reserved.
198
Assessment Tip: Total 5 points
Grade 3, Unit 3

Lesson 13
READER'S NOTEBOOK

Yonder Mountain:
A Cherokee Legend
Spelling:
Contractions

Spelling Words

Basic
1. I'd
2. he's
3. haven't
4. doesn't
5. let's
6. there's
7. wouldn't
8. what's
9. she's
10. aren't
11. hasn't
12. couldn't
13. he'd
14. they're

Review
can't
isn't

Challenge
we're
weren't

Name _____ Date _____

Proofreading

Circle the ten misspelled Spelling Words in the following story. Then write each word correctly. (10 points)

My Relatives

My aunt and uncle are very different from a lot of people. Hes a clown in a circus, and she works as a stuntwoman. Theyr'e always doing crazy stuff. For example, my aunt has'nt cut her hair in fifteen years. I know I couln'ot go six months without getting a haircut. Then theres the house where they live. Lets just say that it is unique. For starters, it do'snt have any corners. You wouldnt believe how odd it looks. When we stay with them, I feel like wer'e living in a donut! If they were'nt so nice, I might think that there was actually something wrong with them.

1. He's (1)
2. They're (1)
3. hasn't (1)
4. couldn't (1)
5. there's (1)
6. Let's (1)
7. doesn't (1)
8. wouldn't (1)
9. we're (1)
10. weren't (1)

Read directions to students.
Spelling
© Houghton Mifflin Harcourt Publishing Company. All rights reserved.
199
Assessment Tip: Total 20 points
Grade 3, Unit 3

Name _____ Date _____

Words with *ar, or, ore*

**Read each sentence. Choose the missing word from the box.
Write the word. Then reread the sentence.**

Mars	morning	cart
chores	parking	largest
artistic	explore	parlor

1. This tree is the ___largest (1 point)___ tree on the street.

2. "Have a seat in the ___parlor (1)___," said the butler to the guest.

3. The bold scientists planned to ___explore (1)___ the bottom of the ocean.

4. The driver looked for a ___parking (1)___ space for five minutes.

5. Put your groceries into the ___cart (1)___.

6. My favorite time of day is ___morning (1)___.

7. Painting, singing, and dancing are ___artistic (1)___ hobbies.

8. I wish I could fly to the planet ___Mars (1)___.

9. Taking out the trash and making my bed are on my list of ___chores (1)___.

Read directions to students.
Phonics   201
© Houghton Mifflin Harcourt Publishing Company. All rights reserved.

Assessment Tip: Total 9 points
Grade 3, Unit 3

Lesson 13
READER'S NOTEBOOK

Yonder Mountain:
A Cherokee Legend
Grammar:
Connect to Writing

Name _____ Date _____

Connect to Writing

Proofreading is important to make writing correct and clear to the reader. Pay attention to endings of verbs as you proofread.

Singular Subject	Plural Subject
The Native American chief leads.	Chiefs lead.
He mixes an herb as medicine.	They mix herbs as medicine.
The chief thinks about his people.	Chiefs think about their people.
He works for a solution.	They work for a solution.

Proofread the paragraph. Find and underline five errors with the spelling of present tense verbs. Write the corrected sentences.

The chief of the Native American group knows it is time to move. The land lack the food needed for their people. It is time to go south. The women carries the things they want to bring. Some men on horses searches for a place to stay. They find a wonderful place by the river. The children rushes to get there first. Everyone enjoys the new area. A horse splash through the river water. Everyone smiles for the first time in a long time.

1. The land lacks the food needed for their people. (1 point)

2. The women carry the things they want to bring. (1)

3. Some men on horses search for a place to stay. (1)

4. The children rush to get there first. (1)

5. A horse splashes through the river water. (1)

Read directions to students.
Grammar   200
© Houghton Mifflin Harcourt Publishing Company. All rights reserved.

Assessment Tip: Total 5 points
Grade 3, Unit 3

Name _____ Date _____

Lesson 14
READER'S NOTEBOOK

Aero and Officer Mike
Grammar:
Pronoun-Verb Agreement

Pronoun-Verb Agreement

- Verbs show action in sentences and when that action happens. **Verbs** that tell about actions that are happening now are in the present tense.
- You add -s or -es to the verb when the **subject** is *he, she,* or *it.*
- You do not add -s or -es to the verb when the pronoun in the subject is *I, you, we,* or *they.*

  She barks very loudly.
  They bark even more loudly.

Thinking Question
Does the subject pronoun refer just to one person or does it refer either to me or to more than one person?

Underline the present-tense verb in parentheses that agrees with the subject pronoun. Then write each sentence correctly.

1. You (find, finds) dogs of all different types. (2 points)

  You find dogs of all different types.

2. He (choose, chooses) the ones that are the best.

  He chooses the ones that are the best. (2)

3. It (seem, seems) that you know dogs well.

  It seems that you know dogs well. (2)

4. We (feel, feels) that you should choose the dogs.

  We feel that you should choose the dogs. (2)

5. They (want, wants) to pick out some dogs, too.

  They want to pick out some dogs, too. (2)

Assessment Tip: Total 10 points
Grade 3, Unit 3

Name _____ Date _____

Lesson 14
READER'S NOTEBOOK

Aero and Officer Mike
Grammar:
Pronoun-Verb Agreement

When to Add -*es*, -*ies*

- Most **verbs** in the present end with -s when the **pronoun** in the **subject** is *he, she,* or *it.* Add -*es* to verbs that end in -s, -sh, -ch, or -x.
- Do not add -s or -*es* to verbs when the pronoun in the subject is *I, you, we,* or *they.*
- Some verbs end with a consonant and *y*. Change the *y* to *i* and add -*es* when the pronoun in the subject is *he, she,* or *it.*
- You do not change the *y* to *i* and add -*es* when the pronoun in the subject is *I, you, we,* or *they.*

Thinking Question
Does the verb end in s, sh, ch, x or with a consonant and y, and what is the pronoun in the subject?

Underline the present-tense verb in parentheses that agrees with the subject pronoun. Then write each sentence correctly.

1. You (push, pushes) the cart filled with hay out to the fields.

  You push the cart filled with hay out to the fields. (2 points)

2. It (pass, passes) over the old bridge. (2)

  It passes over the old bridge. (2)

3. We (guess, guesses) when you will reach the horses.

  We guess when you will reach the horses. (2)

4. They (march, marches) across the hills to the food.

  They march across the hills to the food. (2)

Assessment Tip: Total 8 points
Grade 3, Unit 3

Name _____ Date _____

Words with Vowel + /r/ Sounds

Write the correct Basic Words in each box.

Spelling Words

Basic
1. horse
2. mark
3. storm
4. market
5. acorn
6. artist
7. March
8. north
9. barking
10. stork
11. thorn
12. forest
13. chore
14. restore

Review
dark
story

Challenge
partner
fortune

Write the words that contain the vowel + r sound in *far*.	Write the words that contain the vowel + r sound in *or*.
mark (1 point)	horse (1)
market (1)	storm (1)
artist (1)	acorn (1)
March (1)	north (1)
barking (1)	thorn (1)
	stork (1)
	forest (1)
	chore (1)
	restore (1)

Challenge

1. Does *partner* contain the vowel sound in *far* or the vowel sound in *or*? _____ far (1)

2. Does *fortune* contain the vowel sound in *far* or the vowel sound in *or*? _____ or (1)

Read directions to students.
Spelling
© Houghton Mifflin Harcourt Publishing Company. All rights reserved.

204

Assessment Tip: Total 16 points
Grade 3, Unit 3

Name _____ Date _____

Focus Trait: Purpose
Choosing a Topic

An explanatory essay uses ideas, facts, and details to explain a topic to readers. Good writers ask, *What is my purpose for writing? What topic am I interested in? What ideas do I have about the topic? How can I use facts and details to explain the topic clearly?*

Read the information in the chart. Look at the topics and the author's purpose. Which topic interests you the most? Circle it. Responses will vary. Students should explain why they chose the topic and list their ideas. (6 points)

Topics	Author's Purpose
how dogs help people	to explain a topic to readers
how monkeys help people	
how horses help people	
how dolphins help people	

Tell why you chose the topic. Also list one or two ideas that you have about the topic.

_____

_____

_____

_____

Read directions to students.
Writing
Copyright © Houghton Mifflin Harcourt Publishing Company. All rights reserved.

205

Assessment Tip: Total 6 points
Grade 3, Unit 3

Name _____ Date _____

Cumulative Review

Write words from the box to complete the lines of the poem.

arm	garden	I'd	shark	storm
bored	harm	I've	shore	thorns

What Didn't Go Wrong Today?

I worked in my ___garden (1 point)___, but I soon came to ___harm (1)___ .

The sharp ___thorns (1)___ of a rose badly scratched up

my ___arm (1)___ !

So I went to the ___shore (1)___ for a swim and some sun,

Until a ___shark (1)___ showed its fin and scared everyone!

Then ___I'd (1)___ just reached the woods, the shade of tall trees,

When a dark ___storm (1)___ filled the sky and rained on the seas!

Now ___I've (1)___ come home sad, with nothing to do.

If you are ___bored (1)___, too, may I come play with you?

Read directions to students.
Phonics
© Houghton Mifflin Harcourt Publishing Company. All rights reserved.

Assessment Tip: Total 10 points
Grade 3, Unit 3

Name _____ Date _____

Reader's Guide

Aero and Officer Mike

Aero Tells His Story

Hi, I'm Aero! I just found out that there is a book written about me and my pal Officer Mike. I am going to read this selection and see what the author said about us! Answer my questions about the selection.

Read page 506. It is good that the author mentioned my collar first thing! Do you know why? (2 points)

It shows that you will be working today as a police dog. ___(2 points)___

Read pages 508–509. The author mentioned Officer Mike's police car. Why do you think the car is important?

The car is set up differently for a dog to ride in it. This book explains where you sit and how you get out of the car when Officer Mike needs your help. ___(2)___

Read pages 510–511. I love playing ball with Mike! I also listen to Mike when he talks to me. Can you guess why?

You are loyal to Mike, and you want to do what he says. ___(2)___

Read directions to students.
Independent Reading
© Houghton Mifflin Harcourt Publishing Company. All rights reserved.

Assessment Tip: 6 Points
Grade 3, Unit 3

Name _____ Date _____

Pronoun-Verb Agreement

Write the present-tense form of the verb in parentheses that agrees with the subject pronoun.

1. My dogs ___sleep (1 point)___ all day. (sleep)

2. They ___learn (1)___ my smell and trust me. (learn)

3. He ___uses (1)___ other ways to get close to his dogs. (use)

4. She ___feeds (1)___ them right out of her hand. (feed)

5. You ___sit (1)___ here and watch us do it. (sit)

6. The dogs ___splash (1)___ as they play in the rain. (splash)

7. It ___catches (1)___ your attention when you see it. (catch)

8. He ___mixes (1)___ a special blend of pet food. (mix)

9. One ___catches (1)___ a ball that he throws. (catch)

10. They ___study (1)___ the different ways to train pets. (study)

Assessment Tip: Total 10 points
Grade 3, Unit 3

Name _____ Date _____

Read page 512. I remember that training! I still don't really like looking at those pictures. What can you tell me about the training from looking at the pictures? How did I feel about it?

The pictures show what you learned to walk over. You did not really like this training. (2)

_____

_____

Read pages 516-518. There is important information on these pages. Do you know why the author included this information in this selection?

She wanted to show what happens when you visit schools. She explained how Officer Mike works with you to show what you can do. She also explained how children should pet you. (2)

_____

Read pages 519-521. I thought this was a really good book! It explained a lot about Officer Mike and me! Now you tell me what you thought of this selection. Did you like it? Why or why not?

(Accept all reasonable responses that include details from the book.) (4)

_____

Assessment Tip: 8 Points
Grade 3, Unit 3

Name _____ Date _____

Prefixes *in-*, *im-*

Read each base word. Add the prefix shown and write a new word and its meaning.

Base Word	Prefix	New Word	Meaning
active	in	inactive (1 point)	not active (1)
visible	in	invisible (1)	not visible (1)
definite	in	indefinite (1)	not definite (1)
patient	im	impatient (1)	not patient (1)
perfect	im	imperfect (1)	not perfect (1)
measurable	im	immeasurable (1)	not measurable (1)

Now write a sentence for each word above with a prefix. Make sure your sentence shows the word's meaning. Possible responses shown.

1. When Josh was sick, he stayed in bed and was totally inactive. (1)

2. We wrapped the package using invisible tape that wouldn't show. (1)

3. We had several ideas about what to do on our trip, but our plans were indefinite. (1)

4. We had stood in line a long time and were growing impatient. (1)

5. Since everyone makes mistakes, all people are imperfect. (1)

6. The girl's puppy brings her immeasurable happiness. (1)

Read directions to students.
Vocabulary Strategies
© Houghton Mifflin Harcourt Publishing Company. All rights reserved.

Assessment Tip: Total 18 points
Grade 3, Unit 3

Name _____ Date _____

Words with Vowel + /r/ Sounds

Write eight words that are names for people, places, or things.

Any eight of the following nouns:

horse, mark, storm, market,

March, acorn, artist, north,

stork, thorn, forest, chore (8 points)

_____

_____

Spelling Words

Basic
1. horse
2. mark
3. storm
4. market
5. acorn
6. artist
7. March
8. north
9. barking
10. stork
11. thorn
12. forest
13. chore
14. restore

Review
dark
story

Challenge
partner
fortune

Challenge

1. A person you work with is your _____ partner (1) .

2. If you make a lot of money, you make a

_____ fortune (1) .

Read directions to students.
Spelling
© Houghton Mifflin Harcourt Publishing Company. All rights reserved.

Assessment Tip: Total 10 points
Grade 3, Unit 3

Name _____ Date _____

Words with Vowel + /r/ Sounds

Find the misspelled words and circle them. Then write each word correctly. (10 points)

An (ortist) was traveling through a deep, dark (forest). He carried his paints and brushes in a bag that hung from his back. His (harse) was white, just like a blank canvas. He was riding to the (morket,) a day's ride to the (narth,) to sell his pictures.

Suddenly, huge gray clouds moved overhead. A (storem) was coming! The wind rose, and an (acarn) fell from a tree, hitting the man on the head. A sharp (tharn) from a bush scratched his hand. A big white (stark) flapped its wings as it flew toward its nest. Then the traveler heard the (barrking) of wild dogs in the distance. "Don't worry," he told his horse. "They're afraid of thunder and lightning."

1. _____ artist (1)
2. _____ forest (1)
3. _____ horse (1)
4. _____ market (1)
5. _____ north (1)

6. _____ storm (1)
7. _____ acorn (1)
8. _____ thorn (1)
9. _____ stork (1)
10. _____ barking (1)

Spelling Words

Basic
1. horse
2. mark
3. storm
4. market
5. acorn
6. artist
7. March
8. north
9. barking
10. stork
11. thorn
12. forest
13. chore
14. restore

Review
dark
story

Challenge
partner
fortune

Read directions to students.
Spelling
Assessment Tip: Total 20 points
Grade 3, Unit 3

213

Name _____ Date _____

Subjects and Predicates

- The subject of a sentence tells whom or what the sentence is about.
- The predicate of a sentence tells what the subject is, was, or will be, or what the subject is, was, or will be doing.

The sheep ate grass in the valley.
An old wolf watched them from the bushes.

Write the subject of each sentence on the line.

1. The old gray coyote came out of the hills. ___The old gray coyote (1 point)___

2. This smart animal will eat almost anything. ___This smart animal (1)___

3. His little pups hide right behind him. ___His little pups (1)___

4. These sweet babies are hungry and tired. ___These sweet babies (1)___

Write the predicate of each sentence on the line.

5. Three fat sheep walk away from the others. ___walk away from the others. (1)___

6. A big blue truck drives by them. ___drives by them. (1)___

7. A man with boots grabs the sheep. ___grabs the sheep. (1)___

8. The coyote finds food for the pups. ___finds food for the pups. (1)___

Read directions to students.
Grammar
Assessment Tip: Total 8 points
Grade 3, Unit 3

212

Name _____ Date _____

Words with *er, ir, ur, or*

Read each sentence. Choose the missing word from the box.
Write the word. Then reread the complete sentence.

curb	nerve	curves
worker	furry	birth
thirty	germs	

1. The road ___curves (1 point)___ up ahead, so be ready to turn.

2. Having hair on the furniture is one of the problems with having a
___furry (1)___ dog.

3. I knew you wouldn't have the ___nerve (1)___ to stand up to your
big brother.

4. As Danielle crossed the street, she tripped on the ___curb (1)___ and
hurt her ankle.

5. Adam does well in school because he is a hard ___worker (1)___.

6. The zoo announced the ___birth (1)___ of a baby panther last week.

7. Mr. Perkins has ___thirty (1)___ students in his classroom.

8. Colds and the flu are caused by ___germs (1)___.

Name _____ Date _____

Connect to Writing

Combining two sentences that have the same noun in
the subject makes your writing smoother and easier to
read. Remember to use a comma and the word *and*.

Same Noun in the Subject	Pronoun Replacing Noun in the Subject
These dogs are for sports. These dogs make great pets.	These dogs are for sports, and they make great pets.
Border collies are herding dogs. Border collies are very smart.	Border collies are herding dogs, and they are very smart.

Combine each pair of sentences. Change each underlined subject
to a pronoun. Write the new sentence.

1. Maltese dogs are friendly. Maltese dogs make good pets.

   Maltese dogs are friendly, and they make good pets. (1 point)

2. My male Great Dane is very gentle. My male Great Dane stands very tall.

   My male Great Dane is very gentle, and he stands very tall. (1)

3. Your female collie tends sheep. Your female collie gets burrs in her fur.

   Your female collie tends sheep, and she gets burrs in her fur. (1)

4. The people who breed dogs work very hard. The people who breed dogs
   love animals.

   The people who breed dogs work very hard, and they love animals. (1)

5. My family and I look for the perfect dog. My family and I find a funny
   one we love.

   My family and I look for the perfect dog, and we find a funny one we love. (1)

Name _____ Date _____

Verbs in the Past

- Most verbs show **past tense** by adding *-ed*.
- Some verbs end with *e*. Drop the *e* and add *-ed*.

They allowed us to cook alone.
He needed eggs for the recipe.
Evan's parents liked our cooking.

Thinking Question
Can I add -ed to the verb to show past tense? Does the verb end in e?

Write each sentence using the correct past tense of the verb in parentheses.

1. Evan _____ his parents to send him to cooking school. (want)

Evan wanted his parents to send him to cooking school. (1 point)

2. We _____ to answer a newspaper ad for a school. (decide)

We decided to answer a newspaper ad for a school. (1)

3. Many cooking students _____ there. (work)

Many cooking students worked there. (1)

4. Evan and I _____ that they would like our letter. (hope)

Evan and I hoped that they would like our letter. (1)

5. We _____ the school with the good work we did. (surprise)

We surprised the school with the good work we did. (1)

Grammar
Assessment Tip: Total 5 points
Grade 3, Unit 3
216
© Houghton Mifflin Harcourt Publishing Company. All rights reserved.
Read directions to students.

Name _____ Date _____

Verbs in the Present

- Add *-s* to most **present tense** verbs when when the noun in the subject is singular. For most verbs that end in *y*, change the *y* to *i* and add *-es*.
- Do not add *-s* to the verb when the noun in the subject is plural.
- Do not add *-s* to the verb when the subject is *I* or *you*.

Mario eats in the kitchen. He studies alone.
We eat together. We study together.
I eat alone. I study with my sister.

Thinking Questions
Is the noun in the subject singular or plural? Is the noun I or you? Does the verb end in y?

Write each sentence, using the correct present tense of the verb in parentheses.

1. Uncle Raul _____ a cutting board. (use)

Uncle Raul uses a cutting board. (1 point)

2. He _____ his tea while we slice onions. (sip)

He sips his tea while we slice onions. (1)

3. I _____ when I slice onions. (cry)

I cry when I slice onions. (1)

4. Even my dad _____ when he slices onions. (cry)

Even my dad cries when he slices onions. (1)

Grammar
Assessment Tip: Total 4 points
Grade 3, Unit 3
217
© Houghton Mifflin Harcourt Publishing Company. All rights reserved.
Read directions to students.

Name _____ Date _____

Focus Trait: Elaboration
Using Formal Language

Writers change their voice, or how they use their words and language, based on the purpose of their writing. For example, they use formal language with an explanatory essay to clearly state facts, definitions, and details.

For example:

Dolphins live in the ocean in groups called pods. They are highly intelligent mammals that communicate through sound, vision, touch, and taste.

The sentences below are written using informal language. Rewrite them using formal language. Possible responses shown.

1. Tiny monkeys are so cute, and they help people, too!

   Small monkeys can be trained to assist people. (1 point)

2. That police officer is riding a cool bike. He is in a pretty big park.

   The police officer rides a bicycle to get through a large park quickly. (1 point)

3. I think horses work too hard. They chase cows and carry around people and stuff.

   Horses are hard workers. They help cowboys and cowgirls chase cattle. (1 point)

4. There's a brush fire! You'd better call 911!

   When you see a brush fire, call an operator immediately by dialing 911. (1 point)

Read directions to students.
Writing
Copyright © Houghton Mifflin Company. All rights reserved.

219

Assessment Tip: Total 4 points
Grade 3, Unit 3

Name _____ Date _____

Vowel + /r/ Sound in *nurse*

Write each Basic Word under the correct heading.

Words with the vowel + /r/ sound in *nurse* spelled *ur*	Words with the vowel + /r/ sound in *nurse* spelled *ir*
nurse (1 point)	shirt (1)
hurt (1)	first (1)
curly (1)	dirt (1)
turn (1)	stir (1)
	third (1)
	firm (1)

Words with the vowel + /r/ sound in *nurse* spelled *or*	Words with the vowel + /r/ sound in *nurse* spelled *er*
work (1)	serve (1)
word (1)	
worry (1)	

Challenge: Which Challenge Word can only be placed in the last box? _perfect (1)_

Which Challenge Word can be placed in both the first and the last box? _hamburger (1)_

Spelling Words

Basic
1. nurse
2. work
3. shirt
4. hurt
5. first
6. word
7. serve
8. curly
9. dirt
10. third
11. worry
12. turn
13. stir
14. firm

Review
her
girl

Challenge
perfect
hamburger

Read directions to students.
Spelling
© Houghton Mifflin Harcourt Publishing Company. All rights reserved.

218

Assessment Tip: Total 16 points
Grade 3, Unit 3

Name _____ Date _____

Cumulative Review

Write a word from the box to complete each sentence. Then read the sentence.

certainly	herd	working
firmly	turning	burger
spark	report	before

1. This restaurant is known for having a great
   __burger (1 point)__ and tasty fries.

2. I love to help cook dinner. I think I'm __turning (1)__
   into a chef!

3. Damon gave a very interesting __report (1)__ about
   the rain forests.

4. I __certainly (1)__ don't want to spend all weekend
   studying.

5. The forest fire began with just a single __spark (1)__

6. Nicole was being silly when she said that she always ate
   __lunch__ __before (1)__ breakfast.

7. Frank held the ball __firmly (1)__ as he ran.

8. The cowboys rounded up the __herd (1)__ of
   cattle.

9. Because the dryer is not __working (1)__ my clothes
   are still wet.

Read directions to students.
Phonics
© Houghton Mifflin Harcourt Publishing Company. All rights reserved.

Assessment Tip: Total 9 points
Grade 3, Unit 3

Name _____ Date _____

Reader's Guide

The Extra-good Sunday

Cooking with Beezus and Ramona

Hi, I am Todd Allen, host of *Cooking at Home!* Beezus and Ramona created a delicious chicken dish for dinner. We are going to find out how they made it!

Read pages 543–544 to answer Todd's questions.

Todd Allen: Ramona, you had to cook dinner one night for the family. How did you feel about that?

Ramona: I was unhappy. I did not know how to
cook or what to make.   (5 points)

Read page 545 to answer Todd's question.

Todd Allen: Beezus, you wanted to make something awful! Why? What made you change your mind?

Beezus: I wanted our parents to know how we felt
when we ate tongue. I didn't want to make anything
too bad though because we had to eat it, too.   (5)

Read pages 546–549 to answer to the next question.

Todd Allen: How did you come up with your special dish?

Ramona: We did not have all the ingredients, so we
had to find other ingredients that looked or tasted
like them.   (5)

Read directions to students.
Independent Reading
© Houghton Mifflin Harcourt Publishing Company. All rights reserved.

Assessment Tip: 15 Points
Grade 3, Unit 3

Name _____ Date _____

Verbs in the Future

- A verb that tells about an action that will happen is in the **future tense.**
- Add the word *will* before a verb to form the future tense.

I will cook the food.
My family will eat the food.

Write each sentence, using the correct future tense of the verb in parentheses.

1. Theo _____ the recipe cards. (study)

Theo will study the recipe cards. (1 point)

2. He _____ which recipe to make. (decide)

He will decide which recipe to make. (1)

3. Doug _____ the chicken. (fry)

Doug will fry the chicken. (1)

4. Both boys _____ the sauce. (taste)

Both boys will taste the sauce. (1)

5. The younger kids _____ the table. (set)

The younger kids will set the table. (1)

6. Theo _____ the meal. (serve)

Theo will serve the meal. (1)

Read directions to students.
Grammar
© Houghton Mifflin Harcourt Publishing Company. All rights reserved.

Assessment Tip: Total 6 points
Grade 3, Unit 3

223

Name _____ Date _____

Read pages 550–552. Use these pages to help Beezus talk about what happened next.

Todd Allen: Beezus, how did you feel about the dinner you were making? Was Ramona helping?

Beezus: I was worried that everything would go wrong! Ramona kept spilling things, and we forgot the peas and salad. We didn't think anything would taste good. (5)

Read page 554. Use this page to help the girls talk about serving the dinner and about their parents' reaction.

Todd Allen: All right, Ramona. Let's see this famous chicken dish. Mmm, it looks good! How did you feel when you brought it out to the table?

Ramona: I was really worried that our parents would not like it, but our dad said it was good. We were so happy! (5)

Read pages 555–557. What did Ramona think?

Todd Allen: Tell me, Ramona, what was the best part of making dinner?

Ramona: I liked cooking the dinner, but the best part of all was that Mom and Dad cleaned up! (5)

Read directions to students.
Independent Reading
© Houghton Mifflin Harcourt Publishing Company. All rights reserved.

Assessment Tip: 15 Points
Grade 3, Unit 3

222

Name _____ Date _____

Vowel + /r/ Sound in *nurse*

Use the Basic Words to complete the puzzle. (14 points)

Across
1. Item of clothing
3. Comes before "second"
5. Soil
7. The opposite of play
8. "Please" is the magic _____
9. A hospital worker
10. Not soft
12. The opposite of straight

Down
1. To mix
2. Comes after "second"
4. To present or give
6. Move a car right or left
7. Be concerned
11. Injured

Spelling Words

Basic
1. nurse
2. work
3. shirt
4. hurt
5. first
6. word
7. serve
8. curly
9. dirt
10. third
11. worry
12. turn
13. stir
14. firm

Review
her
girl

Challenge
perfect
hamburger

Read directions to students.
Spelling
© Houghton Mifflin Harcourt Publishing Company. All rights reserved.
224
Assessment Tip: Total 14 points
Grade 3, Unit 3

Name _____ Date _____

Using a Thesaurus

Read the book review. Look up each underlined word in a thesaurus. Write a synonym for each word. Possible responses shown.

> If you haven't already, you'll want to meet Ramona Quimby. The latest adventures of this special girl appear in *Ramona Quimby, Age 8*. With her father in college and her mother back at work, Ramona has to resolve some things for herself. How will she handle her annoying young neighbor? Will her parents be cross with her when she makes a mess? Will things remain tense with Yard Ape?
> There is a reason why Beverly Cleary's books remain some of America's favorites after so many years.

1. newest (2 points)
2. settle (2)
3. irritating (2)
4. angry (2)
5. uncomfortable (2)
6. stay (2)

Write two sentences that could be in your own review of *The Extra-good Sunday*. Choose a word in each sentence to look up in a thesaurus and underline it. Write a synonym for that word. Possible responses shown.

7. Ramona is a funny character. hilarious (2)
8. The story is very interesting. fascinating (2)

Read directions to students.
Vocabulary Strategies
© Houghton Mifflin Harcourt Publishing Company. All rights reserved.
225
Assessment Tip: Total 16 points
Grade 3, Unit 3

Kinds of Pronouns

- A **pronoun** is a word that can take the place of one or more nouns in a sentence. The pronouns *I, you, he, she, it, we,* and *they* are subject pronouns. Pronouns can be singular or plural.
- The words *me, you, him, her, it, us,* and *them* are object pronouns. Object pronouns follow action verbs and words like *to, for, at, of,* and *with.*

  Claude did not understand his parents.
  He did not understand them.

Write each sentence. Replace the underlined word or words with a subject or object pronoun.

1. Claude thinks his parents are good people.

   He thinks his parents are good people. (1 point)

2. Claude shows respect to his parents.

   Claude shows respect to them. (1)

Replace the repeated noun in these sentences with a pronoun. Write the new sentences on the lines.

3. Claude loves to eat. Claude enjoys eating with his family.

   Claude loves to eat. He enjoys eating with his family. (1)

4. Claude loves his friends. His friends see him every day.

   Claude loves his friends. They see him every day. (1)

Read directions to students.
Grammar
Assessment Tip: Total 4 points
Grade 3, Unit 3

Proofread for Spelling

Circle the ten misspelled Spelling Words in this diary entry. Then write each word correctly. (10 points)

June 2nd

Today was the (purfect) day. Dad decided to take a day off from (wirk) and we went to the baseball game. Our seats were on the (frist) base side of the field. The grass looked so green, and the (durt) on the infield looked so soft. As we sat down, Dad smiled and asked if my hair was getting more (cirly). Before I could say a (wurd) I saw my favorite player. He is the (therd) baseman, and he wears number 20 on his (shurt). That's my favorite number, too! The last time we came to a game, he was (hirt) but he was healthy today. Dad ordered me a (hambirgur) and we settled in to watch a great game.

1. _perfect_ (1)   6. _word_ (1)
2. _work_ (1)   7. _third_ (1)
3. _first_ (1)   8. _shirt_ (1)
4. _dirt_ (1)   9. _hurt_ (1)
5. _curly_ (1)   10. _hamburger_ (1)

Spelling Words

Basic
1. nurse
2. work
3. shirt
4. hurt
5. first
6. word
7. serve
8. curly
9. dirt
10. third
11. worry
12. turn
13. stir
14. firm

Review
her
girl

Challenge
perfect
hamburger

Read directions to students.
Spelling
Assessment Tip: Total 20 points
Grade 3, Unit 3

Connect to Writing

Lesson 15
READER'S NOTEBOOK

The Extra-good Sunday
Grammar:
Connect to Writing

Using incorrect verb tenses in your writing can confuse the reader. Use the correct verb tense to show when actions happen. Remember to use the correct verb endings or the word *will* before the verb.

Present Tense	Past Tense	Future Tense
I talk.	I talked.	I will talk.
She talks.	She talked.	She will talk.
They talk.	They talked.	They will talk.

Choose the correct tense for each sentence. Write the verb.

1. The family (cooked, will cook) breakfast together. (future tense)

   will cook (1 point)

2. Dad (mixes, mixed) the pancake batter in a bowl. (past tense)

   mixed (1)

3. Harry (pours, will pour) the batter in the pan. (present tense)

   pours (1)

4. When the pancakes are ready, Harry (flipped, will flip) them. (future tense)

   will flip (1)

5. Mom, Dad, and Harry (enjoy, will enjoy) their breakfast. (present tense)

   enjoy (1)

Contents

Name _____ Date _____

Words with *air, ear, are*

Write a word from the box to complete each sentence. Then read the complete sentence.

airfare	hear	wear
airline	pear	year
dairy	share	
prepare	tear	

1. The ___airline (1 point)___ has ten airplanes.

2. Gently ___tear (1)___ the paper into two pieces.

3. The teacher will ___prepare (1)___ the lesson for the day.

4. Did you ___hear (1)___ the bell ring?

5. You must pay the ___airfare (1)___ before you can ride on the plane.

6. Milk and cheese are in the ___dairy (1)___ food group.

7. You and I were born in the same ___year (1)___.

8. It's cold outside, so you'll need to ___wear (1)___ your coat.

9. This is a juicy ___pear (1)___!

10. It's kind to ___share (1)___ your toys.

Lesson 16
READER'S NOTEBOOK

Judy Moody Saves the World!
Grammar:
What Are Adjectives and Articles?

Name _____ Date _____

Adjectives That Tell How Many

An **adjective** is a word that describes, or tells about, a noun. Some adjectives tell how many. An adjective that tells how many comes before the noun it describes.

She saw three birds in a nest. (How many birds?)

Thinking Question
Which word tells how many?

Write the adjective that tells about the underlined noun.

1. There are two paths along the river. _____ two (1 point)

2. My dad hikes to the river with four friends. _____
   four (1)

3. They bring five bags to collect trash. _____ five (1)

4. My dad picks up many cans. _____ many (1)

5. Soon two bags are filled with trash. _____ two (1)

6. Then they see several cans in the shallow river. _____
   several (1)

7. Three men have boots and wade into the water. _____
   Three (1)

8. They use a net and pull seventeen cans out of the river. _____
   seventeen (1)

9. A few more pieces of trash are under the bench. _____
   few (1)

10. Their walk home is about one mile. _____ one (1)

Lesson 16
READER'S NOTEBOOK

Judy Moody Saves the World!
Grammar:
What Are Adjectives and Articles?

Name _____ Date _____

Adjectives That Tell What Kind

Adjectives are words that describe, or tell about, nouns. Some adjectives tell what kind.

We went for a long walk. (What kind of walk?)

An adjective usually comes before the noun it describes.

Thinking Question
Which word tells what kind?

Write the adjective that tells about the underlined noun.

1. Our class started a recycling project. _____ recycling (1 point)

2. Mr. Thomas put several big bins in the room. _____
   big (1)

3. The blue bin was for paper. _____ blue (1)

4. Jason added a stack of old newspapers. _____ old (1)

5. Lee Ann brought wrapping paper. _____ wrapping (1)

6. Melissa used the colorful paper for a collage. _____
   colorful (1)

7. We added our cereal boxes to the bin. _____ cereal (1)

8. Our small class collected a lot of paper. _____
   small (1)

9. We took the bins to a green truck. _____ green (1)

10. The workers wore thick gloves. _____ thick (1)

Lesson 16
READER'S NOTEBOOK

Judy Moody Saves
the World!
Spelling:
Vowel + /r/ Sounds in *air* and *fear*

Name _____ Date _____

Spelling Word Sort

Write each Basic Word under the correct heading.

Vowel + /r/ Sound in *air* spelled *air*	Vowel + /r/ Sound in *fear* spelled *ear*
air (1 point)	near (1)
chair (1)	ear (1)
stairs (1)	beard (1)
hair (1)	Review: year (1)
pair (1)	Challenge: earring (1)

Vowel + /r/ Sound in *air* spelled *ear*	Vowel + /r/ Sound in *air* spelled *are*
wear (1)	bare (1)
bear (1)	care (1)
pear (1)	share (1)
	Challenge: compare (1)

Review Add one Review Word to your Word Sort.

Which Review Word cannot be added to the Word Sort?

buy (1)

Challenge: Add the Challenge Words to your Word Sort.

Assessment Tip: Total 18 points   **Grade 3, Unit 4**

4

Spelling Words

Basic
1. air
2. wear
3. chair
4. stairs
5. bare
6. bear
7. hair
8. care
9. pear
10. pair
11. share
12. near
13. ear
14. beard

Review
buy
year

Challenge
earring
compare

Lesson 16
READER'S NOTEBOOK

Judy Moody Saves
the World!
Writing: Opinion Writing

Name _____ Date _____

Focus Trait: Purpose
Introducing the Topic and Opinion

The purpose of a persuasive letter is to try to make someone believe something or take an action. Good writers state their opinion clearly and convince readers it is correct by giving specific reasons. For example, Monique does not like the school lunch menu because it includes too much junk food. She wants to convince the school board to change the menu so it includes more healthful foods, like fruits and vegetables. She might offer reasons, such as healthful foods help kids think better and have stronger bodies.

Read each writer's opinion and think about the writer's purpose and goal. Then read the reasons that could support the opinion. Underline the strongest, most convincing reasons.

1. We should help rescued dogs and cats. I want to convince people to adopt rescued animals. (2 points)

REASONS

A. Pets are good.
B. Adopting a rescued pet saves a life.
C. Rescued pets have a lot of love to give owners.
D. Some rescued pets are injured or sick.

2. We should clean up our local park. I want to convince my classmates to volunteer to help clean up the park. (2)

REASONS

A. Kids are getting hurt on broken glass and metal litter.
B. A lot of people use the park.
C. We can be proud of the place where we play.
D. Litter makes the park look bad.

Assessment Tip: Total 4 points   **Grade 3, Unit 4**

5

Cumulative Review

**Write a word from the box to complete each sentence in the story.
Then read the story.**

careful	energy	wear
center	shirt	worry
dirty	turned	
disappeared	stairs	

"I want to ___wear (1 point)___ my new clothes," said Julia. She went up
                        1

the ___stairs (1)___ to her room and put them on.
        2

Julia went back downstairs. She ___turned (1)___ the doorknob to
                                           3

go outside.

"Julia," said Mom, "don't get your new clothes ___dirty (1)___."
                                                    4

"Don't ___worry (1)___, Mom. I'll be ___careful (1)___!"
            5   6

Julia ___disappeared (1)___ into the backyard. She used a lot of
              7

___energy (1)___ playing outside. As she came back in, she saw a big
      8

spot in the ___center (1)___ of her new ___shirt (1)___. "Oh, no!"
                  9   10

she gasped. "I should have listened to Mom!"

Reader's Guide

Judy Moody Saves the World!

Judy Moody's Class Presentation

"Judy Moody will come up to the front of the class and
talk about what she has learned about the environment,"
said Mr. Todd.

**Read pages 18–20. Use the information on these pages to help
Judy tell the class how she got the idea to save the world.**

It all started when I got home from school. I thought about

saving the earth. I started a compost bucket with bananas

in it. I was excited to tell Mr. Todd about it.   (5 points)

**Read pages 21–22. Use these pages to help Judy tell the
class about the Crazy Strips contest.**

I got this idea for the Crazy Strips contest. I drew a

picture of a bandage with banana peels and the world

on it. It said "Heal the World."   (5)

**Read pages 24–27. Use these pages to help Judy tell the class
about her work the next morning. Then tell how her family felt
about her plan.**

I collected all the stuff from around our house that

came from the rain forest. My family did not like it.

They wanted all their stuff back.   (5)

Name _____ Date _____

Lesson 16
READER'S NOTEBOOK

Judy Moody Saves the World!
Grammar:
What Are Adjectives and Articles?

This, *That* and Articles

- The adjectives *this* and *that* tell "which one."
- The words *a, an,* and *the* are adjectives called **articles.**
- Use *a* before nouns that begin with a consonant sound. Use *an* before nouns that begin with a vowel sound.

Underline the adjective that tells *which one*. Write the noun the adjective describes.

1. My friends and I helped clean this park. _____ park (2 points)

2. We put the trash we collected in that can. _____ can (2)

3. This playground could use a good cleaning. _____ playground (2)

Choose the article in parentheses to go with the underlined word. Write the article.

4. I have (a, an) can to recycle. _____ a (1)

5. You should recycle (the, an) paper. _____ the (1)

6. There is (a, an) empty bin. _____ an (1)

7. (The, An) bin is not full yet. _____ The (1)

Assessment Tip: Total 10 points
9
Grade 3, Unit 4

Read pages 28–29. Use these pages to help Judy tell about her next plan.

I had a Plan B. Every time someone threw something out, I was

going to write it down. I wanted to get to know our garbage. (5)

_____

Read pages 31–32. Help Judy tell how her family responded to this plan.

Nobody was listening to me. They were throwing things out that they

should have recycled! (5)

_____

Read pages 35–36. Help Judy tell the class how she decided to save trees and energy.

I decided to use my old lunch box instead of a paper bag. That would

save trees. Then I decided to ride my bike instead of taking the bus to

school. That would save energy. (5)

_____

Assessment Tip: 15 Points
8
Grade 3, Unit 4

Lesson 16
READER'S NOTEBOOK

Judy Moody Saves
the World!
Spelling:
Vowel + /r/ Sounds in *air* and *fear*

Name _____ Date _____

Word Towers

**Read each clue. Write the Basic Word that matches
each clue. (1 point each)**

Clues

1. A body part you use
   to hear
2. Two of something
3. Hair on a man's chin

4. Fills the open space
   around you
5. A large, strong animal
6. Split something with
   a friend
7. Steps

	e	a	r	
		p	a	i	r
b	e	a	r	d

	a	i	r	
	b	e	a	r	
s	h	a	r	e	
s	t	a	i	r	s

**Challenge Use Basic, Review, and Challenge Words to
complete the Word Tower.**

Clues

8. Pay money for
   something
9. Feel love and concern
   for someone
10. Furniture you can
    sit on
11. Steps
12. Tell how two things
    are alike

b	u	y	
c	a	r	e
c	h	a	i	r
s	t	a	i	r	s
c	o	m	p	a	r	e

Spelling Words

Basic
1. air
2. wear
3. chair
4. stairs
5. bare
6. bear
7. hair
8. care
9. pear
10. pair
11. share
12. near
13. ear
14. beard

Review
buy
year

Challenge
earring
compare

Lesson 16
READER'S NOTEBOOK

Judy Moody Saves
the World!
Vocabulary Strategies:
Context Clues

Name _____ Date _____

Context Clues

**Write the meaning of the underlined word as it is used
in each sentence. Circle the words that help you know
the meaning of the underlined word.**

1. One weekend each fall, our family goes on a yearly campout.

   happens once a year (1 point)

2. When it gets dark, we gather kindling to start a campfire.

   twigs and wood to burn (1)

3. Last year, our tent was leaky. Rain dripped in while we were sleeping.

   letting liquid inside (1)

4. Our new tent is made from recycled bottles.

   made from things that have been used (1)

5. This year, we forgot to put our garbage in the trash can with a lid.

   trash (1)

6. A raccoon gobbled up the food we threw away.

   ate (1)

7. My brother and I quarreled with loud voices over who was supposed
   to put the lid on the trash can.

   argued (1)

8. Pop got us to stop fighting when he suggested that we all go fishing.

   recommended (1)

9. We got the necessary gear to catch fish and headed to the pond.

   needed, required (1)

10. We were sad to see the pollution in the pond.

    trash (1)

Lesson 16
READER'S NOTEBOOK

Judy Moody Saves
the World!
Spelling:
Vowel + /r/ Sounds in *air* and *fear*

Name _____ Date _____

Proofreading for Spelling

Spelling Words

Basic
1. air
2. wear
3. chair
4. stairs
5. bare
6. bear
7. hair
8. care
9. pear
10. pair
11. share
12. near
13. ear
14. beard

Review
buy
year

Challenge
earring
compare

**Read the following journal entry. Find and circle the
misspelled words.** (10 points)

May 8

Today I went camping in a park (nere) my

home. Before I left, I took (cair) as I decided what

to (where) I put on a jacket because the (aer) was

crisp. I put a cap over my (haire.) I wore a (pare) of

hiking boots, too.

I got to the campsite and set up my tent. I sat

in my camp (chare) and started to eat a juicy (paire.)

All of a sudden I saw a big, brown (bair.) He was

looking at my food, but I did not want to (shear.)

I ended my camping trip right then and there!

Write the misspelled words correctly on the lines below.

1. _____ near (1 point)   6. _____ pair (1)

2. _____ care (1)   7. _____ chair (1)

3. _____ wear (1)   8. _____ pear (1)

4. _____ air (1)   9. _____ bear (1)

5. _____ hair (1)   10. _____ share (1)

Read directions to students.
Spelling
© Houghton Mifflin Harcourt Publishing Company. All rights reserved.

Assessment Tip: Total 20 points
Grade 3, Unit 4

13

Lesson 16
READER'S NOTEBOOK

Judy Moody Saves
the World!
Grammar: Spiral Review

Name _____ Date _____

More Plural Nouns

- Form the **plural of a noun** that ends with a consonant
  and *y* by changing the *y* to *i* and adding *-es*.
- Identify nouns that change their spelling to form
  their plurals.

The <u>families</u> enjoyed watching the <u>geese</u>.

Write the plural form of each singular noun in parentheses.

1. two beautiful (butterfly) _____ butterflies (1 point)

2. six new (hobby) _____ hobbies (1)

3. two intelligent (woman) _____ women (1)

4. many falling (leaf) _____ leaves (1)

5. a crowd of (child) _____ children (1)

Write *singular* or *plural* for each underlined noun.

6. A <u>man</u> gathered bottles. _____ singular (1)

7. The <u>geese</u> flew over the recycling area. _____ plural (1)

8. Many <u>families</u> recycle their own garbage. _____ plural (1)

9. One <u>city</u> saves money by reusing paper. _____ singular (1)

10. <u>Mice</u> will eat garbage if it isn't cleaned up. _____ plural (1)

Read directions to students.
Grammar
© Houghton Mifflin Harcourt Publishing Company. All rights reserved.

Assessment Tip: Total 10 points
Grade 3, Unit 4

12

Lesson 16
READER'S NOTEBOOK

Judy Moody Saves
the World!
Grammar:
Connect to Writing

Name _____ Date _____

Connect to Writing

Short Sentences	Longer, Smoother Sentence
Our class watched a video about recycling. The video about recycling was interesting.	Our class watched an interesting video about recycling.
There was a talking can in the video. The talking can was green.	There was a green talking can in the video.

Combine two short sentences by moving an adjective to make one longer sentence. Write the new sentence on the line.

1. The video was about a recycling center. The recycling center was big.

   The video was about a big recycling center. (1 point)

2. Many people work in the recycling center. It is noisy in the recycling center.

   Many people work in the noisy recycling center. (1)

3. One worker wore a hat. The hat was huge.

   One worker wore a huge hat. (1)

4. The wind blew paper into the air. The paper was yellow.

   The wind blew yellow paper into the air. (1)

5. The workers take a bus home. The bus is new.

   The workers take a new bus home. (1)

Read directions to students.
Grammar
© Houghton Mifflin Harcourt Publishing Company. All rights reserved.

Assessment Tip: Total 5 points
Grade 3, Unit 4

14

Lesson 17
READER'S NOTEBOOK

The Albertosaurus
Mystery
Phonics:
Words with /j/ and /s/

Name _____ Date _____

Words with /j/ and /s/

Read each sentence. Choose the missing word from the box. Write the word. Then reread the complete sentence.

season	decide	squirt
jelly	scale	jumping
force	edge	engine

1. Which _____ season (1 point) _____ of the year is your favorite?

2. Close the door with _____ force (1) _____!

3. I would love to drive a fire _____ engine (1) _____.

4. Place the apples on the _____ scale (1) _____.

5. Felice likes to put _____ jelly (1) _____ on her toast.

6. The _____ edge (1) _____ on these scissors is too dull to cut cardboard.

7. "Did you _____ decide (1) _____ who is the winner?" the girl asked.

8. If you _____ squirt (1) _____ me with water, I'll have to change my clothes.

9. We saw grasshoppers _____ jumping (1) _____ into the bushes.

Read directions to students.
Phonics
© Houghton Mifflin Harcourt Publishing Company. All rights reserved.

Assessment Tip: Total 9 points
Grade 3, Unit 4

15

Lesson 17
READER'S NOTEBOOK

The Albertosaurus
Mystery
Grammar:
Adjectives That Compare

Name _____ Date _____

One-Syllable Adjectives That Compare

- Add -er to most **adjectives** that have one syllable.
- For adjectives with one syllable that end in a single vowel followed by a consonant, double the last consonant and then add -er.

Are the Badlands <u>hotter</u> than a desert?

Thinking Questions
Does the adjective have only one syllable? Does it end in a single vowel followed by a consonant?

Write the correct form of the adjective that compares two nouns.

1. fresh _____ fresher (1 point)

2. green _____ greener (1)

3. fat _____ fatter (1)

4. sad _____ sadder (1)

5. hard _____ harder (1)

6. cool _____ cooler (1)

7. thin _____ thinner (1)

8. tight _____ tighter (1)

9. soft _____ softer (1)

10. ripe _____ riper (1)

Read directions to students.

Grammar 17

Assessment Tip: Total 10 points
Grade 3, Unit 4

Lesson 17
READER'S NOTEBOOK

The Albertosaurus
Mystery
Grammar:
Adjectives That Compare

Name _____ Date _____

Adding -er, -ier, or More

- Add -er to most **adjectives** that have one syllable.
- For adjectives that have two syllables and end in -y, such as *happy*, replace the *y* with *i* and then add -er.
- Add *more* before adjectives that have two or more syllables.

The pottery is <u>larger</u> than the arrowheads.
The arrowheads were shinier than the pottery.
The Native American exhibit is <u>more modern</u> than the dinosaur exhibit.

Thinking Questions
Does the adjective have more than one syllable? Does it end in -y?

Choose the correct form of the adjective in parentheses. Write it on the line.

1. The (younger, more young) of the two students found an arrowhead made of stone. _____ younger (1 point)

2. The arrowhead was in a location (deeper, more deep) than the clay pot. _____ deeper (1)

3. One of the bones was (tinier, more tiny) than the arrowhead. _____ tinier (1)

4. It was (difficulter, more difficult) to unearth the arrowheads than the bones. _____ more difficult (1)

5. The circle of stones was (interestinger, more interesting) than the bones they found. _____ more interesting (1)

Read directions to students.

Grammar 16

Assessment Tip: Total 5 points
Grade 3, Unit 4

Name _____ Date _____

Spelling Words with /j/ and /s/

Spelling Words

Basic
1. age
2. space
3. change
4. jawbone
5. jacket
6. giant
7. pencil
8. circle
9. once
10. large
11. dance
12. jeans
13. bounce
14. huge

Review
nice
place

Challenge
excited
gigantic

1. Write the Basic Words that use the letter *j* to spell the sound /j/.

jawbone (1 point) , jacket (1) ,

jeans (1)

2. Write the Basic Words that use the letter *g* to spell the sound /j/.

age (1) , change (1) ,

giant (1) , large (1) ,

huge (1)

3. Write the Basic Word that uses the letter *s* to spell the sound /s/.

space (1)

4. Write the Basic Words that use the letter *c* to spell the sound /s/.

space (1) , pencil (1) ,

circle (1) , once (1) ,

dance (1) , bounce (1)

Challenge

1. **gigantic** Circle the letter in *gigantic* that makes one of this week's spelling sounds. (1)

2. **excited** Circle the letter in *excited* that makes one of this week's spelling sounds. (1)

Read directions to students.
Spelling

18

Assessment Tip: Total 17 points
Grade 3, Unit 4

Name _____ Date _____

Focus Trait: Elaboration
Interesting and Supporting Details

Good writers elaborate on their ideas with interesting details that support their opinions. Interesting details can make your writing seem more convincing.

Weak Details: I think computers are a waste of time.

Interesting Details: Computers can be a big help doing some tasks, but it's important to do more than just sit in front of a monitor all day. How about getting outside and playing with friends? Which sentence is more interesting?

Read each sentence. Revise sentences so they include more interesting details. Possible responses shown.

1. Our cafeteria food is not very good.
Our cafeteria food tastes OK, but a lot of it is not good for you.

_____

We should have more healthful choices. (2 points)

_____

2. I think school sports are great.
I know that some people don't like playing school sports, but I think they help

_____

students learn to work as a team. Exercise is for your brain as well as

_____

your body. (2)

_____

3. I think homework should be more fun.
Teachers and parents think homework is a good thing that helps us learn.

_____

I think we would learn more if our homework was more like video games.

_____

Everyone would want to do their homework! (2)

Read directions to students.
Writing

19

Assessment Tip: Total 6 points
Grade 3, Unit 4

Reader's Notebook

125

Volume 2, pp. 18–19

Name _____ Date _____

Lesson 17
READER'S NOTEBOOK

The Albertosaurus
Mystery
Phonics:
Words with the VCCCV Pattern

Words with the VCCCV Pattern

**Write a word from the box to complete each
sentence. Then read the complete sentence.**

explore	partner	improve
instant	complaining	laundry
complicated	dolphin	athlete

1. I know that if I practice I will ___improve (1 point)___

2. We made ___instant (1)___ oatmeal since we had no
time to cook breakfast.

3. Cara is a great ___athlete (1)___ who swims and plays
soccer.

4. When we paired up, I chose Gloria as my
___partner (1)___

5. Tran is always ___complaining (1)___ that it is too cold.

6. This puzzle is too ___complicated (1)___ for young children.

7. When we were at the beach, we saw a
___dolphin (1)___ in the sea.

8. Mom is teaching me to do my own ___laundry (1)___

9. I would like to travel and ___explore (1)___ the world.

Read directions to students.
Phonics
© Houghton Mifflin Harcourt Publishing Company. All rights reserved.

Assessment Tip: Total 9 points
Grade 3, Unit 4

20

Name _____ Date _____

Lesson 17
READER'S NOTEBOOK

The Albertosaurus
Mystery
Independent Reading

Reader's Guide

The Albertosaurus Mystery:
Philip Currie's Hunt in the Badlands

Clues in the Attic

You are exploring an old attic and you find a large wooden
chest. You read the name *Barnum Brown* scrolled across
the back. The chest must belong to Barnum Brown! As you
uncover each object inside the chest, help tell the story of
Barnum Brown's discoveries.

First, you find a photograph of an old plow.

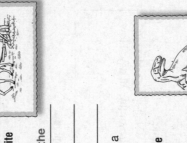

**Read page 64. Use what you learn on this page and write
why Barnum Brown kept this photo.**
The first fossil he ever saw was pulled out of the

___ground by a plow. (2 points)___

You continue digging through the chest and find a
photograph of T. rex bones.

**Read page 65. Use information from this page to decide
why this photograph was important to Barnum Brown.**
Barnum Brown was the first person to find

___a T. rex skeleton. (2)___

Read directions to students.
Independent Reading
© Houghton Mifflin Harcourt Publishing Company. All rights reserved.

Assessment Tip: 4 Points
Grade 3, Unit 4

21

Name _____ Date _____

Comparing More Than Two Nouns

Thinking Questions
Does the adjective compare more than two nouns? Does it have more than one syllable? Does it end in -y?

- Add *-est* to most **adjectives** that have one syllable.
- For adjectives with two or more syllables, add the word *most* before the adjective.
- For adjectives with two syllables that end in *-y*, such as *happy*, replace the *y* with an *i* and then add *-est*.
- For adjectives that have one syllable and end in a single vowel followed by a consonant, first double the last consonant and then add *-est*.

Which of the world's oceans is the *deepest*?
She chose the *most expensive* book.
Of the three jokes, Ben's is the *funniest*.

Write the correct form of the adjective that compares more than two nouns.

1. happy _____ happiest (1 point)
2. wonderful _____ most wonderful (1)
3. fast _____ fastest (1)
4. thin _____ thinnest (1)
5. sleepy _____ sleepiest (1)
6. dangerous _____ most dangerous (1)

Read directions to students.
Grammar
© Houghton Mifflin Harcourt Publishing Company. All rights reserved.

Assessment Tip: Total 6 points
Grade 3, Unit 4

23

Name _____ Date _____

Inside the wooden chest, you also find an old journal wrapped in cloth. You open to a page and begin reading Philip Currie's journal entries.

Read pages 69–70. What did Philip Currie write in his journal about his findings in the museum basement? What did he do as a result? Write as if you were Philip Currie.

I found some Albertosaurus bones in the basement of the museum. Using clues, I was able to locate the place where Barnum Brown found those bones. **(2 points)**

Read pages 71–72. Use this information to write in Philip Currie's journal about his main question.

After we saw the bones from the basement, we really wanted to know why all those fossils were together. Did the animals live together as a group? (2)

Read pages 73–75. Use this information to write in Currie's journal about Rodolfo Coria and what the two scientists concluded.

Rodolfo Coria also found fossils of meat-eating dinosaurs buried in a group. This made me think that meat-eaters lived in groups, even though we thought they lived separately. (2)

Read directions to students.
Independent Reading
© Houghton Mifflin Harcourt Publishing Company. All rights reserved.

Assessment Tip: Total 6 Points
Grade 3, Unit 4

22

Lesson 17
READER'S NOTEBOOK

The Albertosaurus
Mystery
Spelling:
Words with /j/ and /s/

Name _____ Date _____

Spelling Words with /j/ and /s/

Spelling Words

Basic
1. age
2. space
3. change
4. jawbone
5. jacket
6. giant
7. pencil
8. circle
9. once
10. large
11. dance
12. jeans
13. bounce
14. huge

Review
nice
place

Challenge
excited
gigantic

1. Four of the words on the list are synonyms for *big*.
Write them on the lines. You may write Basic Words
and Challenge Words.

giant (2 points) , ___large___ (2) ,

___huge___ (2) , ___gigantic___ (2)

2. Write three sentences about a dinosaur. Use
four of the spelling words. Don't use any synonyms
for *big!*

Responses will vary. (8)

_____

_____

_____

_____

_____

_____

Lesson 17
READER'S NOTEBOOK

The Albertosaurus
Mystery
Vocabulary Strategies:
Suffix -ly

Name _____ Date _____

Suffix -ly

**Circle the word in each sentence that has the suffix *-ly*.
On the line, write the meaning of the word.**

1. The angry dog growled (fiercely).

in a fierce way (2 points) _____

2. The truck driver honked the horn (loudly) when the light
turned green.

in a loud way (2) _____

3. Maria won the race (easily) because she is the fastest
runner in our class.

in an easy way (2) _____

4. We watched (hopefully) as Sean tried to score the winning
goal.

in a hopeful way (2) _____

5. When he saw his birthday present, Jason laughed (happily).

in a happy way (2) _____

6. The students read (quietly) in the library until the bell rang.

in a quiet way (2) _____

7. Mom told Sara that she sang (beautifully) in the school play.

in a beautiful way (2) _____

8. We walked (carefully) across the shaky bridge.

in a careful way (2) _____

The Albertosaurus
Mystery
Spelling:
Words with /j/ and /s/

Spelling Words

1. age
2. space
3. change
4. jawbone
5. jacket
6. giant
7. pencil
8. circle
9. once
10. large
11. dance
12. jeans
13. bounce
14. huge

Review
nice
place

Challenge
excited
gigantic

Name _____ Date _____

Proofreading for Spelling

Find the misspelled words and circle them. (10 points)

A long, long time ago, a jiant ship flew through outer spase. It was the shape of a pensil, but it was gijantic. It flew in a sircle around the Earth. It flew around the Earth onse, then twice, then three times. In fact, it flew around the Earth a hundred times! What was it doing? What was it looking for? No one knows. Maybe the people on the ship wanted to chanje planets. Maybe they liked to bounse from world to world and never stop. Maybe their world was not larje enough for them. I have a different answer, though. I think they were looking for a place to buy geans. They just came here thousands of years too soon.

Write the misspelled words correctly on the lines below.

1. giant (1)	6. once (1)	
2. space (1)	7. change (1)	
3. pencil (1)	8. bounce (1)	
4. gigantic (1)	9. large (1)	
5. circle (1)	10. jeans (1)	

Assessment Tip: Total 20 points
Grade 3, Unit 4

27

The Albertosaurus
Mystery
Grammar:
Spiral Review

Name _____ Date _____

Writing Proper Nouns

- A **proper noun** names a particular person, pet, place, holiday, person's title, or book title.
- Always begin a proper noun with a capital letter.

Aunt Liz took me to the Museum of Natural History.

Identify the proper nouns in each sentence. Then write each sentence correctly.

1. My favorite holiday is hanukkah, and it is in december. (2 points)

My favorite holiday is Hanukkah, and it is in December.

2. That is one of mrs. hubbard's favorite movies.

That is one of Mrs. Hubbard's favorite movies. (2)

Use proofreading marks to write each proper noun in this letter correctly. (6)

Grandma
Dear grandma,

                    Beacon School
Last week our class at beacon school learned about cats. We looked
        All Kinds of Cats   Tracy
at a book called all kinds of cats. My friend tracy brought her cat to class.
        Fuzzy   Valentine's Day
Her cat's name is fuzzy. Her cat was a valentine's day present.

                    Love,
                    Amy

Assessment Tip: Total 10 points
Grade 3, Unit 4

26

129

Words with /k/ and /kw/

Read each sentence. Choose the missing word from the box. Write the word. Then reread the complete sentence.

croaking	music	squeal
jacket	quiet	joke
squirrel	sock	tractor

1. Kim told a silly ___joke (1 point)___ that made us all giggle.

2. It is cold outside, so wear a warm ___jacket (1)___.

3. After everyone went to bed, the house was very ___quiet (1)___.

4. My brother's band plays loud ___music (1)___.

5. "Here is my shoe, but where is my ___sock (1)___?" Ana asked.

6. We saw a ___squirrel (1)___ in a tree at the park.

7. Mr. Martin got a new ___tractor (1)___ for his farm.

8. The scared little pig let out a loud ___squeal (1)___.

9. You can hear frogs ___croaking (1)___ down by the pond.

Connect to Writing

Lesson 17
READER'S NOTEBOOK

The Albertosaurus
Mystery
Grammar:
Connect to Writing

Use adjectives to describe how people, places, or things are different. To compare two nouns, add -er to most adjectives. To compare more than two nouns, add -est to most adjectives.

Compare Two	Compare More Than Two
This bone is older than that one.	This is the oldest bone we have found.
It is hotter today than yesterday.	We went digging on the hottest day of the week.

Use the correct form of the adjective in parentheses. Write the sentence.

1. *Tyrannosaurus Rex* was (big) than *Albertosaurus.*

   Tyrannosaurus Rex was bigger than Albertosaurus. (1 point)

2. The (long) dinosaur measured more than 100 feet in length.

   The longest dinosaur measured more than 100 feet in length. (1)

3. Sauropod eggs are (thick) than chicken eggs.

   Sauropod eggs are thicker than chicken eggs. (1)

4. One of the (large) dinosaur eggs was found in China.

   One of the largest dinosaur eggs was found in China. (1)

Lesson 18
READER'S NOTEBOOK

A Tree Is Growing
Grammar:
Using the Verb *be* and
Helping Verbs

Name _____ Date _____

The Verb *be*

The verb *be* has different forms. Different subjects use these different forms. *Am*, *is*, and *are* show present tense. *Was* and *were* show past tense.

Ms. Greene **was** our teacher last year.
We **were** interested in her book on deserts.
One large desert **is** in Africa.

Thinking Question
What is the subject, and do I want to show present tense or past tense?

Choose the correct verb in ( ), and write it on the line.

1. My science project (am, is) finished. _____ is (1 point)

2. Ms. Burns (was, were) happy that I finished. _____ was (1)

3. Leaves (was, were) part of my project. _____ were (1)

4. They (was, were) very colorful. _____ were (1)

5. Mike's project (is, are) also finished. _____ is (1)

6. Forest animals (is, are) in his project. _____ are (1)

7. They (was, were) fun for him to draw. _____ were (1)

8. We (am, are) proud of our projects. _____ are (1)

9. The projects (is, are) on a table. _____ are (1)

10. Our room (is, are) ready for Parent Night. _____ is (1)

Lesson 18
READER'S NOTEBOOK

A Tree Is Growing
Grammar:
Using the Verb *be* and
Helping Verbs

Name _____ Date _____

Helping Verbs

Helping verbs work with the main verb to help show time. Singular and plural subjects use different forms.

Subject	Helping Verbs
Singular nouns Pronouns: he, she, it	is, was, has
Plural nouns Pronouns: you, we, they	are, have, were
Pronoun: I	am, was, have

The tree **was** growing taller.
It **has** grown many branches.
The two friends **were** talking quietly.
We **have** tried to count the leaves.
They **are** blowing in the wind.
I **am** going to stop counting.
I **was** excited about the falling leaves.

Thinking Questions
Is the subject of the sentence singular or plural? If it is a pronoun, what form of helping verb does it take?

Write the correct verb in ( ) to complete the sentence.

1. Those workers (is, are) planting trees in the park. _____ are (1 point)

2. My brother (is, are) helping the workers. _____ is (1)

3. He (has, have) asked me to come with him. _____ has (1)

4. I (am, is) going to walk with them. _____ am (1)

5. One tree's leaves (has, have) already turned brown. _____ have (1)

6. Some squirrels (was, were) collecting acorns. _____ were (1)

Focus Trait: Conventions
Exact Words

Good writers of persuasive problem-and-solution paragraphs use exact words—nouns, adjectives, adverbs, and verbs—to express clearly what they want to say. Compare a sentence without exact words and a sentence with exact words.

Without Exact Words: The dog chased the cat.

With Exact Words: The large, playful golden retriever chased the tiny calico cat.

Rewrite each sentence, adding exact words to express the writer's thoughts more clearly. Make up your own specific details and exact words. Possible responses shown.

1. The piano fell.

As it was being lowered to the ground, the expensive piano crashed and splintered into pieces. (1 point)

2. The puppy tripped.

The tiny golden-haired puppy ran and tripped clumsily over its own paws. (1)

3. The store manager told me to leave.

The store manager scowled, yelled at me, and gruffly ordered me to leave. (1)

4. From the window, you can see many things.

From the huge picture window, you can see snow-capped mountains, crystal blue lakes, and huge forests. (1)

5. The food was great.

The perfectly cooked salmon just melted in my mouth. (1)

Spelling the /k/ and /kw/ Sounds

Write each Basic Word where it belongs in the chart.

kite	trick
shark (1 point)	check (1)
flake (1)	crack (1)
	quick (1)

camp	quack
circus (1)	queen (1)
second (1)	squeeze (1)
coldest (1)	quart (1)
Africa (1)	squeak (1)
Mexico (1)	quick (1)
(challenge) correct (1)	(challenge) question (1)

Challenge: Add the Challenge Words to your Word Sort.

Spelling Words

Basic
1. shark
2. check
3. queen
4. circus
5. flake
6. crack
7. second
8. squeeze
9. quart
10. squeak
11. quick
12. coldest
13. Africa
14. Mexico

Review
black
thank

Challenge
correct
question

Name _____ Date _____

Lesson 18
READER'S NOTEBOOK

A Tree Is Growing
Phonics:
Cumulative Review

Cumulative Review

Write a word from the box to complete each sentence about one family's love for the zoo. Then read the complete sentence.

complain	kiss	quality
exchange	monkey	question
instead	pick	surprise

1. I have never heard anyone _____complain (1 point)_____ about our local zoo.

2. It isn't a huge zoo, but its _____quality (1)_____ is very good.

3. Our zookeepers have managed to _____exchange (1)_____ animals with zoos in faraway places.

4. My favorite animal is a _____monkey (1)_____ from India.

5. He likes to blow you a _____kiss (1)_____ when you visit his exhibit.

6. My little brother would _____pick (1)_____ the zebra as his favorite animal.

7. It's probably no _____surprise (1)_____ that my sister likes the koalas best.

8. Our family would choose a visit to the zoo _____instead (1)_____ of almost any other form of entertainment.

9. We all often ask the _____question (1)_____, "Can we go to the zoo this weekend?"

Reader's Guide

A Tree Is Growing

Label a Growing Tree

What did you learn about trees? Use the features in *A Tree Is Growing* to help you draw and label a growing tree.

Read pages 94–96. Draw and label three different leaves. Write a caption telling what leaves do for trees.

(Students should create drawings of three leaves with correct identification labels, such as Ginko, White Oak, Palm.) Leaves make food for trees. (5 points)

Read pages 97–99. What is sap? What is special about some kinds of sap? Use the captions to find some of this information.

Sap is a kind of juice in the tree. Sap takes food to different parts of the tree. Some sap smells spicy, and some can be made into maple syrup. (5)

Lesson 18
READER'S NOTEBOOK

A Tree Is Growing
Grammar:
Using the Verb *be* and
Helping Verbs

Name _____ Date _____

Using Verbs

Choose the correct verb in ( ), and write it on the line.

1. The pine tree (is, are) the tallest tree in the woods. _____ is (1 point)

2. The lakes in our state (is, are) very pretty. _____ are (1)

3. The Hudson River (is, am) the longest river in New York State.
_____ is (1)

4. Our trip to Lake Erie (was, were) interesting. _____ was (1)

5. We (was, were) happy viewing the lake. _____ were (1)

Write *has* or *have* to complete each sentence correctly.

6. We _____ have (1) read books about the ocean.

7. Jack _____ has (1) written a report on rivers.

8. My friends _____ have (1) worked hard on their desert project.

9. The librarian _____ has (1) shown me books on mountains.

10. I _____ have (1) found pictures of tall mountains for my report.

Name _____ Date _____

Read pages 100–101. What are some important things about a tree's roots?

Roots grow into the ground and hold the tree in place.

Roots absorb water. (2)

Read pages 102–105. What are some important things about a tree's bark?

The outer layer of bark protects the tree. Under the outer layer of bark, there is a layer of growing bark. (2)

Now draw a picture of your own growing tree. Use the information from the text and illustrations to label your tree's parts.

(The tree should be labeled with leaves, roots, bark, and sap.) (10)

Name _____ Date _____

Word Roots

Identify the root and tell its meaning. Use the meaning of the root to figure out the meaning of the word. (1 point each)

1. telephone

Root: tele

Meaning of the root: far away

Meaning of the word: thing you use to talk to someone far away

2. telescope

Root: tele

Meaning of the root: far away

Meaning of the word: something you look through to see far away

3. autocorrect

Root: auto

Meaning of the root: self

Meaning of the word: something that corrects mistakes by itself

4. autopilot

Root: auto

Meaning of the root: self

Meaning of the word: able to fly by itself

5. automatic

Root: auto

Meaning of the root: self

Meaning of the word: done by itself

Read directions to students.
Vocabulary Strategies
© Houghton Mifflin Harcourt Publishing Company. All rights reserved.

Assessment Tip: Total 15 points

Grade 3, Unit 4

39

Name _____ Date _____

Spelling the /k/ and /kw/ Sounds

Spelling Words

Basic
1. shark
2. check
3. queen
4. circus
5. flake
6. crack
7. second
8. squeeze
9. quart
10. squeak
11. quick
12. coldest
13. Africa
14. Mexico

Review
black
thank

Challenge
correct
question

Write the Basic Word that best replaces the underlined word or words in each sentence.

1. The recipe called for four cups of milk.

2. The mouse let out a high, little sound and then ran away.

3. The little piece of snow melted as soon as it touched my warm skin.

4. This is the chilliest winter day we have had this year.

5. Will you look over my report for spelling mistakes?

6. We have tickets to go to the fun show in the big tent!

7. With one fast kick, the player scored the winning goal.

8. When the king died, the king's wife became the country's leader.

9. Hold the egg carefully so that it won't break open.

10. My baby sister likes to grab my finger and hold tightly to it.

1. quart (1 point)   6. circus (1)

2. squeak (1)   7. quick (1)

3. flake (1)   8. queen (1)

4. coldest (1)   9. crack (1)

5. check (1)   10. squeeze (1)

Challenge: On a separate sheet of paper, write a sentence using each Challenge Word. Then rewrite your sentences replacing each Challenge Word with a synonym. Use a dictionary or thesaurus if you need help. (2)

Read directions to students.
Spelling
© Houghton Mifflin Harcourt Publishing Company. All rights reserved.

Assessment Tip: Total 12 points

Grade 3, Unit 4

38

Abstract Nouns

- Nouns are words that name people, places, or things.
- **Abstract nouns** name things that *cannot* be seen, touched, heard, smelled, or tasted.

  idea   energy   growth   happiness

  Mira had a good idea about saving energy.

  The growth of my plants fills me with happiness.

Thinking Question
Can I see, touch, hear, smell, or taste it?

Write the abstract noun in each sentence.

1. Fear stopped him from opening the door.   fear (1 point)

2. Ben's disappointment made him very quiet.   disappointment (1)

3. The puppy barked with joy.   joy (1)

4. Jan had the freedom to pick her own books.   freedom (1)

5. Jill was filled with relief when she found her lost hamster.

   relief (1)

Proofreading for Spelling

Find the misspelled words and circle them. (10 points)

Dear Sam,

I am having a great time in Mexico. On the seckond day of our trip, Dad took me snorkeling. I had to wear a wetsuit because the water here is the koldest I've ever felt! Before we got in the water, Dad called the beach patrol to ask a very important qwestion. He had to chek and make sure there was no shark danger!

Snorkeling was fun. We saw all kinds of fish. I even saw one called a clownfish. It was as colorful as a real circus clown! Dad pointed out a fish trying to catch a little squid. We watched the squid scueeze out black ink. Then it made a quik getaway. It was amazing to see!

Today my parents and I went to the market. We used some of the Spanish words we've learned. People smile and try to understand us even when we don't say things the korrect way. Sometimes we get the words all mixed up and just crac up laughing.

We are having a lot of fun. I hope you are having fun back at home. I'll see you in a few days.

Your friend,
Mark

On a separate sheet of paper, write the misspelled words correctly. (10)

Spelling Words

Basic

1. shark
2. check
3. queen
4. circus
5. flake
6. crack
7. second
8. squeeze
9. quart
10. squeak
11. quick
12. coldest
13. Africa
14. Mexico

Review

black
thank

Challenge

correct
question

Name _____ Date _____

Vowel Sounds in *spoon* and *wood*

Read each sentence. Choose the missing word from the box. Write the word. Then reread the complete sentence.

hooded	juicy	screws
sunroof	reduce	shouldn't
clue	youth	rules

1. Max hid a present for his mother and left a very good _____ clue (1 point) about where to look for it.

2. To help the environment, we are trying to _____ reduce (1) _____ the amount of trash we create.

3. We should use _____ screws (1) _____, not nails, to put the birdhouse together.

4. The large dog stuck his head out the _____ sunroof (1) _____ when his owner took him for a ride in the sports car.

5. My grandfather likes to tell stories about what life was like in his _____ youth (1) _____.

6. Before the game, the umpire reminded us to play by the _____ rules (1) _____.

7. You _____ shouldn't (1) _____ run when the sidewalk is slippery.

8. Dad told me to wear my _____ hooded (1) _____ jacket to keep my ears warm.

9. The _____ juicy (1) _____ watermelon dripped on my shirt.

Read directions to students.
Phonics 43
© Houghton Mifflin Harcourt Publishing Company. All rights reserved.
Assessment Tip: Total 9 points
Grade 3, Unit 4

Name _____ Date _____

Connect to Writing

Short Sentences	Longer, Smoother Sentence
Mount Whitney is very high. White Mountain is very high.	Mount Whitney and White Mountain are very high.
Elise has hiked in the woods. Jamik has hiked in the woods.	Elise and Jamik have hiked in the woods.

Combine two short sentences by moving one subject to make one longer sentence with two subjects. Write the new sentence on the line. Be sure to change the forms of the verbs to match the subject of the new sentence.

1. A goat lives in the mountains. A wolf lives in the mountains.
   A goat and a wolf live in the mountains. (1 point)

2. A hiker has stopped at the ranger station. A camper has stopped at the ranger station.
   A hiker and a camper have stopped at the ranger station. (1)

3. My aunt likes hiking in the woods. My uncle likes hiking in the woods.
   My aunt and my uncle like hiking in the woods. (1)

4. Ellen has reached the top of the mountain. Steven has reached the top of the mountain.
   Ellen and Steven have reached the top of the mountain. (1)

5. Ali was on the bridge. Jane was on the bridge.
   Ali and Jane were on the bridge. (1)

Read directions to students.
Grammar 42
© Houghton Mifflin Harcourt Publishing Company. All rights reserved.
Assessment Tip: Total 5 points
Grade 3, Unit 4

Name _____ Date _____

Eat, Give, Grow, Take, and *Write*

Thinking Questions
Is the verb in the past tense? Is the verb used with has, have, or had?

The verbs **eat, give, grow, take,** and **write** have special spellings to show past tense. These verbs also have other spellings when they are used with *has, had,* and *have.*

My mother gave me a book about bears.
The author has written books about other animals.

Write the correct past tense of the verb in parentheses to complete each sentence.

1. I (wrote, written) my name on the cover of my book. _____ wrote (1 point)

2. The first chapter (gave, given) facts about bears. _____ gave (1)

3. I have (took, taken) the book to my friend's house. _____ taken (1)

4. She (gave, given) me a book about mountain lions. _____ gave (1)

5. She had (wrote, written) her name in her book, too. _____ written (1)

6. Her dog had (ate, eaten) a corner of the book. _____ eaten (1)

7. That dog has (grew, grown) a lot this year! _____ grown (1)

8. I (ate, eaten) a cookie before leaving. _____ ate (1)

Read directions to students.
Assessment Tip: Total 8 points
Grade 3, Unit 4

Name _____ Date _____

Come, Do, Go, Run, and See

Thinking Questions
Is the verb in the past tense? Is the verb used with has, have, or had?

The verbs **come, do, go, run,** and **see** are irregular and have special spellings to show past tense. These verbs may also have other spellings when they are used with *has, had,* or *have.*

A mouse had gone into our house.
The mouse ran into the woods yesterday.

Write the correct past tense of the verb in parentheses to complete each sentence.

1. My sister had (went, gone) outside. _____ gone (1 point)

2. Tammy (saw, seen) the mouse in a pile of leaves. _____ saw (1)

3. My brother has (ran, run) outside, too. _____ run (1)

4. Our neighbors had (saw, seen) the mouse on the bird feeder. _____ seen (1)

5. The mice also (did, done) some damage to some feed bags. _____ did (1)

6. They have (ran, run) through the gardens. _____ run (1)

7. The baby mice (go, went) into the nest. _____ went (1)

8. I (did, done) a drawing of a mouse last night. _____ did (1)

Read directions to students.
Assessment Tip: Total 8 points
Grade 3, Unit 4

Name _____ Date _____

Focus Trait: Purpose
Thinking About Your Audience

Good writers ask, "What reasons will convince my audience to agree with me?"

Marla is writing to convince her parents to let her go on a class trip to the zoo. Marla brainstormed reasons. Then she chose the ones that her audience, her parents, would care most about.

- She can learn many things about animals, such as bears, at the zoo.
- The teacher, principal, and five other parents will be on the trip.
- She will promise to follow safety rules.

Read about each writer and his or her purpose. Underline the reason that the writer's audience would care most about. Then add another reason that the audience would care about. Possible responses shown.

1. Jovan is writing to convince his older brother to follow their mother's rules.

   A. When we follow Mother's rules, she is happier. (1 point)

   B. Mother likes to go to the gym in the afternoons while we are at school.

   Another reason: Mother's rules help keep us safe. (1)

2. Stephanie is writing to convince her father to let her join the soccer team.

   A. Soccer is one of the most popular sports in the world.

   B. Soccer is great exercise, and lots of players make new friends. (1)

   Another reason: Exercise is good for your health. (1)

Name _____ Date _____

Vowel Sounds in *spoon* and *wood*

Write each Basic Word under the correct heading.

Vowel Sounds in *spoon*	Vowel Sounds in *wood*
mood (1 point)	wooden (1)
drew (1)	crooked (1)
smooth (1)	foot (1)
blue (1)	
balloon (1)	
true (1)	
chew (1)	
tooth (1)	
hooves (1)	
cool (1)	
food (1)	
pooch (1)	
blew (1)	
Challenge: loose (1)	
Challenge: jewel (1)	

Challenge: Add the Challenge Words to your Word Sort.

Spelling Words

Basic
1. mood
2. wooden
3. drew
4. smooth
5. blue
6. balloon
7. true
8. crooked
9. chew
10. tooth
11. hooves
12. cool
13. food
14. pooch

Review
blew
foot

Challenge
loose
jewel

Lesson 19
READER'S NOTEBOOK

Two Bear Cubs
Independent Reading

Reader's Guide

Two Bear Cubs

Write a Theater Review

Write a review of *Two Bear Cubs* for your local newspaper. First, use details from the text and illustrations to gather information about the play.

Read pages 134–136. Describe the setting and main characters.

The setting is a forest and a mountain. The main characters are

Mother Grizzly, Older Brother, and Younger Brother.   (2 points)

Read page 137. How does the end of Scene 1 change the story?

The cubs fell asleep on the stone, and the stone grew bigger.

Mother Grizzly could not see her cubs anymore.   (2)

Read pages 139–143. What happens in Scene 2? How does it end?

Mother Grizzly and her friends look for the cubs. Hawk sees them,

but no one can reach them. Measuring Worm says he will try.   (2)

Read pages 145–149. Who is the hero of Scene 3? Why?

Measuring Worm is the hero. He climbs to the top of the mountain

and guides the cubs down the mountain.   (2)

Read page 151. What is the message at the very end of the play?

The mountain was named after Measuring Worm because he was

a hero.   (2)

Read directions to students.
Independent Reading
© Houghton Mifflin Harcourt Publishing Company. All rights reserved.

Assessment Tip: Total 10 Points
Grade 3, Unit 4

49

Lesson 19
READER'S NOTEBOOK

Two Bear Cubs
Phonics:
Cumulative Review

Cumulative Review

Choose a word from the box to complete each sentence. Write the word on the line. Then read the sentence.

shampoo	woof
chewing	clues
lookout	
food	

1. In comic strips, dogs often say "arf" or " ___woof___ (1 point) "

2. To keep its owner safe, a guide dog is always on the
___lookout___ (1)

3. Some dogs use their noses to find ___clues___ (1) about the right trail to follow.

4. Most grown dogs eat twice a day, but puppies need ___food___ (1) four times a day.

5. Dogs should be washed with ___shampoo___ (1) made just for dogs. Try not to get the suds in the dog's eyes.

6. Sometimes a dog enjoys ___chewing___ (1) on a special treat to keep its teeth healthy and strong.

Read directions to students.
Phonics
© Houghton Mifflin Harcourt Publishing Company. All rights reserved.

Assessment Tip: Total 6 points
Grade 3, Unit 4

48

Name _____ Date _____

Come, Do, Go, Run, See, Eat, Give, Grow, Take, and Write

Write the correct past tense of the verb in parentheses to complete each sentence.

1. The class (go, went) to the play downtown. _____ went (1 point)

2. Some parents (come, came) with us last year. _____ came (1)

3. The actors have (grow, grown) stronger since last year. _____ grown (1)

4. One person (took, taken) her camera to the play. _____ took (1)

5. We have (wrote, written) about the play for class. _____ written (1)

Write the correct past-tense form of the verb in parentheses to complete the sentence.

6. In the play, actors _____ their best to please the crowd. (do) did (1)

7. The actors pretended to have _____ a huge feast. (eat) eaten (1)

8. A friend _____ to my seat during the play. (come) came (1)

9. He _____ a few pictures with his camera. (take) took (1)

10. We have _____ some interesting plays this year. (see) seen (1)

Read directions to students.
Grammar
© Houghton Mifflin Harcourt Publishing Company. All rights reserved.

Assessment Tip: Total 10 points
Grade 3, Unit 4

Name _____ Date _____

Now use all the details from the previous page to write your review. Include the characters, the setting, and the plot. At the end, be sure to say whether you liked the play and why.

A Review of *Two Bear Cubs*

(The review should include details from the previous page and a sentence that tells whether the student liked the play and why.) (10 points)

Read directions to students.
Independent Reading
© Houghton Mifflin Harcourt Publishing Company. All rights reserved.

Assessment Tip: Total 10 Points
Grade 3, Unit 4

Left worksheet

Name _____ Date _____

Two Bear Cubs
Spelling:
Vowel Sounds in *spoon* and *wood*

Name _____ Date _____

Vowel Sounds in *spoon* and *wood*

Use the Basic Words to complete the puzzle. (1 point each)

Across

2. used to bite
3. to eat
7. not straight
8. what you eat
10. It is filled with air.

Down

1. small dog
4. made of boards
5. traced or sketched
6. opposite of warm
9. feeling

Spelling Words

Basic
1. mood
2. wooden
3. drew
4. smooth
5. blue
6. balloon
7. true
8. crooked
9. chew
10. tooth
11. hooves
12. cool
13. food
14. pooch

Review
blew
foot

Challenge
loose
jewel

Read directions to students.
Spelling
© Houghton Mifflin Harcourt Publishing Company. All rights reserved.

52

Assessment Tip: Total 10 points
Grade 3, Unit 4

Two Bear Cubs
Vocabulary Strategies:
Prefixes *pre-*, *re-*, *bi-*

Name _____ Date _____

Prefixes *pre-*, *re-*, *bi-*

In each sentence, circle the word with the prefix *pre-*, *re-*, or *bi-*. Then write the base word, the prefix, and the word meaning.

1. My mom can fix just about anything that goes wrong on a (bicycle).

cycle (1 point)   bi (1)   vehicle with two wheels (1)
base word   prefix   meaning

2. I always go get popcorn during the (previews) at the movies.

views (1)   pre (1)   before showing (1)
base word   prefix   meaning

3. Jenna liked the book so much that she (reread) it three times.

read (1)   re (1)   read again (1)
base word   prefix   meaning

4. Hector and I meet (biweekly) to work on our social studies project.

weekly (1)   bi (1)   twice a week (1)
base word   prefix   meaning

5. Our class visited a museum to see an exhibit of (prehistoric) art.

historic (1)   pre (1)   before history (1)
base word   prefix   meaning

Read directions to students.
Vocabulary Strategies
© Houghton Mifflin Harcourt Publishing Company. All rights reserved.

53

Assessment Tip: Total 15 points
Grade 3, Unit 4

Name _____ Date _____

Pronoun-Verb Agreement

- Add -s or -es to a verb in the present tense when the pronoun in the subject is *he, she,* or *it.*
- Do not add -s or -es to a verb in the present tense when the pronoun in the subject is *I, you, we,* or *they.*
- Change the *y* to *i* and add -es to form the present tense of verbs that end with *y* when the subject is *he, she,* or *it.*

  I toss the ball.   I fly kites.
  She <u>splashes</u> into the lake.   She <u>flies</u> kites.

Write the correct verb in parentheses to go with each underlined subject.

1. <u>He</u> (drive, drives) to the theater. _____ drives (1 point) _____

2. <u>We</u> (watch, watches) the actors. _____ watch (1) _____

3. <u>They</u> (perform, performs) really well. _____ perform (1) _____

4. <u>She</u> (study, studies) acting. _____ studies (1) _____

Combine each pair of sentences. Change the underlined words to pronouns. Write the new sentences on the lines.

5. <u>Aunt Clara</u> goes to plays. <u>Aunt Clara</u> goes to concerts, too.

   Aunt Clara goes to plays, and she goes to concerts, too. (2)

6. A bus takes <u>them</u> to the theater. <u>A bus</u> brings them back, too.

   A bus takes them to the theater, and it brings them back, too. (2)

54   Assessment Tip: Total 8 points
Grade 3, Unit 4

Name _____ Date _____

Proofreading for Spelling

Find and circle the misspelled words. (8 points)

Dear Grandma,

    Thank you for the wonderful day at the petting zoo. It put me in such a good (moud). I remember hearing hooves as we walked across the (wuden) bridge. Seeing a mule up close was (cule) I liked feeding it hay to (chue).

    It was fun to feed the animals handfuls of their special (fuud). I liked petting the deer's (smooth) fur. I think the lamb smiled at me. It had a cute crooked tooth!

    I really like the blue (ballone) you got me. It reminds me of our fun day. I (droo) a picture that I am sending to you. It shows you, me, the lamb, the mule, and the black pooch we saw. It is true that this day was the best one ever!

                 Love,
                  Quinn

Write the misspelled words correctly on the lines below.

1. _____ mood (1) _____   5. _____ food (1) _____

2. _____ wooden (1) _____   6. _____ smooth (1) _____

3. _____ cool (1) _____   7. _____ balloon (1) _____

4. _____ chew (1) _____   8. _____ drew (1) _____

55

Spelling Words

Basic
1. mood
2. wooden
3. drew
4. smooth
5. blue
6. balloon
7. true
8. crooked
9. chew
10. tooth
11. hooves
12. cool
13. food
14. pooch

Review
blew
foot

Challenge
loose
jewel

Assessment Tip: Total 16 points
Grade 3, Unit 4

Compound Words

Lesson 20
READER'S NOTEBOOK

Life on the Ice
Phonics:
Compound Words

Write a word from the box to answer each clue. Then answer the question below by reading the word in the shaded boxes. (1 point each)

chalkboard	flashlight	toothbrush
cookbook	homework	underwater
fireplace	newspaper	
	outside	
	snowshoes	

1. f l a s h l i g h t

2. s n o w s h o e s

3. t o o t h b r u s h

4. u n d e r w a t e r

5. h o m e w o r k

6. c o o k b o o k

7. o u t s i d e

8. f i r e p l a c e

9. c h a l k b o a r d

10. n e w s p a p e r

1. This helps you see in the dark.
2. You wear these to walk in snow.
3. You need this to brush your teeth.
4. Look here to see fish in a lake.
5. You do this work after school.
6. This is a book of recipes.
7. You might play here after school.
8. A fire in here will warm a room.
9. A teacher may write on this in a classroom.
10. You read this to learn the news.

What is the coldest place on Earth? _____ Antarctica

Read directions to students.   Assessment Tip: Total 11 points
Phonics   Grade 3, Unit 4
© Houghton Mifflin Harcourt Publishing Company. All rights reserved.
57

Connect to Writing

Lesson 19
READER'S NOTEBOOK

Two Bear Cubs
Grammar:
Connect to Writing

Using exact verbs helps the reader better picture what you are describing in your writing.

Less Exact Verb	More Exact Verb
run	sprint, jog, dash, race
talk	whisper, chatter, gossip, debate

For each verb, write a sentence that shows its exact meaning.
Use a dictionary if you need help. Possible responses shown. (2 points each)

1. sprint

We will sprint to the finish line.

2. jog

Because the path is so long, we will jog most of the way.

3. dash

The puppy will dash across the lawn to get its ball.

4. race

I will race my brother to see who runs faster.

5. whisper

Whisper in the library so you don't disturb other people.

Read directions to students.   Assessment Tip: Total 10 points
Grammar   Grade 3, Unit 4
© Houghton Mifflin Harcourt Publishing Company. All rights reserved.
56

Adverbs That Tell *Where* and *When*

Thinking Question
What word tells where or when?

- **Adverbs** can tell *how* an action happens. They can also tell *where* and *when* something happens.
- Adverbs can come before or after the verbs they describe.

The scientists flew there in an airplane.
Then they cleaned the airplane.

Write the adverb that tells about each underlined verb. Then write *where* or *when* to show how each adverb describes the verb.

1. It's too snowy to <u>leave</u> tonight.

tonight, when (1 point)

2. First, we will <u>make</u> a shelter.

first, when (1)

3. Then we will <u>drink</u> hot chocolate.

then, when (1)

4. We can <u>build</u> a shelter there.

there, where (1)

5. We will <u>ride</u> snowmobiles tomorrow.

tomorrow, when (1)

6. We can <u>skate</u> nearby.

nearby, where (1)

7. They hiked <u>away</u>, but then they came back.

away, where (1)

8. The iceberg <u>lies</u> ahead.

ahead, where (1)

Adverbs That Tell *How*

Thinking Question
What word tells how?

- Words that describe verbs are called **adverbs.**
- Adverbs can tell *how* an action happens. Most adverbs that tell *how* end in *-ly.*
- Adverbs can come before or after the verbs they describe.

Lynne <u>happily</u> went skating.
The skaters moved <u>smoothly</u> across the ice.

Write the adverb that tells about the underlined verb in each sentence.

1. They <u>tied</u> their laces tightly.

tightly (1 point)

2. Lynne and Lamont <u>moved</u> cautiously at first.

cautiously (1)

3. Lamont <u>watched</u> the skaters carefully.

carefully (1)

4. Then he <u>skated</u> effortlessly around the rink.

effortlessly (1)

5. Proudly, Lynne <u>spun</u> on the ice.

Proudly (1)

6. Lynne's lace <u>broke</u> unexpectedly.

unexpectedly (1)

7. Slowly, she <u>moved</u> to a bench.

Slowly (1)

8. She <u>arrived</u> at the bench safely.

safely (1)

Spelling Word Sort

Read each Basic Word. Listen to the number of syllables. Write each word under the correct heading.

Spelling Words

Basic
1. birthday
2. anyone
3. sometimes
4. everything
5. homework
6. afternoon
7. airplane
8. grandmother
9. something
10. without
11. himself
12. faraway
13. sunburned
14. daylight

Review
someone
cannot

Challenge
scorekeeper
everybody

Words with Two Syllables	Words with Three Syllables
birthday (1 point)	anyone (1)
sometimes (1)	everything (1)
homework (1)	afternoon (1)
airplane (1)	grandmother (1)
something (1)	faraway (1)
without (1)	Challenge: scorekeeper (1)
himself (1)	
sunburned (1)	
daylight (1)	
Review: someone (1)	
Review: cannot (1)	

Review: Add the Review Words to your Word Sort.

Challenge: Which Challenge Word has four syllables?

everybody (1) _____

Add the other Challenge Word to your Word Sort.

Focus Trait: Organization
Paragraphs for Reasons

Good writers make a separate paragraph for each reason in a persuasive essay.

Reasons Together	Reasons in Paragraphs
In Antarctica, scientists can learn about pollution. For example, they can find ash from Mount Vesuvius. They learn about how the climate is changing. They can see how quickly ice is melting.	In Antarctica, scientists can learn about pollution. For example, they can find ash from Mount Vesuvius. Additionally, they learn about how the climate is changing. They can see how quickly ice is melting.

Rewrite the following paragraph so that each reason has its own paragraph. Add linking words between paragraphs. Possible response shown.

A century ago, explorers built huts in Antarctica. Today, the huts are falling apart. We should save the huts because they are an important part of history. The huts are full of food and clothing. These items can teach us what the explorers' lives were like. The huts are full of books. By reading them, we can learn how explorers prepared for their trip.

A century ago, explorers built huts in Antarctica. Today, the

huts are falling apart. We should save the huts because they are an

important part of history.

First of all, the huts are full of food and clothing. These items

can teach us what the explorers' lives were like.

Secondly, the huts are full of books. By reading them, we can

learn how explorers prepared for their trip. (10 points)

Name _____ Date _____

Reader's Guide

Life on the Ice

A Travel Guide to the Poles

Gather information about the North and South Poles.
Use the information to create a travel guide.

Read pages 170–171. Where are the Poles? What are they like?

The North Pole is in the Arctic. The South Pole is in Antarctica.

Both places are very cold.   (2 points)

Read pages 174–175. What is traveling to the Poles like?

You have to fly thousands of miles to reach the Poles. Planes use

skis to land, and they slide like giant sleds until they stop.   (2)

Read pages 180–181. How do you need to dress at the Poles?

You need to wear many layers of clothing at the Poles. You also need

goggles to prevent blindness from the snow.   (2)

**Read pages 182–183. What are the different seasons like for
people who live at the Poles?**

People work hard in summer while it is warm enough for planes to

fly. They also ski in summer. In the winter, people feel tired because

of the constant darkness. In the spring, planes fly in again.   (2)

Read directions to students.
Independent Reading
© Houghton Mifflin Harcourt Publishing Company. All rights reserved.

Assessment Tip: 8 Points
Grade 3, Unit 4

Name _____ Date _____

Cumulative Review

**Read each sentence. Choose two words from the Word Bank
to form a compound word to complete each sentence. Then read
the complete sentence.**

bare	brush	eye	sun
bath	brow	fire	room
boat	butter	fly	sail
glasses	camp	foot	paint

1. When you do not have a shoe or sock on your foot, you

   are ____ barefoot (2 points) ____.

2. You use ____ sunglasses (2) ____ to protect your eyes.

3. To make a colorful picture, you use a ____ paintbrush (2) ____.

4. The hair that grows just above your eye is called an

   ____ eyebrow (2) ____.

5. You take a shower in a room called a ____ bathroom (2) ____.

6. An insect that uses its pretty wings to fly from flower to

   flower is called a ____ butterfly (2) ____.

7. A boat that uses wind and sails is called a

   ____ sailboat (2) ____.

8. When you want to cook something while you are

   camping, you build a ____ campfire (2) ____.

Read directions to students.
Phonics
© Houghton Mifflin Harcourt Publishing Company. All rights reserved.

Assessment Tip: Total 16 points
Grade 3, Unit 4

Name _____ Date _____

Now use the information you collected to design a travel guide for the North and South Poles. Be sure to point out interesting details that would make visitors eager to go. Remember to let your excitement show!

Come to the North and South Poles! An adventure awaits you!

(Students should use details from the previous page, along with an enthusiastic voice, to create the travel guide.) (10)

Read directions to students.
Independent Reading
© Houghton Mifflin Harcourt Publishing Company. All rights reserved.

Assessment Tip: 10 Points
Grade 3, Unit 4

Name _____ Date _____

Adverbs That Tell *How, Where,* and *When*

Write the adverb that tells *how* the underlined verb happened.

1. The airplane noisily landed on the runway. _____ noisily (1 point)

2. The engines roared loudly as we waited. _____ loudly (1)

3. Cheerfully, we waved at the scientists. _____ cheerfully (1)

4. The pilots sternly nodded at us. _____ sternly (1)

Write the adverb that describes the underlined verb. Then write *where* or *when* to show how each adverb describes the verb.

5. First, we showed the scientists their rooms. _____ first, when (1)

6. We talked with them inside. _____ inside, where (1)

7. We walked upstairs for a snack. _____ upstairs, where (1)

8. Another group arrives tomorrow. _____ tomorrow, when (1)

Read directions to students.
Grammar
© Houghton Mifflin Harcourt Publishing Company. All rights reserved.

Assessment Tip: Total 8 points
Grade 3, Unit 4

Name _____ Date _____

Spelling Compound Words

Read each book title. Add a Basic Word to complete each title.

Spelling Words

Basic
1. birthday
2. anyone
3. sometimes
4. everything
5. homework
6. afternoon
7. airplane
8. grandmother
9. something
10. without
11. himself
12. faraway
13. sunburned
14. daylight

Review
someone
cannot

Challenge
scorekeeper
everybody

1. *Teacher, My Dog Ate My* __Homework (1 point)__ *!*

2. *Using Sunblock to Avoid Getting* __Sunburned (1)__

3. *Happy* __Birthday (1)__ *, Rosalinda!*

4. *Sixteen Hours of* __Daylight (1)__

5. *Traveling in an* __Airplane (1)__

6. *Scott's* __Faraway (1)__ *Pen Pal*

7. *Spending the Summer with* __Grandmother (1)__ *and Grandpa*

8. *An* __Afternoon (1)__ *at the Zoo*

9. *In the Rain* __Without (1)__ *an Umbrella*

10. *Does* __Anyone (1)__ *Know What Time It Is?*

Review: **Choose a Review Word. Use it in a book title.**

__Answers will vary. (1)__

Challenge: **Choose a Challenge Word. Use it in a book title.**

__Answers will vary. (1)__

Name _____ Date _____

Dictionary/Glossary

Read each word. Write the base word to use to find its dictionary entry. Then find each entry word in a dictionary. Write the words with all their endings.

Word	Entry Word in Dictionary	Part(s) of Speech	Word with Endings
1. gliding	glide (1 point)	verb (1)	glides, gliding, glided (1)
2. hesitate	hesitate (1)	verb (1)	hesitated, hesitating, hesitates (1)
3. dripping	drip (1)	verb, noun (1)	dripped, dripping, drips (1)
4. rippling	ripple (1)	verb, noun (1)	rippled, rippling, ripples (1)
5. horrifying	horrify (1)	verb (1)	horrified, horrifying, horrifies (1)

Now write a sentence for one form of each word. Possible responses shown.

1. __The children glided across the ice in their skates. (1)__

2. __The child hesitated before approaching the dog. (1)__

3. __The steady drip of melting snow formed a puddle. (1)__

4. __Laughter rippled through the room. (1)__

5. __The hero was horrified by the monsters. (1)__

Name _____ Date _____

Simple Verb Tenses

- A verb that tells about an action that has already happened shows **past tense.** Add *-ed* to most verbs to show past tense.
- A verb that tells about an action happening now shows **present tense.** Add *-s* to the verb when the noun in the subject of a sentence is singular. Do not add *-s* to the verb when the noun in the subject is *I, you,* or a plural.
- A verb that tells about an action that will happen in the future shows **future tense.** Use the helping verb *will* for verbs in the future tense.

Write the correct past tense of the verb in parentheses.

1. They ___hurried (1 point)___ to get inside. (hurry)

2. The snow ___stopped (1)___ after two hours. (stop)

Write the correct present tense of the verb in parentheses.

3. The girl ___plays (1)___ in the snow. (play)

4. The adults ___clap (1)___ for the skaters. (clap)

Write the correct future tense of the verb in parentheses.

5. We ___will sweep (1)___ the snow from the steps. (sweep)

6. The snow ___will melt (1)___ when the sun comes up. (melt)

Read directions to students.
Grammar
© Houghton Mifflin Harcourt Publishing Company. All rights reserved.

Assessment Tip: Total 6 points
Grade 3, Unit 4

68

Name _____ Date _____

Proofreading for Spelling

Read the following letter. Circle the misspelled words.
(12 points)

Dear Grandmoter,

Thank you for my birthday card. It came in the mail this afternoon. I love everthing you send me.

I wish you didn't live in such a farawy place. Sumtimes I wish I had an airplan I would fly to see you all the time. I could be back home when it was still daylite.

Yesterday, I came home from school and played outside. I got sunberned. I canot play outside today. I have a lot of homwork to do.

I can't say goodbye withowt saying I love you and I miss you. I hope you can come see us soon!

Love,
Tony

Write the misspelled words correctly on the lines below.

1. Grandmother (1)
2. birthday (1)
3. afternoon (1)
4. everything (1)
5. faraway (1)
6. Sometimes (1)
7. airplane (1)
8. daylight (1)
9. sunburned (1)
10. cannot (1)
11. homework (1)
12. without (1)

Read directions to students.
Spelling
© Houghton Mifflin Harcourt Publishing Company. All rights reserved.

Assessment Tip: Total 24 points
Grade 3, Unit 4

69

Spelling Words

Basic
1. birthday
2. anyone
3. sometimes
4. everything
5. homework
6. afternoon
7. airplane
8. grandmother
9. something
10. without
11. himself
12. faraway
13. sunburned
14. daylight

Review
someone
cannot

Challenge
scorekeeper
everybody

Unit 4
READER'S NOTEBOOK

Boy, Were We Wrong
About Dinosaurs!
Segment 1
Independent Reading

Name _____ Date _____

Boy, Were We Wrong About Dinosaurs!

An Ancient Chinese Scroll

Imagine you were in ancient China and helped find the giant bones! You will write on a Chinese scroll to explain what you saw. First, answer some questions that will help you write about your findings.

Read pages 4–6. How were the first dinosaur bones found? (2 points)

They were dug up by people in China. (2 points)

_____

Why did wise men think the bones came from dragons?

They thought that only dragons could have bones

so large. (2)

Why didn't they know the bones came from dinosaurs?

They did not know what dinosaurs were. They did not know the

bones came from creatures that lived long ago. (2)

How do you think the men in ancient China felt once they discovered the huge bones?

They might have felt afraid because the bones were so big and they

thought the dragons were still alive. (2)

Name _____ Date _____

Connect to Writing

Short, choppy sentences can be combined to make your writing smoother. Combine two sentences by moving an adverb.

Short Sentences	Longer, Smoother Sentences
Sam walked up the hill. The hill was nearby.	Sam walked up the nearby hill.
They wait to skate. They wait eagerly.	They wait eagerly to skate.

Combine two short, choppy sentences by moving the adverb. Write the sentence.

1. We rode our sleds. We rode today.

We rode our sleds today. (2 points)

2. I screamed as I flew downhill. I screamed loudly.

I screamed loudly as I flew downhill. (2)

3. I ran back up the hill. I ran eagerly.

I eagerly ran back up the hill. (2]]

4. I reached the top. I reached it first.

I reached the top first. (2)

Name _____ Date _____

Then and Now Pictures

Scientists had some wrong ideas about dinosaurs! Draw pictures that show how scientists' ideas about dinosaurs have changed. First, use the text and illustrations to answer the questions below.

Read page 8. What did scientists first think about the horn-shaped bone of the iguanodon? (2 points)

They thought it fit onto the iguanodon's nose.

Read page 9. What did scientists realize later about the horn-shaped bone?

They saw that there were two bones and they were part of iguanodon's hands. (2)

Read page 10. What did scientists first think about the elbows and knees of dinosaurs?

They thought that they pointed out to the side, like a lizard's. (2)

How did scientists first think that dinosaurs moved?

They thought they waddled on all fours or floated underwater. (2)

Name _____ Date _____

Now use your answers to write a scroll. Tell how you found the bones. Tell what you thought they were. Tell how you felt about your find.

(Accept all reasonable responses that include how the bones were found and what they think the bones came from.) (10 points)

Name _____ Date _____

Unit 4
READER'S NOTEBOOK

Boy, Were We Wrong About Dinosaurs!
Segment 1
Independent Reading

Now use your answers to draw two pictures of an iguanadon. First, draw what scientists used to think they looked like. Next, draw what scientists now believe. Write captions to explain your drawings.

Iguanodon Then

(Students should draw iguanodon with the horn-shaped bone on its nose.) (5 points)

Scientists thought iguanodons had spikes on their noses. (5 points)

Iguanodon Now

(Students should draw iguanondon with horn-shaped bones on its hands.) (5)

Scientists now know that iguanodons had spikes on their hands. (5)

Name _____ Date _____

Unit 4
READER'S NOTEBOOK

Boy, Were We Wrong About Dinosaurs!
Segment 1
Independent Reading

Now answer some questions about dinosaurs' tails. You will use your answers to draw more Then and Now pictures.

Read page 12. What did scientists think about dinosaurs' tails? (2 points)

They thought their tails dragged in the dirt.

What evidence made them believe that?

They saw fossils of tail drags. They thought the tails were too heavy to be held up. (2)

Read page 13. Now what do scientists think that dinosaurs did with their tails?

They think that many dinosaurs used their tails for balance. (2)

What clues helped them to realize this?

They found clues in dinosaur fossils that showed their tailbones had stiff tendons inside to hold them up straight. (2)

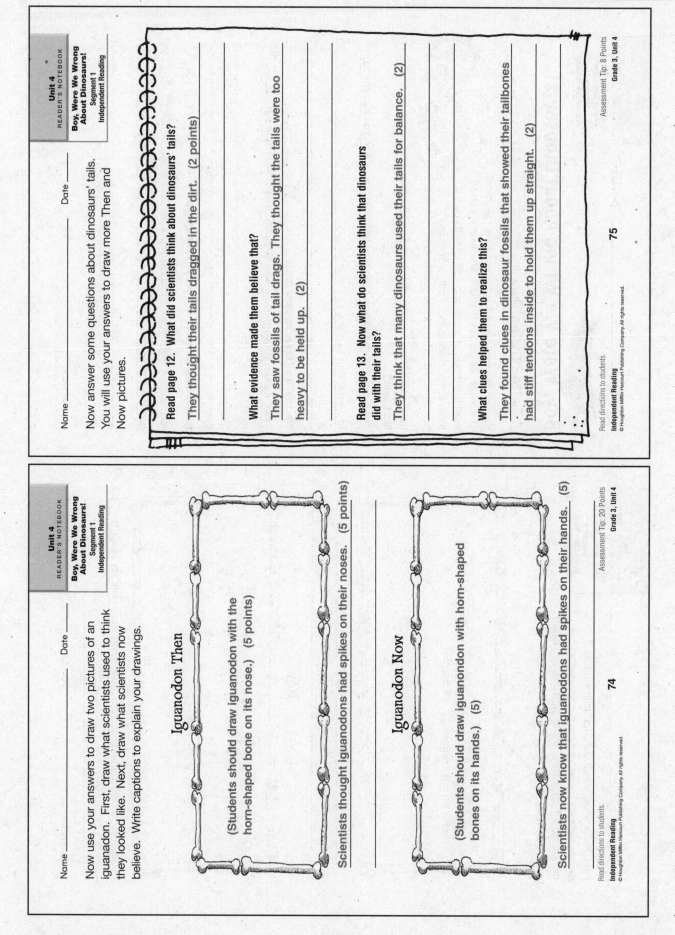

Unit 4
READER'S NOTEBOOK
Boy, Were We Wrong
About Dinosaurs!
Segment 2
Independent Reading

Reader's Guide

Boy, Were We Wrong About Dinosaurs!

A Letter to the Past

You are going to send a letter in a time machine! The letter will go to scientists who worked and lived hundreds of years ago. What will you tell them about dinosaurs? First, gather facts from the text. Then, write your letter.

Read page 14. How did scientists think dinosaurs were like lizards?

They thought they were cold-blooded and needed to bask in the sun

to warm their bodies. (2 points)

_____

What do lizard bones look like inside?

They do not have many blood vessels. There are rings where new

bone grows. (2)

_____

How do dinosaur bones compare with lizard bones?

Dinosaur bones have many blood vessels inside. New bone grows

around each one. (2)

_____

Unit 4
READER'S NOTEBOOK
Boy, Were We Wrong
About Dinosaurs!
Segment 1
Independent Reading

First, draw what scientists used to think about dinosaurs' tails. Next, draw what scientists now believe about their tails. Write captions to explain your drawings.

Then

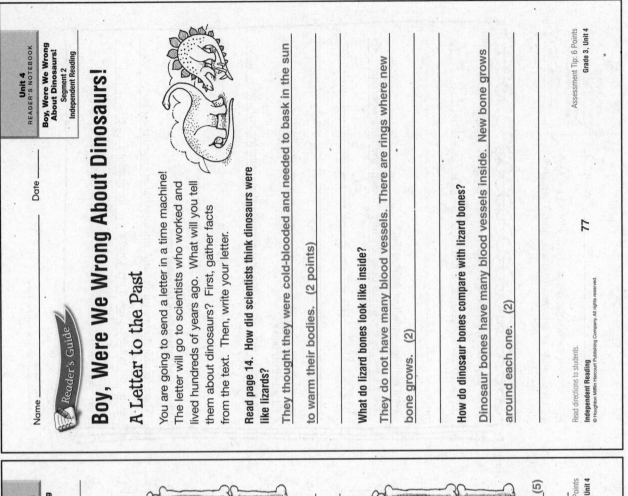

(Students should draw a picture of a dinosaur with its tail dragging.) (5 points)

Scientists thought dinosaurs dragged their tails. (5)

Now

(Students should draw a dinosaur with its tail up in the air.) (5)

Scientists now know that dinosaurs used their tails for balance. (5)

Unit 4
READER'S NOTEBOOK

Boy, Were We Wrong About Dinosaurs!
Segment 2
Independent Reading

Read page 15. How do scientists think dinosaurs were like birds? (2 points)

They think their bodies might have been warm and full of

energy. (2 points)

Read pages 16–18. Why do scientists think big dinosaurs did not have fur or feathers?

They think that big dinosaurs did not need fur or feathers to keep

themselves warm. (2)

Read page 19. Why do scientists think little dinosaurs had feathers?

They needed a way to keep warm. (2)

Read page 20. What do scientists now think about the colors of dinosaurs?

They think dinosaurs were colorful to protect them from being found

and eaten. (2)

Unit 4
READER'S NOTEBOOK

Boy, Were We Wrong About Dinosaurs!
Segment 2
Independent Reading

Now use this information to write a letter to scientists of the past. Explain in this letter what we now know about the bones, blood, feathers, and colors of dinosaurs.

Dear Scientists of the Past,

(Accept all reasonable responses that include information

about the bones, blood, feathers, and colors of

dinosaurs.) (10 points)

Sincerely yours,

Look Under the Microscope

Unit 4
READER'S NOTEBOOK
**Boy, Were We Wrong
About Dinosaurs!**
Segment 2
Independent Reading

Suppose you are the leader of a group of scientists who are digging up dinosaur bones. When your group has gathered all the fossils you need, you will be looking at the fossils under a microscope. Draw and label everything you find. Then write a lab report.

Read page 14. You have just found a dinosaur bone and sliced it open. Draw and label what you see under the microscope.

(Students should show many blood vessels inside the bone. They should label the blood vessels.) (5 points)

_____
_____
_____

Read page 16. You have just found a fossil with some marks that look like feathers. Draw and label what you see under the microscope.

(Students should draw feather marks and label them.) (5)

_____
_____
_____

Unit 4
READER'S NOTEBOOK
**Boy, Were We Wrong
About Dinosaurs!**
Segment 2
Independent Reading

Read page 18. You have just found the skin of a large dinosaur. Is it smooth or bumpy? Does it have feathers or fur? Draw and label what you see under the microscope.

(Students should show smooth skin.) (5 points)

_____
_____
_____

Read page 19. Now you have found the skin of a small dinosaur. Is it smooth or bumpy? Does it have feathers or fur? Draw and label what you see under the microscope.

(Students should show skin with feathers.) (5)

_____
_____
_____

Name _____ Date _____

Unit 4
READER'S NOTEBOOK
Boy, Were We Wrong
About Dinosaurs!
Segment 3
Independent Reading

Boy, Were We Wrong About Dinosaurs!

Dinosaur Short Story

After reading this book, you know a lot about baby dinosaurs! Use the text and illustrations to write a short story about a baby dinosaur. First, answer the questions below to get the main details.

Read pages 22–23. What is the same about dinosaur babies and lizard babies? (2 points)

They both come from eggs that are laid by their mothers. (2 points)

_____

What is different about dinosaur babies and lizard babies?

Lizard mothers laid their eggs on the ground and left. Dinosaur

mothers made nests for their babies. The dinosaur mothers may

have brought food back to the nest. (2)

_____

Read page 24. What did the nests of dinosaurs tell us about them?

Dinosaur mothers made their nests in the same place every year. (2)

_____

What did fossil footprints of dinosaurs tell us about dinosaur babies?

The babies walked together with other dinosaurs. They were

protected by walking in the middle of the herd. (2)

83

Name _____ Date _____

Unit 4
READER'S NOTEBOOK
Boy, Were We Wrong
About Dinosaurs!
Segment 2
Independent Reading

Now use what you saw under the microscope to write a lab report. Describe your discoveries about the different parts of dinosaurs.

Lab Report

(Accept all reasonable responses that include details

from their drawings about the bones and skin of

dinosaurs.) (10 points)

_____

82

Unit 4
READER'S NOTEBOOK

Boy, Were We Wrong
About Dinosaurs!
Segment 3
Independent Reading

Name _____ Date _____

Draw a Comic Strip

Scientist had many different ideas about what killed off the dinosaurs. Use the text and illustrations to draw a comic strip showing what you think might have happened. The questions below will help you think of some ideas.

Read page 26. What did scientists first think killed off the dinosaurs? (2 points)

They thought that the world got too dry and hot. _____

Why did scientists change their minds about what killed off the dinosaurs?

They found a layer of space dust. They think that a comet hit Earth

and that the dust blocked the sun. (2) _____

Read page 27. Why would dinosaurs die if the sun was blocked?

Without the sun, the plants would die. Then the animals

would starve. (2) _____

Dinosaurs

Unit 4
READER'S NOTEBOOK

Boy, Were We Wrong
About Dinosaurs!
Segment 3
Independent Reading

Name _____ Date _____

Now write your story about a baby dinosaur. You can include details about how the baby was born, how the mother took care of it, and how it traveled with its family.

(Accept all reasonable responses that include details

about baby dinosaurs such as being born in a nest,

being taken care of by their mother, and walking

together with their family.) (10 points)

_____

_____

_____

_____

_____

_____

_____

_____

Unit 4
READER'S NOTEBOOK
Boy, Were We Wrong
About Dinosaurs!
Segment 3
Independent Reading

Name _____ Date _____

Write a Speech

We may still be wrong about the dinosaurs. Scientists keep making discoveries. Be a scientist! You have just made an important discovery about dinosaurs. Plan the speech you are going to give to a group of scientists about your discovery. Then write the speech.

Read pages 22–24. What don't we know about dinosaur babies?

We do not know if their mothers brought them food or

if they got food themselves. (2 points)

_____

Read pages 26–27. What don't we know about why dinosaurs died?

We do not know what killed them. It might have been a cloud of

space dust. (2)

_____

Read page 29. Why do some scientists believe that some dinosaurs are still alive?

They believe that some small dinosaurs became birds. (2)

_____

What are some other things we don't know about dinosaurs yet?

(Accept all reasonable responses.) (2)

_____

Unit 4
READER'S NOTEBOOK
Boy, Were We Wrong
About Dinosaurs!
Segment 3
Independent Reading

Name _____ Date _____

Now draw a comic strip showing how scientists think the dinosaurs died.

(Accept all reasonable drawings/explanations.) (10 points)

Base Words and -ed, -ing

Read each sentence. Choose the missing word from the box.
Write the word. Then reread the complete sentence.

juggling	skipped	sliced
rattled	exciting	practiced
excused	tasting	unzipped

1. Travis ___unzipped (1 point)___ his jacket, took it off, and hung it up.

2. The two girls ___skipped (1)___ across the playground instead of walking.

3. The clown is ___juggling (1)___ four balls high into the air.

4. The polite man ___excused (1)___ himself before he got up from the table.

5. "It was ___exciting (1)___ to see real giraffes at the zoo!" Keisha said.

6. Did your eyes water when you ___sliced (1)___ the onions?

7. When the snake ___rattled (1)___ its tail, we took off running.

8. I ___practiced (1)___ my spelling words over and over.

9. The chef is ___tasting (1)___ the stew to see if it needs more salt.

Read directions to students.

Phonics

89

Unit 4
READER'S NOTEBOOK

Boy, Were We Wrong
About Dinosaurs!
Segment 3
Independent Reading

Now write your speech about your latest discovery. You are going to talk to a group of scientists. Describe the new information you have about dinosaurs and why you believe it is true.

(Accept all reasonable responses.) (10 points)

Read directions to students.

Independent Reading

88

Name _____ Date _____

Adverbs That Compare

Thinking Question
Does the adverb have more than one syllable or does it end in -ly?

- **Adverbs** can be used to compare two actions.
- Add *-er* to one-syllable adverbs to show comparison. If the adverb ends with *e*, drop the *e* before adding *-er*.
- Use *more* before adverbs that end in *-ly*. Sometimes, an adverb that ends with *-ly* will use an *-ier* ending.

The moon shines brighter than the stars.

Linda could see the moon earlier than she could notice the stars.

The stars twinkled more brilliantly than the moon glowed.

Write the correct form of the adverb in parentheses to complete the sentence.

1. The truck arrived (late) today than the bus did.
   later (1 point)

2. The cornstalks stood (rigidly) than the tall grass.
   more rigidly (1)

3. She watched the sheep (closely) than she watched the cows.   more closely (1)

4. They climbed (high) than we could.
   higher (1)

5. The wind is blowing (strong) now than it did this morning.
   stronger (1)

Assessment Tip: Total 5 points
Grade 3, Unit 5
91

Name _____ Date _____

Adverbs That Compare

Thinking Question
Are two actions compared?

- **Adverbs** can tell *where*, *when*, or *how* something happens. Adverbs are used to describe verbs. Adverbs can also be used to compare actions.
- To compare two actions, use the ending *-er* with most adverbs, such as *hard, late,* or *slow.*
- Use *more* before adverbs that end in *-ly*, such as *carefully* or *quickly.*

She practiced harder than her brother needed to practice.

She danced more awkwardly than her brother did.

Choose the correct adverb in parentheses. Write it on the line.

1. The brother and sister acted (bashfully, more bashfully) than their father.   more bashfully (1 point)

2. Abby waited (eagerly, more eagerly) than her brother did.   more eagerly (1)

3. The woman sang (gently, more gently) than the wind blew.   more gently (1)

4. She swayed (gracefully, more gracefully) than the prairie grasses moved outside.   more gracefully (1)

5. The song sounded (stronger, more stronger) than it did before.   stronger (1)

6. The little girl held her toy bear (carefully, more carefully) than she would hold a ball.   more carefully (1)

Assessment Tip: Total 6 points
Grade 3, Unit 5
90

Name _____ Date _____

Spelling Word Sort

Sarah, Plain and Tall
Spelling
Words with -ed and -ing

Write each Basic Word under the correct heading.

Words with -ed	Words with -ing
invited (1 point)	coming (1)
stared (1)	swimming (1)
planned (1)	dropping (1)
loved (1)	tapping (1)
gripped (1)	taping (1)
tasted (1)	saving (1)
Review: stopped (1)	changing (1)
Challenge: scared (1)	joking (1)
	Review: making (1)
	Challenge: freezing (1)

Review: Add the Review Words to your Word Sort.

Challenge: Add the Challenge Words to your Word Sort.

Spelling Words

Basic
1. coming
2. swimming
3. dropping
4. tapping
5. taping
6. invited
7. saving
8. stared
9. planned
10. changing
11. joking
12. loved
13. gripped
14. tasted

Review
making
stopped

Challenge
freezing
scared

Name _____ Date _____

Focus Trait: Development
Setting the Scene

Sarah, Plain and Tall
Writing: Narrative Writing

Setting the scene means telling the reader who the main character or narrator is and what is happening as the story begins.

The chart below lists questions that a writer answers to set the scene. Read the example answers, and then complete the chart with answers of your own. Possible responses shown.

Questions	Example Answers	Your Answers
Who is the main character or narrator?	a young scientist	Abby, a girl in the fourth grade (2 points)
What is he or she doing?	She is studying elephants, and she has found an injured baby elephant.	She is looking for her classroom. (2)
Where and when are events taking place?	Events take place in the rain forest in Africa. It is early in the morning.	Events take place at Abby's new school. It is her first day. (2)
What problem does the main character or narrator face?	The scientist must take care of the baby and bring it to an animal refuge.	Abby does not know anyone and is lost. (2)

Name _____ Date _____

Reader's Guide

Sarah, Plain and Tall

Write in Caleb's Diary

Help complete Caleb's diary entries with details from the story.

Read pages 209–211. How did Caleb feel before Sarah arrived?

Dear Diary,

Today Papa is bringing Sarah home. I wonder if she will be
_____ nice and if she will like us. I hope so. (5 points)

Read pages 213–215. What was it like when Caleb met Sarah?

Dear Diary,

Sarah gave me a shell! I love it. She gave Anna
_____ a sea stone and told us about the sea. (5)

Read page 216. How did Sarah feel about living with the family? What did this make Caleb think?

Dear Diary,

Sarah seems sad and lonely living with us. She misses
_____ the sea. I am worried she will not want to stay with us. (5)

95

Name _____ Date _____

Cumulative Review

Read each sentence. Choose the missing word from the box. Write the word. Then reread the complete sentence.

chopped	haircut	tripped
described	included	watermelon
driveway	racing	
driving	spinning	

1. The man admired his new short __haircut (1 point)__ in the mirror.

2. In the dark, Lee Ann __tripped (1)__ and fell over a chair.

3. Martin __chopped (1)__ the carrot into small pieces.

4. Mr. Ward parked his truck in the __driveway (1)__.

5. The puppy is __spinning (1)__ in a circle, chasing its tail!

6. A cap is __included (1)__ as part of your baseball uniform.

7. We ate juicy __watermelon (1)__ at the school picnic.

8. Braden __described (1)__ every detail of the painting.

9. It was fun to watch the two squirrels __racing (1)__ up and down the tree.

10. I saw an electric car __driving (1)__ past our school.

94

Name _____ Date _____

Adverbs That Compare

Write the correct form of the adverb that compares more than two actions.

1. easily _____most easily___ (1)

2. furiously ___most furiously__ (1)

3. late ____latest___ (1)

4. perfectly ___most perfectly__ (1)

5. rigidly ___most rigidly__ (1)

6. high ___highest___ (1)

Write the form of the adverb that compares more than two actions in parentheses.

1. Sam worked ___most slowly__ (1) of all the workers. (slowly)

2. Jim shoveled the ___most quickly__ (1) of all the adults. (quickly)

3. Sally worked the ___hardest__ (1) of the three people on her team. (hard)

4. Jenny always arrived ___earliest__ (1) at work. (early)

Grammar
© Houghton Mifflin Harcourt Publishing Company. All rights reserved.

Read directions to students.
Assessment Tip: Total 10 points
Grade 3, Unit 5

97

Name _____ Date _____

Read pages 217–218. How did Caleb feel when he and Anna picked flowers with Sarah?

Dear Diary,

We picked flowers with Sarah today. She talked about drying them for the winter. I think that means she will be staying until the winter! I made up a song about a flower that lives by the sea. Everyone laughed. It was fun. (5)

Read pages 219–220. How did Caleb feel later that evening?

Dear Diary,

After dinner, Sarah cut my hair. Sarah said the birds would use my hair later for their nests. I was so happy when she said that. I knew she would be staying with us! (5)

Read page 221. What happened at the end of the evening?

Dear Diary,

We all sang on the porch. Sarah taught us a new song. It was about summer. I knew that summer was coming. I was so happy because I knew that Sarah would stay. (5)

Independent Reading
© Houghton Mifflin Harcourt Publishing Company. All rights reserved.

Read directions to students.
Assessment Tip: 15 Points
Grade 3, Unit 5

96

Name _____ Date _____

Words with -ed and -ing

Write the Basic Word that replaces the underlined word or words in each book title.

Spelling Words

Basic
1. coming
2. swimming
3. dropping
4. tapping
5. taping
6. invited
7. saving
8. stared
9. planned
10. changing
11. joking
12. loved
13. gripped
14. tasted

Review
making
stopped

Challenge
freezing
scared

1. *Kidding and Laughing*   Joking (1 point)

2. *Moving to California*   Coming (1)

3. *Stop Letting Go of the Ball*   Dropping (1)

4. *Sticking Together and Gluing Projects*
   Taping (1)

5. *Moving in Water Sports*   Swimming (1)

6. *Asked to the Party*   Invited (1)

7. *Pets I Have Liked a Lot*   Loved (1)

8. *Keeping Money in a Bank*   Saving (1)

9. *We Arranged a Party*   Planned (1)

10. *Making Different Weather*   Changing (1)

11. *He Held a Baseball Bat*   Gripped (1)

12. *Hitting Lightly at the Door*   Tapping (1)

13. *Teas I Have Tried*   Tasted (1)

14. *The Monster Looked at Me!*   Stared (1)

Review   What Review Word completes this title?

The Art of   Making (1)   *Bread*

Challenge   Write your own title using one of the Challenge Words.

Answers will vary. (1)

Assessment Tip: Total 16 points
Grade 3, Unit 5

98

Name _____ Date _____

Prefix *non-*

Read each question. Add the prefix *non-* to the underlined word and write a new word. Use the new word to write an answer to each question.   Possible responses shown.

1. A cat is a living thing. What is an example of something that is not living?
   nonliving; An example of a nonliving thing is a rock or a stone. (2 points)

2. Violent storms, such as tornadoes, can occur on the prairie. What kind of a storm is not violent?
   nonviolent; A gentle rainstorm without lighting and thunder is nonviolent. (2)

3. Anna and Caleb are productive when they do their chores. During the day, when are you not productive?
   nonproductive; When I watch television, I am being very nonproductive. (2)

4. Caleb could not stop talking to Sarah. What is something you would like to do and not stop?
   nonstop; I could read books nonstop all day and all night long. (2)

5. *Sarah, Plain and Tall* is fiction. What is your favorite book that is not fiction?
   nonfiction; My favorite nonfiction book is *A Tree Is Growing*. (2)

6. Papa, Anna, and Caleb write letters to Sarah. What is another way of communicating with someone that is not verbal?
   nonverbal; Waving and smiling at someone is a nonverbal way of showing you're glad to see her. (2)

Assessment Tip: Total 12 points
Grade 3, Unit 5

99

Name _____ Date _____

Kinds of Adjectives

Words that describe, or tell about, nouns are called **adjectives.** Adjectives can tell **what kind** or **how many** about a noun.

Jasmine loves sweet foods.

Write the adjective that tells *what kind or how many* **about the underlined noun.**

1. Tara made chocolate cake. _____ chocolate (1 point)

2. Our diet has little sugar. _____ little (1)

3. We eat three kinds of vegetables. _____ three (1)

4. We drink many glasses of water daily. _____ many (1)

5. My mother makes healthful meals. _____ healthful (1)

Combine each pair of sentences. In the new sentence, use two adjectives to describe the same noun.

6. The vegetables are healthful. The vegetables are delicious.

The vegetables are healthful and delicious. (1)

7. The pie was sweet. It was also juicy.

The pie was sweet and juicy. (1)

8. The drink was thick. It was icy, too.

The drink was thick and icy. (1)

Read directions to students.
Grammar
© Houghton Mifflin Harcourt Publishing Company. All rights reserved.
100
Assessment Tip: Total 8 points
Grade 3, Unit 5

Lesson 21
READER'S NOTEBOOK

Sarah, Plain and Tall
Spelling:
Words with -ed and -ing

Spelling Words

Basic
1. coming
2. swimming
3. dropping
4. tapping
5. taping
6. invited
7. saving
8. stared
9. planned
10. changing
11. joking
12. loved
13. gripped
14. tasted

Review
making
stopped

Challenge
freezing
scared

Name _____ Date _____

Proofreading for Spelling

Read the following invitation. Find and circle the misspelled words. (10 points)

You Are Invited To A (Swiming) Party!

Parents will be (droping) kids at the (planed) meeting place: the (changing) rooms at Bayview Park. Everyone is coming at 11:00.

I have been (saveing) plastic flowers. We will be (tapeing) them onto our bathing caps. People stared when we did this at my sister's party. I think they all (looved) how we looked and knew we were only (jokeing).

We will play in the water until noon. We (griped) hands at my sister's party and jumped over waves. Maybe we can do that again! Then my dad will make a tapping signal. He will serve chicken and salad for lunch. I've (tastted) his cooking and it will be great! Finally, we'll have a second swim. It will be a fun party. I hope you can make it!

Write the misspelled words correctly on the lines below.

1. swimming (1)
2. dropping (1)
3. planned (1)
4. changing (1)
5. saving (1)
6. taping (1)
7. loved (1)
8. joking (1)
9. gripped (1)
10. tasted (1)

Read directions to students.
Spelling
© Houghton Mifflin Harcourt Publishing Company. All rights reserved.
101
Assessment Tip: Total 20 points
Grade 3, Unit 5

Lesson 22
READER'S NOTEBOOK

The Journey:
Stories of Migration
Phonics: Spelling Changes:
-s, -es, -ed, -ing

Name _____ Date _____

Spelling Changes: -s, -es, -ed, -ing

Read each sentence. Choose the missing word from the box. Write the word. Then reread the complete sentence.

hurried	drying	cities
replied	pennies	grazed
traveled	memories	
pillows	paintbrushes	

1. April ___replied (1 point)___ to the question with another question.

2. I have such good ___memories (1)___ of kindergarten!

3. Most of the big ___cities (1)___ in California are on the coast.

4. The goats ___grazed (1)___ on the hillside.

5. Ten ___pennies (1)___ equal one dime.

6. Alexander ___hurried (1)___ to school so he wouldn't be late.

7. The class ___traveled (1)___ to the zoo on a bus.

8. Joshua broke a plate as he was ___drying (1)___ the dishes.

9. Mom set two fluffy ___pillows (1)___ on the bed.

10. The artist had many ___paintbrushes (1)___ of different sizes.

Assessment Tip: Total 10 points
Grade 3, Unit 5

Name _____ Date _____

Connect to Writing

You can make your ideas clearer by using adverbs that compare. To compare two actions, add *-er* to most adverbs. Use *more* before an adverb that ends in *-ly*. To compare more than two actions, add *-est* to most adverbs. Use *most* before an adverb that ends in *-ly*.

Incorrect Adverb Form	Correct Adverb Form
Mary will arrive soonest than Ellen.	Mary will arrive sooner than Ellen.
The gray kitten acts the more lively of all the cats.	The gray kitten acts the most lively of all the cats.

Use the correct form of the adverb in parentheses. Write the sentence.

1. Ellen ran to the barn (fast) than Mary.

   Ellen ran to the barn faster than Mary. (1 point)

2. Mary climbed the ladder (quickly) than Ellen.

   Mary climbed the ladder more quickly than Ellen. (1)

3. The white kitten moved (slow) of all the kittens.

   The white kitten moved slowest of all the kittens. (1)

4. The gray kitten cried (loud) than the white kitten.

   The gray kitten cried louder than the white kitten. (1)

5. Mary played with the kittens (carefully) than Ellen did.

   Mary played with the kittens more carefully than Ellen did. (1)

Assessment Tip: Total 5 points
Grade 3, Unit 5

Lesson 22
READER'S NOTEBOOK

The Journey:
Stories of Migration
Grammar:
Making Comparisons

Name _____ Date _____

Adjectives That Compare

- **Adjectives** are used to describe nouns. Adjectives can also be used to **compare** two or more nouns.
- Add the ending -*er* to most adjectives to compare two nouns. Add -*est* to compare more than two nouns.

Adjective	Comparing Two Nouns	Comparing More Than Two Nouns
tall	taller	tallest
high	higher	highest
large	larger	largest

Thinking Question
How many nouns are being compared?

Kim's hair is long. Morgan's hair is longer than Kim's. Jamie's hair is the longest of all.

Write the correct form of the adjective in parentheses.

1. Monarch butterflies are (quick) than turtles.
   quicker (1 point)

2. One book showed that the butterfly was (bright) than the flower it landed on. brighter (1)

3. The (long) section in the book was about migration.
   longest (1)

4. Male monarchs are (big) than female monarchs.
   bigger (1)

Lesson 22
READER'S NOTEBOOK

The Journey:
Stories of Migration
Grammar:
Making Comparisons

Name _____ Date _____

Adverbs That Compare

- **Adverbs** tell *when*, *where*, or *how* something happened. They can also be used to **compare actions.**
- Add the ending -*er* to adverbs to compare two actions.
- To compare more than two actions, add the ending -*est*.

Adverb	Comparing Two Actions	Comparing More Than Two Actions
late	later	latest
quickly	more quickly	most quickly
fast	faster	fastest

Thinking Question
How many actions are being compared?

Len jumped high. I jumped higher than Len. Lou jumped the highest of all.

Write the correct form of the adverb in parentheses.

1. I thought the whale swam (fast) than the dolphin.
   faster (1 point)

2. Lee thought the dolphins swam the (fast) of all the animals we saw.
   fastest (1)

3. We talked (softly) than we do in school.
   more softly (1)

4. The dolphin dived (deep) than the school of fish.
   deeper (1)

Lesson 22
READER'S NOTEBOOK

The Journey:
Stories of Migration
Writing:
Narrative Writing

Name _____ Date _____

Focus Trait: Elaboration
Using Similes

Description	Simile Added
My face turned red.	My face turned as red as a tomato.

A. Read each description. Create a clearer picture by adding a simile using *like* or *as*. Possible responses shown.

Description	Simile Added
1. Huge rain clouds blocked the sun and made it dark outside.	Huge rain clouds blocked the sun and made _____ it as dark as night outside. (1 point)
2. The children walking in the hallway are loud.	The children walking in the hallway are _____ like a herd of stampeding elephants _____. (1)

B. Read each description. Add a simile to each description to create a clearer picture for the reader. Write your new sentences. Possible responses shown.

Description	Simile Added
3. The freshly washed floor was slippery.	The freshly washed floor was as slippery as a frozen pond. (1)
4. The new mall is huge.	The new mall is like a city. (1)

Pair/Share Work with a partner to brainstorm similes to add to each description.

Lesson 22
READER'S NOTEBOOK

The Journey:
Stories of Migration
Spelling:
Changing Final y to i

Name _____ Date _____

Spelling Word Sort

Write each Basic Word under the correct heading.

Spelling Words

Basic
1. cities
2. cried
3. puppies
4. hurried
5. stories
6. flies
7. parties
8. tried
9. pennies
10. fried
11. carried
12. babies
13. spied
14. ponies

Review
pretty
very

Challenge
countries
libraries

Words ending with -es	Words ending with -ed
cities (1 point)	cried (1)
puppies (1)	hurried (1)
stories (1)	tried (1)
flies (1)	fried (1)
parties (1)	carried (1)
pennies (1)	spied (1)
babies (1)	
ponies (1)	

Challenge: countries (1)

Challenge: libraries (1)

Review: Suppose you were asked to add a column for the Review Words. What would you name the heading of that column? _____ Words ending with -y (2)

Challenge: Add the Challenge Words to your Word Sort.

Lesson 22
READER'S NOTEBOOK

The Journey:
Stories of Migration
Phonics:
Less Common Plurals

Less Common Plurals

Read each sentence. Choose the missing word from the box. Write the word. Then reread each complete sentence.

| knives |
| leaves |
| hooves |
| lives |
| loaves |

1. The blacksmith put shoes on the horses'
   _____ hooves (1 point)

2. Run for your _____ lives (1) ! The volcano is erupting!

3. Do you have any _____ loaves (1) of wheat bread?

4. In autumn, the _____ leaves (1) fall from the trees.

5. Set the table with forks, _____ knives (1) , and spoons.

Read directions to students.

Phonics
© Houghton Mifflin Harcourt Publishing Company. All rights reserved.

108

Assessment Tip: Total 5 points
Grade 3, Unit 5

Reader's Guide

Lesson 22
READER'S NOTEBOOK

The Journey: Stories
of Migration
Independent Reading

The Journey: Stories of Migration

An Interview with Locust and Whale

Hello and welcome to the weekly radio program, *Animal Journeys*. Today we are going to talk with Locust and Whale, two animals that take amazing journeys.

Read pages 241–242. Locust, let's hear your story first. What makes you migrate?

Locust: _____ We have to move whenever there is not enough food. Our bodies change and we become locusts instead of grasshoppers. (2 points)

Read page 243. How interesting. What happens when you all land?

Locust: _____ We eat everything on the ground, including grass, bushes, and plants. Then we fly off again. (2)

Read pages 246–247. Now tell us more about how you travel.

Locust: _____ We ride the winds from one area to the next. We look for places where it rains because those places have more food. We travel in the mornings and rest at night. (2)

Read directions to students.

Independent Reading
© Houghton Mifflin Harcourt Publishing Company. All rights reserved.

109

Assessment Tip: 6 Points
Grade 3, Unit 5

Lesson 22
READER'S NOTEBOOK

The Journey:
Stories of Migration
Grammar:
Making Comparisons

Name _____ Date _____

Adjectives and Adverbs That Compare

Review with students that adjectives compare nouns, and adverbs compare verbs, or actions.

Write an adjective or adverb to complete each sentence. Then write *adjective* or *adverb* to identify the answer you gave.

1. A butterfly's wings move _more quietly (1 point)_ than a locust's wings. (quietly) _adverb (1)_

2. Locusts are the _hungriest (1)_ of all insects. (hungry) _adjective (1)_

3. The waves splashed _higher (1)_ than they had earlier in the day. (high) _adverb (1)_

4. The waters near the Arctic are _colder (1)_ than the waters near Mexico. (cold) _adjective (1)_

Write two sentences. Include an adjective that compares in one sentence and an adverb that compares in the other sentence. Possible answers shown.

5. _The ocean water was the bluest color I had ever seen. (1)_

_____

6. _The boat moved faster than the whale swam. (1)_

_____

_____

Name _____ Date _____

Read pages 248–250. Whale, you migrate too but for different reasons. Why do you migrate?

Whale: In the fall, we leave the Arctic because the water will be too cold for us in the winter and there won't be much food. (2)

_____

What do you do on your migration that is similar to what locusts do?

Whale: We travel together in groups. (2)

_____

Read pages 251–252. When you arrive at the warm tropical waters in January, what happens?

Whale: Baby whales are born. (2)

_____

Read pages 252–253. When spring comes, why do you migrate again?

Whale: We like the food in the Arctic waters. (2)

_____

Thank you both for joining us on *Animal Journeys*. We have learned a lot today about your journeys across the world!

Name _____ Date _____

Changing Final *y* to *i*

Write the Basic Word or Words to answer each question.

1. Which word names big places? _____ cities (1 point)

2. Which words name living things?
   puppies (1) , _____ flies (1) ,
   babies (1) , _____ ponies (1)

3. Which words rhyme with lied?
   cried (1) , _____ fried (1) ,
   tried (1) , _____ spied (1)

4. Which word names money you can carry in a pocket?
   _____ pennies (1)

5. Which verb names what you did when you were late
   to something? _____ hurried (1)

6. What words make you think of food?
   parties (1) , _____ fried (1)

7. Which word names things that you read?
   _____ stories (1)

8. Write two words that name something small.
   Sample answers: pennies,
   babies (1)

Review Name a word that is an adjective. _____
Sample answers: pretty, very (1)

Challenge Write a word that names places. _____
Sample answers: countries,
libraries, cities (1)

Read directions to students.
Spelling
© Houghton Mifflin Harcourt Publishing Company. All rights reserved.

Spelling Words

Basic
1. cities
2. cried
3. puppies
4. hurried
5. stories
6. flies
7. parties
8. tried
9. pennies
10. fried
11. carried
12. babies
13. spied
14. ponies

Review
pretty
very

Challenge
countries
libraries

Name _____ Date _____

Word Roots

Read each question. Write the word root or word roots in each underlined word. Then use the underlined word to write a complete sentence to answer each question. Possible responses shown.

1. How do grasshoppers survive when there is not enough food? (2 points)
   viv; They survive by migrating to find more food.

2. What happens when grasshoppers transform into locusts?
   trans; Their bodies transform from light green to dark yellow or
   red. (2 points)

3. Why are locusts so destructive to people's gardens?
   struct; Locusts are destructive because they eat all the vegetation,
   including gardens, so people don't have enough food to eat. (2 points)

4. How do locusts affect transportation?
   trans; port; Clouds of locusts affect transportation because they
   make it dangerous to fly planes or drive trains or cars. (2 points)

5. When do gray whales start to look for companions?
   com; They look for companions in the fall because they want to
   migrate in small groups to warmer waters. (2 points)

6. What do the bodies of the gray whales demand before
   the whales migrate south?
   mand; Their bodies demand lots of food to keep them going on
   their long journey. (2 points)

Read directions to students.
Vocabulary Strategies
© Houghton Mifflin Harcourt Publishing Company. All rights reserved.

Lesson 22
READER'S NOTEBOOK

**The Journey:
Stories of Migration**
Grammar:
Spiral Review

Name _____ Date _____

Adjectives and Articles

- The words *a*, *an*, and *the* are special adjectives called **articles**. Use *a* and *an* with singular nouns. Use *a* before words that begin with a consonant sound. Use *an* before words that begin with a vowel sound. Use *the* before both singular and plural nouns.
- An adjective formed from a proper noun should begin with a capital letter.

  The class took <u>a</u> bus to see <u>an</u> exhibit of <u>African</u> zebras.

Rewrite each sentence correctly. Capitalize proper adjectives.

1. We also saw european deer.

   We also saw European deer. (1 point)

2. A irish scientist gave a talk.

   An Irish scientist gave a talk. (1)

Use proofreading marks to write *a*, *an*, and *the* correctly. (4)

Dear Diary,

   We took a trip to see butterflies. We also saw a̸ ant as big as a spider.
   An̸ guide told us about butterflies in Mexico. He described the stages of
a
an̸ butterfly's life. I asked him a̸n question, and he answered it.

                              Ken

Assessment Tip: Total 6 points   **Grade 3, Unit 5**

Lesson 22
READER'S NOTEBOOK

**The Journey:
Stories of Migration**
Spelling:
Changing Final *y* to *i*

Name _____ Date _____

Proofreading for Spelling

Find and circle the misspelled words. (10 points)

While helping Ms. Mancia in the library, I have spyed many interesting things. I made a list of some of them.

- Two pennys were found in a book about banking!
- Once a man carryed three babies in at one time. He held all three while he looked something up on the computer. Then he hurreed out.
- Two flys landed on a book titled *Insect Homes*.
- A girl cried as she looked at pictures of puppyes.
- A cookbook showed fryed chicken for Valentine's Day. Chicken on Valentine's Day?
- The title of one book was *Farm Storys from Our Big Cityes*.
- Two ponies tryd to climb in through a window. (Okay, I made that one up!)

Spelling Words

Basic
1. cities
2. cried
3. puppies
4. hurried
5. stories
6. flies
7. parties
8. tried
9. pennies
10. fried
11. carried
12. babies
13. spied
14. ponies

Review
pretty
very

Challenge
countries
libraries

Write the misspelled words correctly on the lines below.

1. spied (1)
2. pennies (1)
3. carried (1)
4. hurried (1)
5. flies (1)
6. puppies (1)
7. fried (1)
8. Stories (1)
9. Cities (1)
10. tried (1)

Assessment Tip: Total 20 points   **Grade 3, Unit 5**

Read directions to students.

Lesson 23
READER'S NOTEBOOK

The Journey of
Oliver K. Woodman
Phonics: Suffixes
-ful, -y, -ous, -ly, -er

Name _____ Date _____

Suffixes -ful, -y, -ous, -ly, -er

**Read each sentence. Choose the missing word from the box.
Write the word. Then reread the complete sentence.**

spoonful	messy	gardener
runner	closely	windy
nervous	bravely	
graceful	joyous	

1. On a __windy (1 point)__ day, I have to hold onto my hat!

2. The first __spoonful (1)__ of soup is the hottest.

3. The __graceful (1)__ dancer leaped across the stage.

4. Damian __bravely (1)__ walked across the swinging bridge.

5. The __gardener (1)__ planted flowers that would attract bees and butterflies.

6. The lamb followed __closely (1)__ behind its mother so it wouldn't get lost.

7. My __messy (1)__ dog spilled her food and tracked mud across the floor.

8. It was a __joyous (1)__ occasion at my house when I brought home a good report card.

9. Do you feel __nervous (1)__ about singing the solo in the school play?

10. When the __runner (1)__ crossed the finish line, she held her hands over her head in celebration.

Read directions to students.
Phonics
© Houghton Mifflin Harcourt Publishing Company. All rights reserved.

117

Assessment Tip: Total 10 points
Grade 3, Unit 5

Lesson 22
READER'S NOTEBOOK

The Journey:
Stories of Migration
Grammar:
Connect to Writing

Name _____ Date _____

Connect to Writing

You can make your descriptions clearer by using adjectives and adverbs that compare. To compare two nouns or actions, add -er to most adjectives and adverbs. To compare more than two nouns or actions, add -est to most adjectives and adverbs.

Adjective	Adverb
The blue fish is big.	Dad eats fast.
The white fish is bigger than the blue fish.	My sister eats faster than Dad.
The gray fish is the biggest fish in the tank.	Mom eats the fastest in the family.

**Use the correct form of the adjective or adverb in parentheses.
Write the sentence.**

1. This aquarium is (new) than the one in Tarpon.

   This aquarium is newer than the one in Tarpon. (1 point)

2. Tony got to the aquarium (late) than Katie.

   Tony got to the aquarium later than Katie. (1)

3. The jellyfish tank was the (dark) tank in the aquarium.

   The jellyfish tank was the darkest tank in the aquarium. (1)

4. Katie stayed at the seahorse display (long) than at the other displays.

   Katie stayed at the seahorse display longer than at the other displays. (1)

Read directions to students.
Grammar
© Houghton Mifflin Harcourt Publishing Company. All rights reserved.

116

Assessment Tip: Total 4 points
Grade 3, Unit 5

Lesson 23
READER'S NOTEBOOK

The Journey of
Oliver K. Woodman
Grammar:
Possessive Nouns and Pronouns

Singular Possessive Nouns

Thinking Question
Which noun owns or has something?

- A **singular possessive noun** shows that a person, animal, place, or thing has or owns something.
- Add an *apostrophe* and *s* to form a singular possessive noun.

The backpack's straps were loose.
Oliver's backpack was once home to a mouse.

Write the possessive for each noun below.

1. friend _____ friend's (1 point)
2. Emma _____ Emma's (1)
3. bus station _____ bus station's (1)
4. river _____ river's (1)
5. Florida _____ 'Florida's (1)
6. car _____ car's (1)

Underline the noun that should be possessive and write the possessive form.

7. The man hobby was to build furniture. _____ man's (1)
8. The workshop tools hung neatly on the wall. _____ workshop's (1)
9. His niece birthday was next week. _____ niece's (1)
10. The day chores would have to wait until he completed the gift. _____ day's (1)

Lesson 23
READER'S NOTEBOOK

The Journey of
Oliver K. Woodman
Grammar:
Possessive Nouns and Pronouns

Plural Possessive Nouns

Thinking Question
Which noun owns or has something?

- To form a **plural possessive noun**, add an *apostrophe* to the end of plural nouns that end in *s*.
- Add an *apostrophe* and *s* to the end of plural nouns that do not end in *s*.

Raymond put the sisters' postcards in the mail.
The children's letters were from all over the country.

Write the possessive form of the plural nouns.

1. men _____ men's (1 point)
2. babies _____ babies' (1)
3. books _____ books' (1)
4. fish _____ fish's (1)
5. shelves _____ shelves' (1)

Write sentences for three of the possessive plural nouns.

6. The men's dressing room is in the back. (1) _____
7. The fish's tank needs cleaning. (1) _____
8. The books' covers are dusty. (1) _____

Name _____ Date _____

Focus Trait: Development
Showing Characters' Feelings

Instead of this...	...a writer wrote this to show feelings.
Wendy is a good friend.	Wendy is lots of fun to spend a Saturday afternoon with!

A. Read the sentence. Rewrite the sentence to show feelings. Possible response shown.

Instead of this...	...the author wrote this to show feelings.
1. I liked the food.	I really loved the lunch Grandma made. (2 points)

B. Read each event below from *The Journey of Oliver K. Woodman.* Look at the pictures on the pages listed below. Write a line of dialogue in which Oliver shows how he might have felt.

Pair/Share Work with a partner to brainstorm words that show feelings. Possible responses shown.

Event	Dialogue with Feelings
2. Oliver rides with three sisters. (pp. 288–289)	I got to have a cup of tea with the nicest sisters! (2)
3. Oliver gets to Tameka's house. (pp. 292–293)	After a long and exciting trip, I finally made it to Tameka's house. (2)

Read directions to students.
Writing
Copyright © Houghton Mifflin Harcourt Publishing Company. All rights reserved.

Assessment Tip: Total 6 points
Grade 3, Unit 5

121

Lesson 23
READER'S NOTEBOOK

The Journey of
Oliver K. Woodman
Spelling:
Suffixes -ful, -ly, and -er

Name _____ Date _____

Spelling Word Sort

Write each Basic Word under the correct heading.

Spelling Words

Basic
1. singer
2. loudly
3. joyful
4. teacher
5. fighter
6. closely
7. powerful
8. farmer
9. quickly
10. careful
11. friendly
12. speaker
13. wonderful
14. truly

Review
hopeful
safely

Challenge
listener
calmly

Words that End with the Suffix -ful	Words that End with the Suffix -ly
joyful (1 point)	loudly (1)
powerful (1)	closely (1)
careful (1)	quickly (1)
wonderful (1)	friendly (1)
	truly (1)
	Review: safely (1)
	Challenge: calmly (1)

Words that End with the Suffix -er	
singer (1)	farmer (1)
teacher (1)	speaker (1)
fighter (1)	Challenge: listener (1)

Review: Add the Review Words to your Word Sort.

Challenge: Add the Challenge Words to your Word Sort.

Read directions to students.
Spelling
© Houghton Mifflin Harcourt Publishing Company. All rights reserved.

Assessment Tip: Total 18 points
Grade 3, Unit 5

120

Lesson 23
READER'S NOTEBOOK

The Journey of
Oliver K. Woodman
Independent Reading

The Journey of Oliver K. Woodman

A Timeline of Oliver's Journey

Oliver K. Woodman spent two months traveling from Uncle Ray's house to Tameka's house. First, use details from the text and illustrations to gather information. Then show Oliver's journey on a timeline.

Read pages 274–278. According to Uncle Ray's second letter, when did Oliver K. Woodman begin his journey? Where did he start? (2 points)

He set out on June 1 from Rock Hill, South Carolina. _____

Read pages 279–280. When did Uncle Ray get news of Oliver again? Where was he? (2)

June 4. He was just outside Memphis, Tennessee. _____

Read page 281. When did Uncle Ray next hear about Oliver? Where was Oliver at that time?

On June 8, Uncle Ray found out that Oliver went to a basketball game in Memphis and then got sent to Fort Smith, Arkansas. (2)

Read page 282. When did Uncle Ray get news next? Where was Oliver?

On June 11, Oliver was driven to Oklahoma City, then to Dallas, to Amarillo, then to Panhandle, and finally to Albuquerque. (2)

Read directions to students.
Independent Reading
© Houghton Mifflin Harcourt Publishing Company. All rights reserved.

Assessment Tip: 8 Points
Grade 3, Unit 5

123

Lesson 23
READER'S NOTEBOOK

The Journey of
Oliver K. Woodman
Phonics:
Cumulative Review

Cumulative Review

Read each sentence. Choose the missing word from the box. Write the word. Then reread the complete sentence.

salty	handful
juicy	baker
beautiful	butcher
finely	dangerous
	numerous
	happily

1. There are __numerous (1 point)__ kinds of snacks, and there are many healthful ones to choose from.

2. A __handful (1)__ of raisins is a good snack. You can grab them and go!

3. Some people like __salty (1)__ snacks like pretzels or nuts.

4. A __baker (1)__ can make muffins and breads.

5. Not only do bakeries smell good but the items are __beautiful (1)__ to look at.

6. __Finely (1)__ sliced cheese goes well with crackers.

7. There is nothing like a __juicy (1)__ orange as a snack. You can eat it or squeeze it into a glass and drink it.

8. A knife is a __dangerous (1)__ tool. The sharp edge could cut a child's fingers.

9. A __butcher (1)__ is trained in using very sharp knives to cut meat.

10. After your snack, smile and go __happily (1)__ on with your day!

Read directions to students.
Phonics
Copyright © Houghton Mifflin Company. All rights reserved.

Assessment Tip: Total 10 points
Grade 3, Unit 5

122

Lesson 23
READER'S NOTEBOOK

The Journey of
Oliver K. Woodman
Grammar:
Possessive Nouns and Pronouns

Name _____ Date _____

Possessive Pronouns

**Read the sentences below. Underline the possessive pronouns.
If the possessive pronoun is not written correctly, write the word
correctly on the line.**

1. Lucy, a friend of our's, is traveling with us to Tennessee.
   ours (2 points)

2. Is this his's map?
   his (2)

3. My favorite part of a road trip is the snacks.
   (1)

4. That is hers backpack.
   her (2)

5. Is this yours sandwich?
   your (2)

Write a sentence for each of the possessive pronouns.
Possible responses shown.

6. their

   Their pencils are on the floor. (1)

7. our

   What color is our suitcase? (1)

8. my

   My jacket is hanging by the door. (1)

125

Name _____ Date _____

**Read pages 286–287. Uncle Ray and Tameka thought Oliver
was lost. When did Uncle Ray get news from Oliver?
Where was Oliver?**

On July 4, Oliver was found on a reservation in New Mexico. Then he

was brought to Utah to a Fourth of July parade.   (2)

Read pages 288–289. Where did Oliver end up next? When?

On July 27, Oliver was brought to a rodeo in Eureka, Nevada, and

then to San Francisco, and then Rough and Ready, California.   (2)

Now use the details that you have gathered to complete
the timeline below. Remember to use all the dates from
the letters to Uncle Ray that told when Oliver was in
each place.

Date

Places

(Students should write a date above and a place below the timeline

at each marked increment. The information should correspond to the

answers provided above.) (10)

124

Lesson 23
READER'S NOTEBOOK

The Journey of
Oliver K. Woodman
Vocabulary Strategies:
Suffixes -er, -est

Name _____ Date _____

Suffixes -er, -est

Read the paragraph. Circle the words with the suffix -er or -est. Then write the words the suffixes were added to on the lines below.

Saturday was the (loveliest) (sunniest) day we have had during our car trip. The weather in San Francisco was (colder) than I had expected, though. We walked across the Golden Gate Bridge and met the (kindest) people. They were nice to take photos of us. Leaving San Francisco was (harder) than leaving Salt Lake City had been, but we were all (happier) when we thought about our next adventure.

1. lovely (1 point)	4.	kind (1)
2. sunny (1)	5.	hard (1)
3. cold (1)	6.	happy (1)

Add the suffix -er or -est to create new words. Complete the sentence.

7. **nice:** Raymond Johnson is the _____ nicest (1) _____ uncle in the world!

8. **dark:** The sky is _____ darker (1) _____ tonight than it was last night.

9. **strange:** This is the _____ strangest (1) _____ trip I have ever taken!

10. **young:** My sister, Lucinda, is two years _____ younger (1) _____ than I am.

Lesson 23
READER'S NOTEBOOK

The Journey of
Oliver K. Woodman
Spelling:
Suffixes -ful, -ly, and -er

Name _____ Date _____

Suffixes -ful, -ly, and -er

Write a Basic Word to complete each sentence.

Spelling Words

Basic
1. singer
2. loudly
3. joyful
4. teacher
5. fighter
6. closely
7. powerful
8. farmer
9. quickly
10. careful
11. friendly
12. speaker
13. wonderful
14. truly

Review
hopeful
safely

Challenge
listener
calmly

1. A person singing in a choir is a _____ singer (1 point) _____.

2. If your friends yell during a game, they are playing _____ loudly (1) _____.

3. A person who grows corn in the country is a _____ farmer (1) _____.

4. If you run fast, you are moving _____ quickly (1) _____.

5. If you are very happy, you are _____ joyful (1) _____.

6. The person whose desk is in the front of your classroom is your _____ teacher (1) _____.

7. Someone who is very strong is _____ powerful (1) _____.

8. When you use scissors, you should be _____ careful (1) _____.

9. A person who smiles and asks you how you are feeling is _____ friendly (1) _____.

10. If you are _____ truly (1) _____ sorry, you will make a sincere apology.

Review: Choose a Review Word that completes the sentence.

If you want something to happen, you are _____ hopeful (1) _____.

Challenge: Choose a Challenge Word. Use it in a sentence.

Responses will vary. (1)
_____

Lesson 23
READER'S NOTEBOOK

The Journey of
Oliver K. Woodman
Grammar:
Spiral Review

Name _____ Date _____

The Special Verb *be*

- The verbs *am, is, are, was,* and *were* are forms of the verb *be.* They do not show action. They tell what someone or something is or was. *Am, is,* and *are* show present tense. *Was* and *were* show past tense.

  The trip is fun.   The trip was fun.

Write the verb. Write *present* or *past* for each verb.

1. The boys are tired of traveling. _____ are—present (1 point)

2. We were away for one week. _____ were—past (1)

3. I am ready to go on another trip. _____ am—present (1)

Combine two short sentences by moving one predicate to make one longer sentence with two predicates. Write the new sentence on the line.

4. Father is a good driver. Father is a good storyteller.

_____

Father is a good driver and is a good storyteller. (1)

5. We are out of the car. We are ready to relax.

_____

We are out of the car and are ready to relax. (1)

6. Mother and Jorge are happy. Mother and Jorge are in the house.

_____

Mother and Jorge are happy and are in the house. (1)

128

Lesson 23
READER'S NOTEBOOK

The Journey of
Oliver K. Woodman
Spelling:
Suffixes *-ful, -ly,* and *-er*

Spelling Words

Basic
1. singer
2. loudly
3. joyful
4. teacher
5. fighter
6. closely
7. powerful
8. farmer
9. quickly
10. careful
11. friendly
12. speaker
13. wonderful
14. truly

Review
hopeful
safely

Challenge
listener
calmly

Name _____ Date _____

Proofreading for Spelling

Read the following letter. Circle the misspelled words.
(10 points)

Dear Marcus,

My class heard a (speeker) today. His name was Mr. Brown. He showed us pictures of different parts of the country. We saw a picture of a (farmar) on his farm. I looked at the picture (closelie) to see all the animals.

We saw pictures of the Rocky Mountains. What a (wunderful) trip that would be! I am (hopefull) that someday I will see the mountains.

Some of my friends were talking (lowdley.) Mrs. Garcia told them to be quiet. Mrs. Garcia is our (teachur.)

Mr. Brown answered all of our questions. He was very (frenly.)

After the speech, we all went (kuikly) back to our classrooms. I was (carefull) not to bump into anyone on the way.

Your friend,
Danny

Write the misspelled words correctly on the lines below.

1. _____ speaker (1)   6. _____ loudly (1)

2. _____ farmer (1)   7. _____ teacher (1)

3. _____ closely (1)   8. _____ friendly (1)

4. _____ wonderful (1)   9. _____ quickly (1)

5. _____ hopeful (1)   10. _____ careful (1)

129

Lesson 24
READER'S NOTEBOOK

Dog-of-the-Sea-Waves
Phonics: Prefixes
un-, pre-, re-, bi-

Name _____ Date _____

Prefixes *un-*, *pre-*, *re-*, *bi-*

**Read each sentence. Choose the missing word from the box.
Write the word. Then reread the complete sentence.**

refilled	preview	unsafe	unbroken
preheat	unopened	biweekly	bicycle
redo	pretest		

1. Did you see the old ____ bicycle (1 point) ____ zoom past?

2. It is ____ unsafe (1) ____ to skateboard without a helmet.

3. The ____ preview (1) ____ showed parts of a new movie.

4. I have to study the words I missed on the spelling
   ____ pretest (1) ____.

5. The ____ biweekly (1) ____ magazine comes out every
   two weeks.

6. Mom ____ refilled (1) ____ my glass after I finished the
   first glass of juice.

7. I was happy to find the vase ____ unbroken (1) ____ after
   I saw it fall.

8. Tomas had to ____ redo (1) ____ the poster after he
   misspelled a word on it.

9. I left the gifts ____ unopened (1) ____ while I waited for my
   sisters to come home.

10. The recipe says to ____ preheat (1) ____ the oven to
    325 degrees before putting the chicken in.

Lesson 23
READER'S NOTEBOOK

The Journey of
Oliver K. Woodman
Grammar:
Connect to Writing

Name _____ Date _____

Connect to Writing

You can make your sentences smoother by replacing
repeated possessive nouns with possessive pronouns. Make
sure the possessive pronoun matches the possessive noun
you replace.

Awkward Sentence	Smoother Sentence
My brother's favorite toy is my brother's wooden car.	My brother's favorite toy is his wooden car.
"My cousins' friends are going to my cousins' house," she said.	"My cousins' friends are going to their house," she said.

**Replace the underlined possessive noun with a possessive
pronoun. Write the sentence.**

1. Lucy's favorite aunt is Lucy's Aunt Debra.

   Lucy's favorite aunt is her Aunt Debra. (1 point)

2. The family's first stop will be at the family's old house.

   The family's first stop will be at their old house. (1)

3. Jack let Lucy borrow Jack's headphones for the trip.

   Jack let Lucy borrow his headphones for the trip. (1)

4. "Will Aunt Debra's new puppy be at Aunt Debra's
   house?" Lucy asked.

   "Will Aunt Debra's new puppy be at her house?" Lucy asked. (1)

5. Dad said, "Hand me Dad's car keys."

   Dad said, "Hand me my car keys." (1)

Subordinating Conjunctions

Thinking Question
Which subordinating conjunction can join the dependent clause to the independent clause?

- A complex sentence is formed by combining one independent clause and at least one dependent clause. If the dependent clause appears first, add a comma after it.
- **Subordinating conjunctions** begin dependent clauses. Some subordinating conjunctions are *after, although, because, before, even though, since, unless, until, when, while.*

  We had fun swimming. Because of the weather.
  We had fun swimming because of the weather.

Underline the dependent clause. Write the subordinating conjunction that begins the dependent clause.

1. We will see the dolphins <u>before we leave</u>.

   before (2 points)

2. <u>After we eat lunch</u>, we will see more of the zoo.

   After (2)

3. <u>Because he forgot his lunch</u>, we went back to the car.

   Because (2)

4. We will miss the dolphins <u>unless we hurry</u>.

   unless (2)

Complex Sentences

Thinking Question
Which part of the sentence tells a complete thought? Which part cannot stand alone?

- An **independent clause** is a simple sentence and tells a complete thought. It has a subject and a verb.
- A **dependent clause** has a subject and a verb, but it does not tell a complete thought.
- A **complex sentence** is formed by combining one independent clause and one or more dependent clauses.

  Although the boat needed a repair. We went sailing.
  Although the boat needed a repair, we went sailing.

Write *complex* if the sentence has an independent clause and one or more dependent clauses. Write *dependent clause* if the sentence does not tell a complete thought.

1. When the boat's rope broke, the boys worked quickly to fix it.

   complex (1 point)

2. Jen retied the ropes since she was good with knots.

   complex (1)

3. While the captain carefully watched her.

   dependent clause (1)

4. Everyone relaxed when they arrived at the dock.

   complex (1)

Lesson 24
READER'S NOTEBOOK

Dog-of-the-Sea-Waves
Spelling:
Prefixes re-, un-

Name _____ Date _____

Spelling Word Sort

Write each Basic Word under the correct heading.

Prefix that means "again"	Prefix that means "not" or "opposite of"
rejoin (1 point)	unfold (1)
reheat (1)	untie (1)
repaid (1)	unfair (1)
rewrite (1)	unclear (1)
recheck (1)	unhurt (1)
reuse (1)	unlucky (1)
Review: reread (1)	unwrap (1)
	unsure (1)
	Review: unsafe (1)
	Challenge: unbuckle (1)
	Challenge: unknown (1)

Review: Add the Review Words to your Word Sort.

Challenge: Add the Challenge Words to your Word Sort.

Spelling Words

Basic
1. unfold
2. rejoin
3. untie
4. reheat
5. unfair
6. unclear
7. repaid
8. rewrite
9. unhurt
10. recheck
11. unlucky
12. unwrap
13. reuse
14. unsure

Review
reread
unsafe

Challenge
unbuckle
unknown

Read directions to students.
Spelling
© Houghton Mifflin Harcourt Publishing Company. All rights reserved.

134

Assessment Tip: Total 18 points
Grade 3, Unit 5

Name _____ Date _____

Focus Trait: Elaboration
Using Vivid Details

Good story writers use vivid details to paint a clear picture. Compare the sentence without vivid details to the one with vivid details.

Without Vivid Details: The beach was beautiful in the morning.

With Vivid Details: The sunrise cast a warm glow over the golden sands of the empty beach.

Rewrite each sentence, adding vivid details. You may use ideas from the box below or think of your own. Possible responses shown.

gently	sparkling	shady	cool

1. They had to cross the ocean to get home.
   They had to paddle across the sparkling blue ocean to get home. (1 point)

2. Manu cleaned the animal's wound.
   Manu gently washed the animal's wound with cool, clean water. (1)

3. He built a shelter from the sun.
   He used tree branches to build a shady shelter from the burning sun. (1)

4. He gathered berries.
   He gathered sweet, ripe blueberries from the bushes. (1)

5. He dived into the water.
   He dived off the rocks into the ice-cold mountain lake. (1)

Read directions to students.
Writing
© Houghton Mifflin Harcourt Publishing Company. All rights reserved.

135

Assessment Tip: Total 5 points
Grade 3, Unit 5

Name _____ Date _____

Cumulative Review

Read each sentence. Choose the missing word from the box. Write the word.

bimonthly	revisit	unequal	rebuild
reelected	preheat	unfriendly	unknown

1. I had so much fun at the park that I hope we ___revisit (1 point)___ it next summer.

2. I asked Uncle Ramon to pour more water into my glass because the amounts in the two glasses were ___unequal (1)___.

3. Be sure to ___preheat (1)___ the oven before you put the biscuits in to bake.

4. The mayor was ___reelected (1)___ for a second term after all the votes were counted.

5. The ___bimonthly (1)___ school newspaper comes out on the first and fifteenth of the month.

6. The ___unfriendly (1)___ store clerk did not look up when I said hello.

7. There was no card on the flowers that were sent by an ___unknown (1)___ person.

8. The carpenter had to ___rebuild (1)___ the wobbly bookshelves.

Read directions to students.
Phonics
© Houghton Mifflin Harcourt Publishing Company. All rights reserved.

136

Assessment Tip: Total 8 points
Grade 3, Unit 5

Name _____ Date _____

Reader's Guide

Dog-of-the-Sea-Waves

Homes for Sale!

When the brothers returned home to the southern sea, they wanted to convince other people to move there. They decided to place an advertisement in the newspaper.

Read page 315. What are some details on this page that will convince people to move to the Hawaiian Islands?

The Hawaiian Islands grew green and lush. The streams and lagoons rippled with fish. The forests flashed with the feathers of birds and the rainbow wings of insects. (2 points)

Read pages 318–319. Here, Manu finds the hurt seal. How can the story of the seal help convince people to move to the islands?

The seal was friendly and like a dog. It was fun for Manu to swim and play with the seal. (2)

Read pages 320–321. On these pages, the brothers were gathering food. What kinds of food did they gather? Do you think these details can help convince other people that Hawaii is a good place to live?

They gathered berries, fish, and roots. People will want to move to Hawaii because a lot of food grows there. (2)

Read directions to students.
Independent Reading
© Houghton Mifflin Harcourt Publishing Company. All rights reserved.

137

Assessment Tip: 6 Points
Grade 3, Unit 5

Name _____ Date _____

Forming Complex Sentences

Combine the clauses to form complex sentences.

1. Even though he is a dog. Rover is Lucy's best friend.

   Even though he is a dog, Rover is Lucy's best friend. (1 point)

2. She takes Rover to the park. After she comes home from school.

   She takes Rover to the park after she comes home from school.

3. Lucy worried she would be late. Unless she hurried.

   Lucy worried she would be late unless she hurried. (1)

4. They stayed at the park. Until it started to rain.

   They stayed at the park until it started to rain. (1)

5. Because it was raining. They ran to the house.

   Because it was raining, they ran to the house. (1)

6. When they got home. Rover shook water everywhere.

   When they got home, Rover shook water everywhere. (1)

Read directions to students.
Assessment Tip: Total 6 points
Grade 3, Unit 5

Name _____ Date _____

Now make the advertisement! Show why Hawaii will be a good place to live. The illustration should show the thing you think people would like best about Hawaii. Label the illustration and use details you gathered to write a caption about Hawaii.

(Possible drawing: a school of fish with the label "Fish are everywhere!" The caption could include any or all of the details from Reader's Notebook page 137.) (10)

Read directions to students.
Assessment Tip: 10 Points
Grade 3, Unit 5

Name _____ Date _____

Shades of Meaning

Read each sentence. Choose the word from the box that best completes each sentence. Explain your choice.

| knows | suspects | wonders | believes | hears |
| know | suspect | wonder | believe | hear |

Possible responses shown.

1. How does Hoku ___know (1 point)___ that the star he

discovered always points north?

Hoku loves stars and probably watched the sky for a while

before he made up his mind. (2)

2. As the brothers sail away from the island, Opua

___wonders (1)___ whether he sees smoke or a cloud.

Opua can't tell for certain whether he is seeing a cloud or

smoke. (2)

3. For a while, the brothers ___believe (1)___ that Manu

has drowned in the sea.

They can't be certain that Manu has drowned, but they don't

see him on the surface of the sea. (2)

4. Although they are leaving the island, Manu

___knows (1)___ that he and his brothers will return.

Because of Dog-of-the-Sea-Waves, Manu has come to love the

island and will return. (2)

Lesson 24
READER'S NOTEBOOK

Dog-of-the-Sea-Waves
Spelling:
Prefixes re-, un-

Name _____ Date _____

Prefixes *re-*, *un-*

Write a Basic Word to answer each clue.

Spelling Words

Basic
1. unfold
2. rejoin
3. untie
4. reheat
5. unfair
6. unclear
7. repaid
8. rewrite
9. unhurt
10. recheck
11. unlucky
12. unwrap
13. reuse
14. unsure

Review
reread
unsafe

Challenge
unbuckle
unknown

1. You might do this with shoelaces. ___untie (1 point)___

2. You would do this to a present wrapped in paper.

   ___unwrap (1)___

3. You might feel this way if you didn't know the answer to

   a question. ___unclear or unsure (1)___

4. To be sure your answers on a test were correct, you

   might do this. ___recheck (1)___

5. If you thought someone had cheated in a game, you

   might think the game was this. ___unfair (1)___

6. You could do this to make some leftover food warm

   again. ___reheat (1)___

7. If you didn't like a poem you had written, you might do

   this to it. ___rewrite (1)___

8. You would do this to a shirt you found folded in a

   drawer. ___unfold (1)___

Review: Choose a Review Word. Write a clue for it.

Answers will vary. (1)

Challenge: Choose a Challenge Word. Write a clue for it.

Answers will vary. (1)

Lesson 24
READER'S NOTEBOOK

Dog-of-the-Sea-Waves
Spelling:
Prefixes *re-, un-*

Proofreading for Spelling

Read each direction. Circle the misspelled words. (8 points)

1. Set up your tent. First, (unfolde) the tent.

2. Next, (unrap) the tent ropes. You need the ropes to set up your tent.

3. If ropes are tied, you need to (untye) them.

4. Try to (reus) plastic bags while at camp. Do not throw them away.

5. Do not (reheet) drinks or food. See your camp leader.

6. Be sure to (rejoyn) your group after lunch.

7. Always walk with a friend. Walking alone at camp is (unsaff).

8. Are you sure you have everything? You should (rechek) your bag.

Write the misspelled words correctly on the lines below.

1. ___unfold (1)___
2. ___unwrap (1)___
3. ___untie (1)___
4. ___reuse (1)___
5. ___reheat (1)___
6. ___rejoin (1)___
7. ___unsafe (1)___
8. ___recheck (1)___

Read directions to students.
Spelling

Assessment Tip: Total 16 points
Grade 3, Unit 5

143

Spelling Words

1. unfold
2. rejoin
3. untie
4. reheat
5. unfair
6. unclear
7. repaid
8. rewrite
9. unhurt
10. recheck
11. unlucky
12. unwrap
13. reuse
14. unsure

Review
reread
unsafe

Challenge
unbuckle
unknown

Lesson 24
READER'S NOTEBOOK

Dog-of-the-Sea-Waves
Grammar:
Spiral Review

Possessive Nouns and Pronouns

- A possessive noun shows that a person, place, or thing has or owns something.
- Add an apostrophe and *s* to a singular noun to make it possessive. Add an apostrophe to a plural noun that ends in *s*.
- Possessive pronouns can take the place of possessive nouns. Possessive pronouns show ownership: *my, your, his, her, its, our, their.*

The family's outing was to the zoo.
The seals' pool was new.
Their bodies moved quickly through the water.

Use the correct possessive form of the noun in parentheses to complete each sentence.

1. It was ___Charlie's (1 point)___ first visit to the zoo. (Charlie)

2. The ___zoo's (1)___ Australia section has koalas. (zoo)

3. The ___workers' (1)___ uniforms are a dark green. (workers)

Use a possessive pronoun to take the place of the underlined possessive noun. Write the sentence.

4. Yolanda saw the dolphin's head peek out of the water.

Yolanda saw its head peek out of the water. (1)

5. The dolphin splashed water onto Yolanda's shoes.

The dolphin splashed water onto her shoes. (1)

Read directions to students.
Grammar

142

Assessment Tip: Total 5 points
Grade 3, Unit 5

Suffixes -less, -ness, -able

Read each sentence. Choose the missing word from the box. Write the word. Then reread the complete sentence.

boneless	predictable	enjoyable
painless	weightless	shyness
breakable	darkness	happiness
		softness

1. Patricia got over her ___shyness (1 point)___ when she met the new neighbors' puppy.

2. That story was so ___predictable (1)___ that I guessed the ending.

3. The newborn chicks are so light that they almost feel ___weightless (1)___

4. I needed a flashlight to see in the ___darkness (1)___

5. Since I didn't need a shot, my doctor's visit was ___painless (1)___

6. Chris smiled and clapped at the end of the ___enjoyable (1)___ movie.

7. Be careful not to drop the box because it contains ___breakable (1)___ items.

8. Mr. Griffin said, "The children in my classroom have brought me much joy and ___happiness (1)___ "

9. When you eat ___boneless (1)___ chicken there are no bones left on the plate!

10. Bradley sank back into the ___softness (1)___ of the pillow.

Read directions to students.
Phonics
© Houghton Mifflin Harcourt Publishing Company. All rights reserved.

145

Assessment Tip: Total 10 points
Grade 3, Unit 5

Connect to Writing

Short, choppy sentences can be combined to make your writing smoother. Use a subordinating conjunction to form complex sentences. Remember to use a comma after the dependent clause if it comes first in the sentence.

Short Sentences	Longer, Smoother Sentences
Sam taught his cat. He thought the cat was clever.	Sam taught his cat since he thought the cat was clever.
Dave played with his pet. He was happy.	While Dave played with his pet, he was happy.

Use a subordinating conjunction from the word bank to combine two short, choppy sentences. Write the new sentence on the line.
Possible responses are shown.

Word Bank

since   while   though   because

1. Tara's dog swims with her. It is not fond of water.
Tara's dog swims with her though it is not fond of water. (1 point)

2. Ernesto worked with his bird. He waited for his friend.
Ernesto worked with his bird while he waited for his friend. (1)

3. His bird escapes often. It knows how to open its cage.
His bird escapes often because it knows how to open its cage. (1)

4. Bennie's cat is still healing. It needs to wear a bandage.
Since Bennie's cat is still healing, it needs to wear a bandage. (1)

Read directions to students.
Grammar
© Houghton Mifflin Harcourt Publishing Company. All rights reserved.

144

Assessment Tip: Total 4 points
Grade 3, Unit 5

Lesson 25
READER'S NOTEBOOK

Mountains: Surviving on
Mt. Everest
Grammar:
Words That Compare

Name _____ Date _____

Adverbs That Compare

- Use *-er* or *more* to compare two verbs, or actions. Use *-est* or *most* to compare three or more.
- Add *-er* or *-est* to most **adverbs** that have one syllable.
- Add *more* or *most* before adverbs that end in *-ly.*

Caroline climbed more carefully than Elena.
Jena climbed the most carefully.
Elena climbed higher then Jena.
Caroline climbed the highest.

Thinking Question
How many does the adverb compare? Does it end in -ly?

Write the correct form of the adverb in parentheses. Then write *two* or *three* or *more* to explain the form you wrote.

1. Will waited (patiently) than Kyle for the storm to pass.
more patiently, two (2 points)

2. Kyle handled the ropes for the tent (roughly) of all the climbers.
most roughly, three or more (2)

3. The ropes were tied (tight) by the oldest climber.
tightest, three or more (2)

4. The climbers sitting by the fire felt (warm) than those inside the tent.
warmer, two (2)

5. Will slept (quietly) of all the campers.
most quietly, three or more (2)

Read directions to students.
Grammar
© Houghton Mifflin Harcourt Publishing Company. All rights reserved.

147

Assessment Tip: Total 10 points
Grade 3, Unit 5

Lesson 25
READER'S NOTEBOOK

Mountains: Surviving on
Mt. Everest
Grammar:
Words That Compare

Name _____ Date _____

Adjectives That Compare

- Use *-er* and *more* to compare two nouns. Use *-est* and *most* to compare three or more nouns.
- Add *-er* or *-est* to most **adjectives** that have one syllable.
- For adjectives that have two syllables and end in *-y*, such as *happy*, replace the *y* with *i* and then add *-er* or *-est.*
- Add *more* or *most* before adjectives that have three or more syllables.

Thinking Question
How many does the adjective compare? Does it have more than two syllables? Does it end in -y?

Write the correct form of the adjective in parentheses. Then write *two* or *three* or *more* to explain the form you wrote.

1. This backpack is (light) than that one.
lighter, two (2 points)

2. I think that mountain climbing is (dangerous) than hiking trails.
more dangerous, two (2)

3. The winds on this mountain are the (powerful) I have ever experienced.
most powerful, three or more (2)

4. The trail going up was (uneven) than the trail coming down.
more uneven, two (2)

5. Our pack mule was the (noisy) animal on the trail.
noisiest, three or more (2)

Read directions to students.
Grammar
© Houghton Mifflin Harcourt Publishing Company. All rights reserved.

146

Assessment Tip: Total 10 points
Grade 3, Unit 5

Lesson 25
READER'S NOTEBOOK

Mountains: Surviving on
Mt. Everest
Spelling:
Suffixes -less and -ness

Name _____ Date _____

Spelling Word Sort

Write each Basic Word under the correct heading.

Suffix that means "without"	Suffix that means "quality of being"
painless (1 point)	sickness (1)
helpless (1)	sadness (1)
thankless (1)	kindness (1)
hopeless (1)	darkness (1)
fearless (1)	thickness (1)
careless (1)	goodness (1)
spotless (1)	softness (1)
Challenge: breathless (1)	Challenge: eagerness (1)

Challenge: Add the Challenge Words to your Word Sort.

Spelling Words

Basic
1. painless
2. sickness
3. sadness
4. helpless
5. thankless
6. kindness
7. hopeless
8. darkness
9. fearless
10. thickness
11. careless
12. goodness
13. spotless
14. softness

Review
useful
weakly

Challenge
breathless
eagerness

Read directions to students.
Spelling
© Houghton Mifflin Harcourt Publishing Company. All rights reserved.

Assessment Tip: Total 16 points
Grade 3, Unit 5

148

Lesson 25
READER'S NOTEBOOK

Mountains: Surviving on
Mt. Everest
Writing:
Narrative Writing

Name _____ Date _____

Focus Trait: Coventions
Misspelled Words

As writers complete the final drafts, they proofread their writing to make sure they have spelled each word correctly.

Find the misspelled word or words in each sentence. Then rewrite the sentence with the words spelled correctly.

1. Mt. Everest is a towering mountin.

   Mt. Everest is a towering mountain. (1 point)

2. Temba made a terrible mistak and took off his gloves

   Temba made a terrible mistake and took off his gloves. (1)

3. After nightfall, the temprature plungd.

   After nightfall, the temperature plunged. (2)

4. Temba fought to reach the summet.

   Temba fought to reach the summit. (1)

5. Climers must be wary of huge peices of ice that could crush them.

   Climbers must be wary of huge pieces of ice that could crush them. (2)

Read directions to students.
Writing
Copyright © Houghton Mifflin Company. All rights reserved.

Assessment Tip: Total 7 points
Grade 3, Unit 5

149

Lesson 25
READER'S NOTEBOOK

Mountains: Surviving on
Mt. Everest
Phonics:
Cumulative Review

Name _____ Date _____

Cumulative Review

Read each sentence. Choose the missing word from the box. Write the word. Then reread the complete sentence.

redo	sleepless	freshness	crispness
preview	erasable	tasteless	valuable

1. Justin spent a _sleepless (1 point)_ night at the campout because he was worried about bears.

2. To test the _crispness (1)_ of celery, see if it makes a snapping sound.

3. The painting is _valuable (1)_ because it is one of a kind.

4. After one sip of the _tasteless (1)_ soup, Tessa switched and ate something with more flavor.

5. I like to draw in pencil because it is _erasable (1)_ , and I can fix my mistakes.

6. Daniel always smells each melon to test its _freshness (1)_ before buying it.

7. I made so many mistakes, I had to _redo (1)_ the whole assignment.

8. We got to _preview (1)_ the movie before it came to the local theater.

Read directions to students.
Phonics
© Houghton Mifflin Harcourt Publishing Company. All rights reserved.
150
Assessment Tip: Total 8 points
Grade 3, Unit 5

Name _____ Date _____

Reader's Guide

Mountains: Surviving on Mt. Everest

Create a Travel Brochure

You are writing a travel brochure about climbing Mount Everest. First, gather details for the brochure.

Read pages 349 and 351. Write important details about Mount Everest and its mountain range.

The summit of Mount Everest is 29,035 feet high.

It is part of the Himalayan Mountains. "Himalaya" means "home of snow." (5 points)

Read page 354. What equipment should travelers bring?

Travelers should bring a climbing suit, gloves, goggles, oxygen mask and tank, climbing ropes, trekking poles, and mountain boots. (5)

Read pages 355 and 360. What should travelers know about the climb? What should they be careful *not* to do?

Campers move from one camp to a higher camp. They rest in between to get used to higher altitudes. Climbers should not leave their trash on Mount Everest. (5)

Read directions to students.
Independent Reading
© Houghton Mifflin Harcourt Publishing Company. All rights reserved.
151
Assessment Tip: 15 Points
Grade 3, Unit 5

Lesson 25
READER'S NOTEBOOK

Mountains: Surviving on
Mt. Everest
Grammar:
Words That Compare

Name _____ Date _____

Adjectives and Adverbs That Compare

Write an adjective or adverb to complete each sentence.
Then write *adjective* or *adverb* to tell about the word or phrase you used.

1. Jeff explained the day's events _more calmly (1)_ than Ella. (calm) _adverb (1)_

2. The water at the bottom of the stream was _murkier (1)_ than the water on the surface. (murky) _adjective (1)_

3. Laurie was the _fastest (1)_ worker of them all. (fast) _adverb (1)_

4. Jason had the _muddiest (1)_ sneakers in the group. (muddy) _adjective (1)_

Write two sentences. Include an adjective that compares in one sentence and an adverb that compares in the other sentence.

5. _Possible answer: The last section was the trickiest section to_ _climb. (1)_ _____

6. _Possible answer: Of the group, Ricky was most eager for a_ _break. (1)_ _____

Assessment Tip: Total 10 points
Grade 3, Unit 5

Name _____ Date _____

Now use all the details from the previous page to write a brochure that will tell climbers what to expect on Mount Everest and what to bring for the climb. Include a title and labeled illustrations on each panel of the brochure to show what that section talks about.

Preparing to Climb Mount Everest.

(The first panel might have facts about the mountain and the range; the second about equipment; the third about the garbage problem. Each should have a relevant illustration.) (10)

Assessment Tip: 10 Points
Grade 3, Unit 5

Lesson 25
READER'S NOTEBOOK

Mountains: Surviving on
Mt. Everest
Spelling:
Suffixes -less and -ness

Name _____ Date _____

Suffixes -*less* and -*ness*

Write the Basic Word that makes sense in the sentence.

Spelling Words

Basic
1. painless
2. sickness
3. sadness
4. helpless
5. thankless
6. kindness
7. hopeless
8. darkness
9. fearless
10. thickness
11. careless
12. goodness
13. spotless
14. softness

Review
useful
weakly

Challenge
breathless
eagerness

1. The hiker thanked the guide for her help and
   __kindness (1 point)__

2. In high mountains, a lack of oxygen can cause
   __sickness (1)__ in the mountains is

3. Being __careless (1)__ in the mountains is
   dangerous.

4. It is not wise to climb mountains in
   __darkness (1)__

5. The __fearless (1)__ guide climbed the
   high cliff.

6. I was amazed at the __softness (1)__ of the
   freshly fallen snow.

7. Scientists measured the __thickness (1)__ of
   the ice at the top.

Challenge: Choose a Challenge Word. Use it in a sentence.
   __Responses will vary. (1)__ _____

Read directions to students.
Spelling
© Houghton Mifflin Harcourt Publishing Company. All rights reserved.

154

Assessment Tip: Total 8 points
Grade 3, Unit 5

Lesson 25
READER'S NOTEBOOK

Mountains: Surviving on
Mt. Everest
Vocabulary Strategies:
Analogies

Name _____ Date _____

Analogies

Complete the analogies with a word from the box.

danger	increase	assist	departure
succeed	brave	slope	strength

1. Believable is to unbelievable as weakness is to __strength (1 point)__

2. Force is to power as achieve is to __succeed (1)__

3. Polite is to rude as fearful is to __brave (1)__

4. Excellent is to wonderful as risk is to __danger (1)__

5. Frequent is to often as aid is to __assist (1)__

6. Up is to down as arrival is to __departure (1)__

7. Sad is to happy as decrease is to __increase (1)__

8. Ocean is to wave as mountain is to __slope (1)__

Read directions to students.
Vocabulary Strategies
© Houghton Mifflin Harcourt Publishing Company. All rights reserved.

155

Assessment Tip: Total 8 points
Grade 3, Unit 5

Name _____ Date _____

Lesson 25
READER'S NOTEBOOK

Mountains: Surviving on
Mt. Everest
Grammar:
Spiral Review

Forming Complex Sentences

- A **complex sentence** is formed by combining one independent clause and one or more dependent clauses. If the dependent clause appears first, add a comma after it.
- **Subordinating conjunctions** begin dependent clauses. Some subordinating clauses are: *after, although, because, before, even though, since, unless, until, when, while.*

Combine the clauses to form complex sentences.

1. Even though he was tired. Tracy hiked up the hill. (1 point)

   Even though he was tired, Tracy hiked up the hill. (1 point)

2. Torry planned to climb the hill. When her father could join her.

   Torry planned to climb the hill when her father could join her. (1)

3. Because she is afraid of heights. Rita will not climb.

   Because she is afraid of heights, Rita will not climb. (1)

4. Until he saw the hill. Robbie was eager to climb.

   Until he saw the hill, Robbie was eager to climb. (1)

5. They played catch. While they waited for the others to climb.

   They played catch while they waited for the others to climb. (1)

6. Mel climbed again. Before they went home.

   Mel climbed again before they went home. (1)

Read directions to students.
Grammar
© Houghton Mifflin Harcourt Publishing Company. All rights reserved.

Assessment Tip: Total 6 points
Grade 3, Unit 5

156

Name _____ Date _____

Lesson 25
READER'S NOTEBOOK

Mountains: Surviving on
Mt. Everest
Spelling:
Suffixes -less and -ness

Proofreading for Spelling

Read each journal entry. Circle the misspelled words.
(8 points)

Journal of a Mountain Guide

Monday: We rescued a hiker who had become lost in the (darkniss.)

Tuesday: It is (hopless) to teach some people how to be careful in the mountains. They just don't pay attention.

Wednesday: We took a short hike to the ranger station. It was (paneless.)

Thursday: Felt a strange (thikness) in my leg. I'll have a doctor check it tomorrow. Was glad for the (softnes) of my sleeping bag.

Friday: Found a hammer and some rope in the snow. Some (careluss) hiker must have dropped them.

Saturday: Some hikers thanked us for our (kineness.) I guess being a mountain guide is not always a (thankliss) job!

Write the misspelled words correctly on the lines below.

1. darkness (1)   5. softness (1)

2. hopeless (1)   6. careless (1)

3. painless (1)   7. kindness (1)

4. thickness (1)   8. thankless (1)

Spelling Words

Basic
1. painless
2. sickness
3. sadness
4. helpless
5. thankless
6. kindness
7. hopeless
8. darkness
9. fearless
10. thickness
11. careless
12. goodness
13. spotless
14. softness

Review
useful
weakly

Challenge
breathless
eagerness

Read directions to students.
Spelling
© Houghton Mifflin Harcourt Publishing Company. All rights reserved.

Assessment Tip: Total 16 points
Grade 3, Unit 5

157

Name _____ Date _____

Lesson 26
READER'S NOTEBOOK

**The Foot Race
Across America**
Phonics: Common Final
Syllables -tion, -sion, -ture

Common Final Syllables

Choose a word from the box to complete each sentence.
Read the completed sentence.

Word Bank			
action	attention	confusion	discussion	furniture
future	motion	nature	picture	protection

1. Give me the camera and I will take your ___ picture (1 point) ___.

2. No one knew what to do, so there was a lot of ___ confusion (1) ___.

3. If you push the toy car, you set it in ___ motion (1) ___.

4. This is important news, so pay ___ attention (1) ___.

5. Yesterday is the past, and tomorrow is the ___ future (1) ___.

6. An umbrella gives you ___ protection (1) ___ from the rain.

7. Let's have a ___ discussion (1) ___ to talk about our plans.

8. Tables, chairs, and sofas are kinds of ___ furniture (1) ___.

9. I like that pirate movie because it has lots of ___ action (1) ___.

10. Trees, animals, and clouds are all parts of ___ nature (1) ___.

Name _____ Date _____

Lesson 25
READER'S NOTEBOOK

**Mountains: Surviving on
Mt. Everest**
Grammar:
Connect to Writing

Connect to Writing

Use adjectives and adverbs that compare to make your
ideas easier for readers to picture. To compare two nouns
or actions, add -er to most adjectives and adverbs. To
compare more than two nouns or actions, add -est to
most adjectives and adverbs. Use more or most before an
adverb that ends in -ly.

	Compare Two	Compare More Than Two
Adjective	Molly's backpack is heavier than Jeff's.	Steven has the heaviest backpack of everyone in the class.
Adverb	Stacy climbs more easily than Brett.	Mike climbs most easily of everyone in the group.

Choose the correct form of the adjective or adverb in parentheses. Write
the sentence.

1. Mrs. Brown's map is (newer, newest) than my map.

Mrs. Brown's map is newer than my map. (1 point)

2. Where are the (higher, highest) mountains in the world?

Where are the highest mountains in the world? (1)

3. Brynn spoke (more eagerly, most eagerly) about climbing than Jo.

Brynn spoke more eagerly about climbing than Jo. (1)

4. Of all the climbers, Lucas climbed (more powerfully, most powerfully).

Of all the climbers, Lucas climbed most powerfully. (1)

Name _____ Date _____

Lesson 26
READER'S NOTEBOOK

The Foot Race
Across America
Independent Reading

The Foot Race Across America

Write a Speech

Andy Payne is receiving an award after the race, but first he must give a speech. Note important details from the text before you write the speech.

Read page 7. What were the specific details of the race that Andy saw in the newspaper?

The race would go from Los Angeles, California, to New York City.

It would be 3,400 miles. The winner would get $25,000.   (2 points)

Why did Andy want to run in the race?

He wanted the money to help his parents pay for their farm and to

persuade his girlfriend to marry him.   (2)

Read pages 8–9. What was the first part of the race like?

The first day was easy, but then it got harder. Many runners dropped

out because of the hot sun or the steep hills.   (2)

Read page 10. What troubles did Andy and the runners face?

The food was not good. They were forced to sleep in barns or

stables. Andy got tonsillitis and a fever.   (2)

Read pages 12–14. What happened at the end of the race?

The runners finally got to New York. Andy won first place and got

the money. He took the train back to Oklahoma.   (2)

Name _____ Date _____

Lesson 26
READER'S NOTEBOOK

The Foot Race
Across America
Independent Reading

The announcer steps onto the stage and says, "We will now present the award for Greatest Running Achievement to Andy Payne. Andy, please tell us about the race!" Write Andy's speech.

(Students should write as if Andy were

speaking and include details from the previous

page, including how he got started, what

happened along the way, and how the race

ended.)   (10)

_____

_____

_____

_____

_____

_____

_____

_____

_____

_____

_____

_____

_____

Word Sort

Name _____ Date _____

Spelling Words

Basic
1. person
2. helmet
3. until
4. carpet
5. Monday
6. enjoy
7. forget
8. problem
9. Sunday
10. garden
11. order
12. mistake
13. umpire
14. herself

Challenge
expect
wisdom

Write each Basic Word next to the correct heading.

Vowel *a* in first syllable	Basic Words: carpet, garden (2 points)
Vowel *e* in first syllable	Basic Words: person, helmet, enjoy, herself (4) Challenge Word: expect (1)
Vowel *i* in first syllable	Basic Words: mistake (1) Challenge Word: wisdom (1)
Vowel *o* in first syllable	Basic Words: Monday, forget, problem, order (4)
Vowel *u* in first syllable	Basic Words: until, Sunday, umpire (3)

Challenge: Add the Challenge Words to your Word Sort.

Words with the VCCV Pattern

Name _____ Date _____

Spelling Words

Basic
1. person
2. helmet
3. until
4. carpet
5. Monday
6. enjoy
7. forget
8. problem
9. Sunday
10. garden
11. order
12. mistake
13. umpire
14. herself

Challenge
expect
wisdom

Basic: Write the Basic Word that best fits each clue.

1. get pleasure from
2. an error
3. a human being
4. where flowers grow
5. opposite of *remember*
6. a baseball official
7. a command
8. protects your head
9. opposite of *solution*
10. soft floor covering

1. enjoy (1 point)
2. mistake (1)
3. person (1)
4. garden (1)
5. forget (1)
6. umpire (1)
7. order (1)
8. helmet (1)
9. problem (1)
10. carpet (1)

Challenge: Write two sentences about how you might help a friend reach a goal. Use both of the Challenge Words.
Possible responses shown. (2)

I would share wisdom with my friend to encourage him. I would

tell him to expect the best and then work to make it happen.

_____

Lesson 26
READER'S NOTEBOOK

The Foot Race
Across America
Grammar
Abbreviations

Name _____ Date _____

Abbreviations for Days and Months

- An **abbreviation** is a shortened form of a word. Most abbreviations begin with a capital letter and end with a period.
  Monday; Mon.
  August; Aug.

Thinking Question
Is the word a day of the week or a month of the year?

Write the correct abbreviation for each day and month.

1. Sunday _____ Sun. (1 point)

2. December _____ Dec. (1)

3. Tuesday _____ Tues. (1)

4. Thursday _____ Thurs. (1)

5. Saturday _____ Sat. (1)

6. November _____ Nov. (1)

7. Wednesday _____ Wed. (1)

8. September _____ Sept. (1)

9. Friday _____ Fri. (1)

10. February _____ Feb. (1)

Assessment Tip: Total 10 points
Unit 5: Going Places

Name _____ Date _____

Proofreading for Spelling

Find the misspelled words and circle them. Write them correctly on the numbered lines below. (2 points each)

Some Really Super Softball!

Last Sundy, the Braden Bobcats' fans got a big thrill when the Bobcats beat the Pinehill Pumas.

The game was tied 1–1 in the last inning. The Bobcat batters came up in ordor. First came Polly Peters, who looked ready to win that game all by herrself. The Puma pitcher, though, couldn't find the plate, and the umpeire called four balls in a row. Polly walked to first base.

The next persen up to bat was Miko Myata. This time, the Puma pitcher's probllem was wild pitches. When one pitch hit Miko's helmit, Miko strolled to first base and Polly moved to second.

The pitcher made one last misteak when he threw a perfect pitch. Shayla Smith swung mightily. CRACK! That ball was out of the park, and it probably didn't land untill Munday. The Bobcats won it, 4–1!

Spelling Words

Basic
1. person
2. helmet
3. until
4. carpet
5. Monday
6. enjoy
7. forget
8. problem
9. Sunday
10. garden
11. order
12. mistake
13. umpire
14. herself

1. Sunday _____   6. problem _____
2. order _____   7. helmet _____
3. herself _____   8. mistake _____
4. umpire _____   9. until _____
5. person _____   10. Monday _____

Assessment Tip: Total 20 points
Grade 3, Unit 6

Lesson 26
READER'S NOTEBOOK

The Foot Race
Across America
Grammar:
Abbreviations

Name _____ Date _____

Writing Abbreviations

1–5. Write the correct abbreviation for each day and month.

1. Tuesday _____ Tues. (1 point)

2. January _____ Jan. (1)

3. Friday _____ Fri. (1)

4. October _____ Oct. (1)

5. Saturday _____ Sat. (1)

6–10. Abbreviate each place name correctly.

6. Myer Lane _____ Myer Ln. (1)

7. Hudson Street _____ Hudson St. (1)

8. Prospect Road _____ Prospect Rd. (1)

9. Lynn Boulevard _____ Lynn Blvd. (1)

10. North Avenue _____ North Ave. (1)

Read directions to students.
Grammar
© Houghton Mifflin Harcourt Publishing Company. All rights reserved.
167
Assessment Tip: Total 10 points
Grade 3, Unit 6

Lesson 26
READER'S NOTEBOOK

The Foot Race
Across America
Grammar:
Abbreviations

Name _____ Date _____

Abbreviations for Places

- An **abbreviation** is a shortened form of a word.
- Places with names that can be abbreviated include roads, streets, lanes, avenues, and boulevards. Examples include *Harrison Rd.*, *Maple St.*, *Elmira Ln.*, *Plainville Ave.*, and *Broad Blvd.*

Thinking Question
Is the word the name of a place?

Write each place name correctly. Use capital letters and abbreviations.

1. King Boulevard _____ King Blvd. (1 point)

2. Jefferson Street _____ Jefferson St. (1)

3. Western Avenue _____ Western Ave. (1)

4. Oak Road _____ Oak Rd. (1)

5. Chestnut Lane _____ Chestnut Ln. (1)

6. Ocean Boulevard _____ Ocean Blvd. (1)

7. Washington Street _____ Washington St. (1)

8. Smith Lane _____ Smith Ln. (1)

9. Vermont Avenue _____ Vermont Ave. (1)

10. Lincoln Street _____ Lincoln St. (1)

Read directions to students.
Grammar
© Houghton Mifflin Harcourt Publishing Company. All rights reserved.
166
Assessment Tip: Total 10 points;
Grade 3, Unit 6

Conventions: Proofreading

Name _____ Date _____

Lesson 26
READER'S NOTEBOOK

The Foot Race
Across America
Grammar
Connect to Writing

Proofreading your work for correctly spelled **abbreviations** will make your writing stronger.

Incorrect Abbreviation	Correct Abbreviation
tues.; mar	Tues.; Mar.
av.; rd	Ave.; Rd.

Use proofreading marks to write abbreviations correctly in this informal note. (6 points)

Sun., Oct.
Sun, Oct 3

Liam,

   We stopped by Pleasant St.
St.
on fri and met your uncle's family. He is a
Fri.
wonderful man, and his kids and wife are great, too. We met Pat Smith, who
is very nice. He lives in Miami. He has a house on Beach Blvd. near the
Blvd.
ocean. We are going to meet him and Cindy Birch next Tues. for a clambake.
Tues.

                             Lucy

Proofreading Marks	
¶ Indent	
∧ Add	
⌢ Delete	
≡ Capital letter	
/ Small letter	

Read directions to students.
Grammar
© Houghton Mifflin Harcourt Publishing Company. All rights reserved.
Assessment Tip: Total 6 points
169
Grade 3, Unit 6

Possessive Nouns

Name _____ Date _____

Lesson 26
READER'S NOTEBOOK

The Foot Race
Across America
Grammar: Spiral Review

- A **possessive noun** shows that a person, an animal, or a thing owns or has something.
- To show that **one** person, animal, or thing has possession, add an **apostrophe** and -s (**'s**).
- To show that **more than one** person, animal, or thing has possession, add an -s and an **apostrophe (s')**.

Noun	Singular Possessive Noun	Plural Possessive Noun
teacher	teacher's	teachers'
book	book's	books'

Activity: Write the word in parentheses as a possessive noun to complete the sentence.

1. Andy's (1 point) home is in Oklahoma. (Andy)

2. He runs in his cousin's (1) neighborhood. (cousin)

3. Andy likes to run with the neighbors' (1) children. (neighbors)

4. He times his running with his sister's (1) stopwatch. (sister)

5. The winner's (1) prize is a huge trophy. (winner)

6. The runners' (1) families all watched the race. (runners)

7. Allen could hear the bird's (1) chirps as he ran. (bird)

8. Each contestant's (1) shirt had a number. (contestant)

9. Every runner could hear the fans' (1) cheers. (fans)

10. The town's (1) statue of Andy shows him running. (town)

Read directions to students.
Grammar
© Houghton Mifflin Harcourt Publishing Company. All rights reserved.
Assessment Tip: Total 10 points
168
Grade 3, Unit 6

Name _____ Date _____

Double Consonants

Choose a syllable from the left box and a syllable from the right box to make a word that completes each sentence. Write the word on the line and read the completed sentence.

Hint: Each word you make will have a double consonant.

First Syllables					Second Syllables				
at	but	dol	fun	hap	den	der	lar	low	nel
lad	sud	tun	yel	zip	ny	pen	per	ter	tract

1. A magnet will _____ attract (1 point) a needle.

2. What do you think will _____ happen (1) next in that story?

3. Bonnie needs a _____ yellow (1) marker to color the sun.

4. I spread _____ butter (1) on warm toast.

5. All of a _____ sudden (1), it started to rain.

6. I can't close my jacket because the _____ zipper (1) is broken.

7. Climb up the _____ ladder (1) carefully.

8. That joke was so _____ funny (1) that I hurt myself laughing.

9. Jake has one _____ dollar (1) to buy a treat.

10. A mole will dig a _____ tunnel (1) under the ground.

Read directions to students.
Phonics

Assessment Tip: Total 10 points
Grade 3, Unit 6

Name _____ Date _____

Focus Trait: Organization

Read each sentence that gives a comparing or contrasting detail. Write whether it compares or contrasts.

Compares ___ Andy Payne and Peter Gavuzzi both competed in the International Trans-Continental Foot Race. (1 point)

Compares ___ Both men were called "Bunioneers." (1)

Contrasts ___ Andy was from Oklahoma, while Peter was from England. (1)

Contrasts ___ Andy won in 1928, but Peter won in 1929. (1)

Think of a topic sentence for a paragraph that compares Andy and Peter. Write the sentence. Then write a topic sentence for a paragraph that contrasts Andy and Peter. Possible responses shown.

Comparing paragraph:
Andy Payne and Peter Gavuzzi were two athletes who shared many of the same qualities. (2)

_____

Contrasting paragraph:
Andy Payne and Peter Gavuzzi were different in a lot of ways, as well. (2)

_____

_____

_____

Read directions to students.
Writing

Assessment Tip: Total 8 points
Grade 3, Unit 6

Reader's Notebook

201

Volume 2, pp. 170–171

Reader's Guide

The Power of Magnets

Your Magnet Invention

Now is your chance to design a magnet to make your life easier! First, answer the questions below to make sure you understand how magnets work. Then, create your own design.

Read pages 20–21. What causes some objects to be attracted to a magnet?

If objects have iron in them, they will be attracted to a

magnet. (2 points)

Read page 22. What happens if you sprinkle iron filings around a magnet?

The iron filings form a pattern of lines. These lines show the

magnetic field where the magnet's force works. (2)

Read page 23. What is important about electromagnets?

Electromagnets can be turned on and off using electricity.

They are very powerful. (2)

Read pages 24–25. How can you create a magnetic field in your own home?

I can create a magnetic field by turning on an electric switch or

plugging in a cord. Electricity coming through a wire creates a

magnetic field. (2)

Assessment Tip: 8 Points
Grade 3, Unit 6

Now think of a way that you can use a magnet to improve your life. Will you use the magnet in your home or outside? Will you use it at school? Will you use a regular magnet or an electromagnet? Draw a picture of your magnet and write an explanation of how it works. Be sure that you include details from the text in your design.

(Accept all reasonable illustrations. Students should

include an explanation about how their magnets will

work to make their lives easier and consider details

from the text in their explanations.) (10)

Assessment Tip: 10 Points
Grade 3, Unit 6

Name _____ Date _____

Double Consonants

Basic: Write the Basic Word that best completes each group.

1. sheet, blanket, ___pillow___ (1 point)

2. chapter, unit, ___lesson___ (1)

3. dime, quarter, ___dollar___ (1)

4. jam, preserves, ___jelly___ (1)

5. fox, raccoon, ___rabbit___ (1)

6. top, side, ___bottom___ (1)

7. postcard, note, ___letter___ (1)

8. peach, plum, ___cherry___ (1)

9. milk, cheese, ___butter___ (1)

10. zipper, snap, ___button___ (1)

Challenge: Use one of the Challenge Words to write
a sentence. Possible response shown. (2)

I placed my grandma's mirror above the dresser in my bedroom.

_____

_____

Spelling Words

Basic

1. jelly
2. bottom
3. pillow
4. happen
5. butter
6. lesson
7. cherry
8. sudden
9. arrow
10. dollar
11. hello
12. rabbit
13. letter
14. button

Challenge
stubborn
mirror

Read directions to students.
Spelling

Name _____ Date _____

Word Sort

Write each Basic Word next to the correct heading.

Words with three letters in both syllables	**Basic Words:** bottom, pillow, happen, butter, lesson, sudden, dollar, rabbit, letter, button (10 points) **Challenge Word:** mirror (1)
Words with two letters in one of the two syllables	**Basic Words:** jelly, cherry, arrow, hello (4)
Words with four letters in both syllables	**Challenge Word:** stubborn (1)

Challenge: Add the Challenge Words to your Word Sort.

Spelling Words

Basic

1. jelly
2. bottom
3. pillow
4. happen
5. butter
6. lesson
7. cherry
8. sudden
9. arrow
10. dollar
11. hello
12. rabbit
13. letter
14. button

Challenge
stubborn
mirror

Read directions to students.
Spelling

Reader's Notebook

203

Volume 2, pp. 174–175

Contractions with *not*

You can put together two words and make a **contraction.** An apostrophe (') takes the place of any letter or letters that are left out. Many contractions combine a verb with *not*. You form it from the words *will not* and change the spelling.

> It **is** *not* always easy to invent something.
> It **isn't** always easy to invent something.
>
> Michael Faraday **was** *not* afraid to try something new.
> Michael Faraday **wasn't** afraid to try something new.

Thinking Questions
Which verb am I putting together with the word not? Which letter should I leave out and replace with an apostrophe?

Write the contraction for the words in parentheses. Use an apostrophe in place of the underlined letter or letters.

1. Electromagnets ____don't (1 point)____ work unless they are turned on. (do n<u>o</u>t)

2. The magnet in the poem ____doesn't (1)____ get used anymore. (does n<u>o</u>t)

3. A computer's hard drive ____won't (1)____ work correctly without an electromagnet. (will n<u>o</u>t)

4. We ____weren't (1)____ aware that doorbells use electromagnets. (were n<u>o</u>t)

5. A blow dryer also ____wouldn't (1)____ work without an electromagnet. (would n<u>o</u>t)

6. The poem's speaker ____hasn't (1)____ been allowed to make her brother disappear. (has n<u>o</u>t)

7. I ____can't (1)____ see a magnetic field, but I know it exists. (cannot)

8. I ____couldn't (1)____ believe all the things magnets do! (could n<u>o</u>t)

Assessment Tip: Total 8 points
Grade 3, Unit 6

177

Proofreading for Spelling

Find the misspelled words and circle them. Write them correctly on the lines below. (2 points each)

Dear Jamal,

Can you believe you're getting a (leter) from me, at last? I think of you a lot, especially when I see a jar of that (charry) (jellie) you love so much. Mom bought some the other day, and all of a (suddin) I find that I love it, too! One of my front teeth fell out last week. I put the tooth under my (pilloaw) The next morning, a (doller) showed up there. Maybe that's enough to buy a treat for my pet (rabit.)

Hey, you're a science buff, right? Do you (happan) to know much about magnets? We had a really neat (lessone) on them in science class last week, and I'd love to talk to you about them.

Well, say (hellow) to your family for me. Please write back if you can. I miss you!

Your friend,

Curtis

Spelling Words
1. jelly
2. bottom
3. pillow
4. happen
5. butter
6. lesson
7. cherry
8. sudden
9. arrow
10. dollar
11. hello
12. rabbit
13. letter
14. button

1. ____letter____
2. ____cherry____
3. ____jelly____
4. ____sudden____
5. ____pillow____
6. ____dollar____
7. ____rabbit____
8. ____happen____
9. ____lesson____
10. ____hello____

Assessment Tip: Total 20 points
Grade 3, Unit 6

176

Name _____ Date _____

Contractions

1–5. Write the contraction for the words in parentheses. Use an apostrophe in place of the underlined letter or letters.

1. We ___haven't (1 point)___ gone to the science fair before. (have no͟t)

2. My family ___didn't (1)___ know how much fun it would be. (did no͟t)

3. My sister ___wouldn't (1)___ stop playing with the projects. (would no͟t)

4. My brother ___can't (1)___ wait to enter the science fair himself. (canno͟t)

5. We ___won't (1)___ mind competing against each other. (will no͟t)

6–10. Write the contraction for the words in parentheses. Use an apostrophe in place of the underlined letter or letters.

6. ___You're (1)___ going to love the science fair. (You a͟re)

7. My teacher says ___I've (1)___ won a prize. (I ha͟ve)

8. ___She'll (1)___ give it to me later. (She wi͟ll)

9. ___It'll (1)___ hang in my bedroom. (It wi͟ll)

10. ___It's (1)___ the best prize I ever won. (It i͟s)

Read directions to students.

Grammar
© Houghton Mifflin Harcourt Publishing Company. All rights reserved.

Assessment Tip: Total 10 points
Grade 3, Unit 6

179

Name _____ Date _____

Contractions with Pronouns

You can put a pronoun and a verb together to make a contraction. An apostrophe replaces the letter or letters that are left out.

*She says that **she is** working on a project.*
*She says that **she's** working on a project.*
We will see if it turns out.
***We'll** see if it turns out.*

> **Thinking Question**
> When I join a pronoun with a verb, which letters should I leave out and replace with an apostrophe to make a contraction?

Write the contraction for the words in parentheses. Use an apostrophe in place of the underlined letter or letters.

1. ___It'll (1 point)___ be exciting to find out if the experiment works. (It will)

2. ___We've (1)___ read a lot about experiments with magnets. (We ha͟ve)

3. Make sure ___you're (1)___ ready for the science fair. (you a͟re)

4. ___I'm (1)___ going to enter the science fair, too. (I a͟m)

5. ___They'll (1)___ judge whose project is the best. (They wi͟ll)

6. ___It's (1)___ going to be competitive. (It i͟s)

7. ___We've (1)___ almost finished our project. (We ha͟ve)

8. She says ___she'll (1)___ enter the science fair next year. (she wi͟ll)

Read directions to students.

Grammar
© Houghton Mifflin Harcourt Publishing Company. All rights reserved.

Assessment Tip: Total 8 points
Grade 3, Unit 6

178

Name _____ Date _____

Writing Proper Nouns

- A **proper noun** always begins with a capital letter.
- Days, months, holidays, historical periods, and special events are proper nouns.
- The first, last, and important words in a book title are capitalized. Book titles are underlined.

Proper Nouns	
day	Wednesday
month	March
holiday	Thanksgiving
book title	The Giver

Activity: Write all proper nouns and book titles from each sentence correctly.

1. The electricity went off last friday. Friday (1 point)

2. I read my favorite book, the dark forest, with a flashlight. The Dark Forest (1)

3. We saved a lot of electricity in april. April (1)

4. My book report on Michael Faraday is due after memorial day. Memorial Day (1)

5. I would rather learn about world war II than about electricity. World War II (1)

6. My sister is writing a book called when the lights go out. When the Lights Go Out (1)

Read directions to students.
Grammar
© Houghton Mifflin Harcourt Publishing Company. All rights reserved.

180

Name _____ Date _____

Conventions: Proofreading

Sentences Without Correct Contractions	Sentences with Correct Contractions
Shes making her project.	She's making her project.
The project is'nt too difficult.	The project isn't too difficult.
We have't decided what we'll make.	We haven't decided what we'll make.

Proofread the paragraphs. Find and underline five mistakes in the spelling of contractions. Write the correct sentences on the lines below.

Theyr'e starting to organize this year's science fair. I cann't miss it this time! Last year I was'nt able to get a project done in time. This year I'm going to make sure I do.

Iv'e heard the fairs are a lot of fun. You get to see all the projects other people have worked on. I would'nt want to miss that.

1. They're starting to organize this year's science fair. (2 points)
_____

2. I can't miss it this time! (2)
_____

3. Last year I wasn't able to get a project done in time. (2)
_____

4. I've heard the fairs are a lot of fun. (2)
_____

5. I wouldn't want to miss that. (2)
_____

Read directions to students.
Grammar
© Houghton Mifflin Harcourt Publishing Company. All rights reserved.

181

Lesson 28
READER'S NOTEBOOK

Becoming Anything
He Wants to Be
Phonics: Words with
ough and *augh*

Name _____ Date _____

Words with *ough*, *augh*

Read each word in the box. Say the sound that *ough* or *augh* stands for. Then write the word in the chart under the correct category.

Word Bank				
bought	caught	fought	naughty	rough	taught
brought	daughter	laugh	ought	sought	thought

ough rhymes with *paw*	*ough* rhymes with *puff*	*augh* rhymes with *paw*	*augh* rhymes with *staff*
bought (1 point)	rough (1)	caught (1)	laugh (1)
brought (1)		daughter (1)	
fought (1)		naughty (1)	
ought (1)		taught (1)	
sought (1)			
thought (1)			

Read directions to students.
Phonics

Assessment Tip: Total 12 points.
Grade 3, Unit 6

Name _____ Date _____

Focus Trait: Elaboration

Read each problem and solution. Add details to elaborate. Explain how the problem was solved and how the solution works. Use information from "The Power of Magnets." Possible responses shown.

1. **Problem:** Kaylie dropped a box of pins.
   Solution: She used a magnet.
   Details:

   The magnet attracted the iron in the pins. The magnet pulled all the

   pins toward it. (2 points)

2. **Problem:** The remote control car does not work.
   Solution: We put a battery in it.
   Details:

   The battery gives power to the electric motor. The motor makes the

   remote control car work. (2)

3. **Problem:** A junkyard owner needs to move a car.
   Solution: He flips a switch.
   Details:

   The switch turns on an electromagnet. The electromagnet is able to

   lift the car. (2)

4. **Problem:** Michael Faraday wanted to produce electricity.
   Solution: He moved a magnet through a coil of wire.
   Details:

   The magnet and wires formed a magnetic field that produced

   electricity. (2)

Read directions to students.
Writing

Assessment Tip: Total 8 points
Grade 3, Unit 6

Name _____

Date _____

Erik Weihenmayer achieved amazing things. How have his achievements inspired you? What is one thing you would like to do but think you cannot do? Draw an illustration of yourself doing this difficult thing. Write a caption that explains what you are doing.

(Accept all reasonable illustrations. Captions should explain the

illustrations.) (10)

Name _____

Date _____

Becoming Anything He Wants to Be

Create a Captioned Illustration

This story of Erik Weihenmayer is told with photographs that have captions. The photographs help us see what Erik can do, and the captions help us understand the photographs. Let's take a closer look.

Look at page 35. What does the caption let you know about the photograph on this page?

It explains that Erik was the first blind person to climb

to the top of Mount Everest.   (2 points)

Look at page 37. What does the caption tell you about the photograph on this page?

It explains in detail what Erik loves about mountain

climbing.   (2)

Look at page 38. In the first photograph, which of the bike riders is Erik? How do you know?

Erik cannot see to steer, so he rides in the back and

his partner steers.   (2)

The caption for the second photograph tells us why this story is important for everybody. Why is it important?

Erik wants people to think about what they can do, not

what they cannot do.   (2)

Lesson 28
READER'S NOTEBOOK

Becoming Anything
He Wants to Be
Spelling: Words with
ough and *augh*

Word Sort

Name _____ Date _____

Spelling Words

Basic
1. taught
2. thought
3. rough
4. laugh
5. bought
6. cough
7. ought
8. caught
9. fought
10. daughter
11. tough
12. through
13. enough
14. brought

Challenge
sought
naughty

Write each Basic Word beside the correct heading.

	Basic Words: taught, thought, bought, ought, caught, fought, daughter, through, brought (9 points) **Challenge Words:** sought, naughty (2 points)
Words in which the letters *gh* are not pronounced	
	Basic Words: rough, laugh, cough, tough, enough (5)
Words in which the letters *gh* are pronounced /f/	

Challenge: Add the Challenge Words to your Word Sort.

Read directions to students.
Spelling
© Houghton Mifflin Harcourt Publishing Company. All rights reserved.
187
Assessment Tip: Total 16 points
Grade 3, Unit 6

Lesson 28
READER'S NOTEBOOK

Becoming Anything
He Wants to Be
Spelling: Words with
ough and *augh*

Words with *ough* and *augh*

Name _____ Date _____

Spelling Words

Basic
1. taught
2. thought
3. rough
4. laugh
5. bought
6. cough
7. ought
8. caught
9. fought
10. daughter
11. tough
12. through
13. enough
14. brought

Challenge
sought
naughty

Basic: Write the Basic Word that completes each sentence.

1. A mother and her ___daughter (1 point)___ had a problem.

2. The little girl had ___caught (1)___ a bad cold.

3. Every day, the child's ___cough (1)___ grew worse.

4. Her sore throat made her voice ___rough (1)___ and scratchy.

5. The girl couldn't sleep ___through (1)___ the night.

6. The mother knew she ___ought (1)___ to take the girl to a doctor.

7. They didn't have ___enough (1)___ money, though, to pay the bill.

8. Then the mother ___thought (1)___ of something.

9. Some of her neighbors had ___fought (1)___ to have a free clinic set up nearby.

10. She picked up her daughter and ___brought (1)___ her to the clinic.

Challenge: Write a sentence about a problem you had and how you solved it. Use both Challenge Words.
Possible response shown. (2)

I sought my mother's help when my brother was being naughty.

_____

_____

Read directions to students.
Spelling
© Houghton Mifflin Harcourt Publishing Company. All rights reserved.
186
Assessment Tip: Total 12 points
Grade 3, Unit 6

Name _____ Date _____

Commas in a Series

Thinking Question
Is there a list of three or more words in the sentence?

- A **series** is a list of three or more words together in a sentence.
- Use a **comma** to separate the words in a series.

It was cold, wet, and windy when he climbed the mountain.

Activity: Rewrite each sentence correctly. Add commas where they are needed.

1. He had a big breakfast of eggs toast and orange juice. (1 point)
   He had a big breakfast of eggs, toast, and orange juice. (1 point)

2. She packed up the tent backpack and sleeping bag.
   She packed up the tent, backpack, and sleeping bag. (1)

3. The weather was cold windy and sunny.
   The weather was cold, windy, and sunny. (1)

4. They wore sunglasses hats and gloves.
   They wore sunglasses, hats, and gloves. (1)

5. Along the path they saw deer raccoons and a fox.
   Along the path they saw deer, raccoons, and a fox. (1)

6. They would tell their story to Anna Julio and Wade.
   They would tell their story to Anna, Julio, and Wade. (1)

Read directions to students.
Grammar
189

Name _____ Date _____

Proofreading for Spelling

Find the misspelled words and circle them. Write them correctly on the lines below. (2 points each)

Not long ago, our old dog, Bella, stopped coming when we called her. At first, we (thouht) she just wanted to show us who was boss. After all the training she'd had, though, she (aught) to know better.

Then the vet found Bella's problem: she had lost her hearing. We worried that Bella would have a (tuff) time in a silent world. That sweet girl has (tawght) us a thing or two!

First, we (baught) a book about living with a deaf dog. We read (throogh) it carefully. We learned to talk to Bella with body signals, not our voices. In a few days, using an arm to beckon her (brout) her to us right away. When it was time for a walk, we held up a leash for her to see. That was (ennough) to get her racing to the door!

Today, we (luagh) to think we ever worried about Bella. She (fough) to overcome her problem, and she's an even more amazing dog now.

Spelling Words

1. taught
2. thought
3. rough
4. laugh
5. bought
6. cough
7. ought
8. caught
9. fought
10. daughter
11. tough
12. through
13. enough
14. brought

1. thought   5. bought   8. enough
2. ought   6. through   9. laugh
3. tough   7. brought   10. fought
4. taught

Read directions to students.
Spelling
188

Name _____ Date _____

Commas with Introductory Words

- Use a **comma** after the introductory words *well*, *yes*, and *no*.
- Use a comma after order words such as *first*, *second*, *next*, and *finally*.
- Do not use a comma after *then*.

    Yes, I might want to try climbing one day.

Rewrite these sentences correctly. Add commas where they are needed.

1. First let's have some lunch.

   First, let's have some lunch. (1 point)

2. Yes that is a very good idea.

   Yes, that is a very good idea. (1)

3. No I did not remember to fill the water bottles.

   No, I did not remember to fill the water bottles. (1)

4. Well we will have to look for a water fountain.

   Well, we will have to look for a water fountain. (1)

5. Yes I can show you how to pack away the blanket.

   Yes, I can show you how to pack away the blanket. (1)

6. First fold it neatly and then in half again.

   First, fold it neatly in half and then in half again. (1)

7. Next smooth out any wrinkles.

   Next, smooth out any wrinkles. (1)

8. Finally roll the blanket carefully, starting at one of the short ends.

   Finally, roll the blanket carefully from one of the short ends. (1)

Name _____ Date _____

Commas in Sentences

Read each pair of sentences. Fill in the circle next to the sentence that uses correct punctuation. (2 points each)

1. (A) Climbers can be tall, short, young, or old.
   (B) Climbers can be tall short, young or, old.

2. (A) Yes, climbing is one of my hobbies.
   (B) Yes climbing is one of my hobbies.

3. (A) Well reaching, a goal takes lots of hard work.
   (B) Well, reaching a goal takes lots of hard work.

4. (A) She used paper, markers, and scissors to draw her plan.
   (B) She used paper, markers, and scissors, to draw her plan.

5. (A) First, you have to decide if you are willing to do the work.
   (B) First you have to decide if you are willing to do the work.

Lesson 28
READER'S NOTEBOOK

Becoming Anything
He Wants to Be
Grammar: Connect to Writing

Sentence Fluency:
Combining Words to Form a Series

Choppy Sentences	Combined Nouns to Make a Series
He needs rope for climbing. He also needs gloves for climbing. He needs boots for climbing.	He needs rope, gloves, and boots for climbing.

Choppy Sentences	Combined Predicates to Make a Series
He wrestles. He scuba dives. He rides a bike.	He wrestles, scuba dives, and rides a bike.

Activity: Combine each group of sentences by forming a series of nouns, verbs, or phrases. Write the new sentence on the lines. Add commas where necessary.

1. Erik climbs walls. He climbs mountains. He also climbs hills.
Erik climbs walls, mountains, and hills. (1 point)

2. Jose wants to share his success with his parents. He wants to share it with his friends. He wants to share his success with his neighbors.
Jose wants to share his success with his parents, his friends, and his neighbors. (1)

3. Anika never gave up. She never complained. She never made excuses.
Anika never gave up, complained, or made excuses. (1)

4. Fong practiced in the morning. He practiced at night. He practiced on the weekend. Fong practiced in the morning, at night, and on the weekend. (1)

Assessment Tip: Total 4 points
Grade 3, Unit 6

Lesson 28
READER'S NOTEBOOK

Becoming Anything
He Wants to Be
Grammar: Spiral Review

Writing Abbreviations

• An **abbreviation** is a short way to write a word. Most abbreviations begin with a capital letter and end with a period.

Abbreviations	
Sunday	Sun.
Monday	Mon.
September	Sept.
title for any woman	Ms.
title for married woman	Mrs.
street	St.
avenue	Ave.

1–10 Write each abbreviation correctly.

1. October Oct. (1 point)

2. avenue Ave. (1)

3. Tuesday Tues. (1)

4. doctor Smith Dr. Smith (1)

5. Thursday Thurs. (1)

6. mister Hill Mr. Hill (1)

7. December Dec. (1)

8. April Apr. (1)

9. mister Adams Mr. Adams (1)

10. street St. (1)

Assessment Tip: Total 10 points
Grade 3, Unit 6

Name _____ Date _____

Words Ending in -er or -le

Read the words in the box. Then choose the word that best matches each clue.

Word Bank			
apple	better	farmer	little	member
middle	rattle	struggle	summer	supper

1. a red fruit that is sweet to eat _____ apple (1 point)

2. someone who belongs to a group _____ member (1)

3. a meal you eat late in the day _____ supper (1)

4. not big; small _____ little (1)

5. a person who grows food crops _____ farmer (1)

6. a toy that a baby shakes _____ rattle (1)

7. in between the first and the last _____ middle (1)

8. the opposite of *worse* _____ better (1)

9. the opposite of *winter* _____ summer (1)

10. a fight or something difficult _____ struggle (1)

Read directions to students.
Phonics
195
© Houghton Mifflin Harcourt Publishing Company. All rights reserved.
Assessment Tip: Total 10 points
Grade 3, Unit 6

Name _____ Date _____

Focus Trait: Conventions

Read each step of the instructions for starting a rock collection. Rewrite the step with exact words and details to give more information. Possible responses shown.

1. **Step:** Get a box.

With Exact Words and Details:

Find a large wooden box with several different sections. (1 point)

2. **Step:** Dig up some rocks.

With Exact Words and Details:

Use a small shovel to dig up rocks from your backyard or a

wilderness area. (1)

3. **Step:** Clean the rocks.

With Exact Words and Details:

Wash your rocks in a bucket or use an old toothbrush to scrub

them clean. (1)

4. **Step:** Put them away.

With Exact Words and Details:

Arrange your rock collection inside your box. (1)

5. **Step:** Read about the rocks.

With Exact Words and Details:

Use an encyclopedia or book about rocks to research and

label the rocks you have collected. (1)

Writing
194
© Houghton Mifflin Harcourt Publishing Company. All rights reserved.
Assessment Tip: Total 5 points
Grade 3, Unit 6

Lesson 29
READER'S NOTEBOOK

A New Team of Heroes
Independent Reading

A New Team of Heroes

The Story of the Game

Choose a character to tell about the soccer game in his or her own words. First, review the play to remember important details.

Read pages 48–50. What can we tell about Carla so far?   (2 points)

Carla is a fast runner. She is a leader on the soccer team.

What do we learn about Lauren?

Lauren thinks Carla is the reason the team wins so much.   (2)

How does Hiro feel about Carla?

He wishes he could play like her.   (2)

How does Gayle feel about Carla?

She thinks Carla is a good player, but they are all important to the

team.   (2)

Read pages 51–52. What can we tell about Manny?

Manny has ideas on how to win the game. He thinks he can be as

good a player as Carla.   (2)

Lesson 29
READER'S NOTEBOOK

A New Team of Heroes
Independent Reading

Think about the characters in the play: Carla, Lauren, Hiro, Gayle, and Manny. Imagine that one of the soccer players is writing a narrative about the game from his or her point of view. Use the box below to write the story.

My Story by _____
(Students should include details from the previous page and

other details that show what happened in the soccer game

from a particular character's point of view.)   (10)

Name _____ Date _____

Words Ending with -er or -le

Basic: Write the Basic Word that answers each clue.

1. The goal of someone who is making funny faces at you is to make you do this. ___giggle___ (1 point)

2. If your aunt is married, her husband is this. ___uncle___ (1)

3. Your goal is to make this color when you mix red and blue. ___purple___ (1)

4. An archer's goal is to hit this part of a target. ___center___ (1)

5. A goal you plan to reach tomorrow is one you'll reach at this time. ___later___ (1)

6. Eating one of these a day can help you reach your goal of keeping the doctor away. ___apple___ (1)

7. If a rooftop is your goal, this tool can help you. ___ladder___ (1)

8. Cooking a turkey dinner is the goal of many people in this month. ___November___ (1)

9. People often have a goal of building a snowman during this season. ___winter___ (1)

10. A common goal during this season is to stay cool. ___summer___ (1)

Challenge: Write two sentences telling how someone might reach a goal. Use both Challenge Words. Possible responses shown. (2)

It takes hard work to learn how to whistle. You have to have strong

character to reach your goal.

Read directions to students.
Spelling
© Houghton Mifflin Harcourt Publishing Company. All rights reserved.
198
Assessment Tip: Total 12 points
Grade 3, Unit 6

Spelling Words

Basic
1. apple
2. river
3. little
4. October
5. ladder
6. summer
7. purple
8. later
9. November
10. giggle
11. uncle
12. winter
13. center
14. double

Challenge
whistle
character

Name _____ Date _____

Word Sort

Write each Basic Word next to the correct heading.

Words that name seasons	Basic Words: summer, winter (2 points)
Words that name months of the year	Basic Words: October, November (2)
Words that name objects you can pick up	Basic Words: apple, ladder (2) Challenge Word: whistle (1)
Other words	Basic Words: river, little, purple, later, giggle, uncle, center, double (8) Challenge Word: character (1)

Challenge: Add the Challenge Words to your Word Sort.

Read directions to students.
Spelling
© Houghton Mifflin Harcourt Publishing Company. All rights reserved.
199
Assessment Tip: Total 16 points
Grade 3, Unit 6

Spelling Words

Basic
1. apple
2. river
3. little
4. October
5. ladder
6. summer
7. purple
8. later
9. November
10. giggle
11. uncle
12. winter
13. center
14. double

Challenge
whistle
character

Name _____ Date _____

What Is a Preposition?

Common Prepositions

about	around	beside	for	near	outside	under
above	at	by	from	of	over	until
across	before	down	in	off	past	up
after	behind	during	inside	on	through	with
along	below	except	into	out	to	without

Underline the preposition in each sentence.

1. Some people like to hike the trails around a lake. (1 point)

2. Hiking over the hills is good exercise. (1)

3. In summer, flowers cover the hills. (1)

4. Some people like the mountains in winter. (1)

5. They ski or snowboard down the steep slopes. (1)

6. A high mountain is a challenge for climbers. (1)

7. Reaching the top of a mountain is a climber's goal. (1)

8. Climbers usually hike with a guide. (1)

9. Guides know the safest way to the top. (1)

10. Which mountains in our country do you know about? (1)

Read directions to students.
Grammar
© Houghton Mifflin Harcourt Publishing Company. All rights reserved.
Assessment Tip: Total 10 points
Grade 3, Unit 6
201

Name _____ Date _____

Proofreading for Spelling

Find the misspelled words and circle them. Write them correctly on the lines below. (2 points each)

Spelling Words

1. apple
2. river
3. little
4. October
5. ladder
6. summer
7. purple
8. later
9. November
10. giggle
11. uncle
12. winter
13. center
14. double

Try Out for the Basketball Team

Welcome back to school! We hope your sumer vacation was super.

As you all know, winnter is the season for basketball. This year, tryouts for our team will be held the last Monday in Ocktober. Practices will begin early in Novembar. In January, we'll travel across the rivier to play our first game against the Dunkers.

We urge all interested students, new or old, big or littel, to try out for the basketball team. You won't have to make a basket from the senter of the court. You must, though, be willing to dubble your efforts when it's needed.

So if you'd like to see yourself in our team's purpul uniform, just try out. That way, you won't be sorry laiter that you didn't.

1. summer   5. river   8. double

2. winter   6. little   9. purple

3. October   7. center   10. later

4. November

Read directions to students.
Spelling
© Houghton Mifflin Harcourt Publishing Company. All rights reserved.
Assessment Tip: Total 20 points
Grade 3, Unit 6
200

Lesson 29
READER'S NOTEBOOK

A New Team
of Heroes
Grammar:
What Is a Preposition?

Name _____ Date _____

Prepositional Phrases

1–5. Underline the prepositional phrase in each sentence. (1 point)

1. Those people in the distance are taking a hike. (1 point)

2. I wonder how far they will hike before lunch? (1)

3. We can follow the hikers up the hill. (1)

4. My friend from the city likes hiking, too. (1)

5. Let's hike to that tall pine tree. (1)

6–10. Underline two prepositional phrases in each sentence. Write the prepositional phrase that tells *when*.

6. On Friday, our class took a hike in the woods. (1)

   On Friday (1)

7. I didn't think we were going on the hike until next week. (1)

   until next week (1)

8. We rested beside a creek at noon. (1)

   at noon (1)

9. During our rest, we looked at a distant mountain. (1)

   During our rest (1)

10. By the afternoon, we were all very tired from the long hike. (1)

   By the afternoon (1)

Read directions to students.
Grammar
© Houghton Mifflin Harcourt Publishing Company. All rights reserved.
202
Assessment Tip: Total 15 points
Grade 3, Unit 6

Lesson 29
READER'S NOTEBOOK

A New Team
of Heroes
Grammar:
What Is a Preposition?

Name _____ Date _____

Prepositional Phrases

1–5. Underline the prepositional phrase in each sentence.

1. We use mountains for many things. (1 point)

2. Rock climbers like to climb up mountain cliffs. (1)

3. Miners search the rock for metals. (1)

4. Trees growing on mountains supply logs for houses. (1)

5. Cows and sheep can graze around a mountain's base. (1)

6–10. Underline the prepositional phrases in each sentence. Write the prepositional phrase that tells *where*.

6. The weather on a mountain can change in a few minutes. (1)

   on a mountain (1)

7. It is very cold at the top of a mountain. (1)

   at the top (1)

8. At great heights, there is little oxygen for breathing. (1)

   At great heights (1)

9. Many of the world's highest mountains are in Asia. (1)

   in Asia (1)

10. Very few people live on these high mountains. (1)

   on these high mountains (1)

Read directions to students.
Grammar
© Houghton Mifflin Harcourt Publishing Company. All rights reserved.
203
Assessment Tip: Total 15 points
Grade 3, Unit 6

Kinds of Adverbs

Lesson 29
READER'S NOTEBOOK

A New Team of Heroes
Grammar: Spiral Review

- An **adverb** is a word that describes a verb.
- **Adverbs** can come before or after the verb they are describing.
- Adverbs tell *how, when,* and *where* an action happens.

Adverb That Tells How	Adverb That Tells When	Adverb That Tells Where
Manny **quickly** passed the ball.	We have to practice **often**.	We practice **here** at the park.

1–4. Write the adverb and what it tells about each underlined verb.

1. Gayle <u>cheered</u> loudly for Manny. loudly; tells how (1 point)

2. They <u>ran</u> away from the fire. away; tells where (1)

3. The game always <u>begins</u> at 4:00. always; tells when (1)

4. Our team <u>shook</u> hands happily with the other team. happily; tells how (1)

5–8. Rewrite the sentences below into one sentence.

5. The team played another game. They played the game later.
The team played another game later; or Later, the team... (1)

6. The goalie blocked the ball. He did it easily.
The goalie easily blocked the ball. (1)

7. We stop for water breaks. We stop often.
We stop often for water breaks. (1)

8. Manny scores a goal. He always scores a goal.
Manny always scores a goal. (1)

Assessment Tip: Total 8 points
Grade 3, Unit 6

Sentence Fluency

Lesson 29
READER'S NOTEBOOK

A New Team of Heroes
Grammar:
Connect to Writing

Short, choppy sentences can be combined to make your writing smoother. You can combine two sentences by **moving a prepositional phrase.**

Two Sentences	Combined Sentence
We watched the film about mountains. We watched the film on Tuesday.	We watched the film about mountains on Tuesday.

Combine two short choppy sentences by moving a prepositional phrase to combine two sentences. Write the new sentence on the line.

1. The map is on the wall.
The map is behind Mrs. Brown's desk.
The map is on the wall behind Mrs. Brown's desk. (2 points)

2. We can see the mountains in Asia.
We can see the mountains on the map.
We can see the mountains in Asia on the map. (2)

3. Please show me the mountains of Africa.
Please show me the mountains on the map.
Please show me the mountains of Africa on the map. (2)

4. We will learn more about mountains.
We will learn more after lunch.
We will learn more about mountains after lunch. (2)

5. Have you ever hiked in the mountains?
Have you ever hiked in our state?
Have you ever hiked in the mountains in our state? (2)

Assessment Tip: Total 10 points
Grade 3, Unit 6

Name _____ Date _____

Sort the Words

Read each word in the box. Find the vowel that makes the schwa sound. Then write the word in the chart under the spelling of the schwa sound.

Word Bank			
about	actor	alive	cactus	circus
engine	kennel	pencil	pilot	salad	wagon

schwa spelled *a*	schwa spelled *e*	schwa spelled *i*
about (1 point)	camel (1)	engine (1)
alive (1)	kennel (1)	pencil (1)
salad (1)		

schwa spelled *o*	schwa spelled *u*
actor (1)	cactus (1)
pilot (1)	circus (1)
wagon (1)	

Read directions to students.
Phonics
© Houghton Mifflin Harcourt Publishing Company. All rights reserved.

Assessment Tip: Total 12 points
Grade 3, Unit 6

Name _____ Date _____

Focus Trait: Evidence

Read each pair of sentences. Underline the fact. Draw a line through the opinion. Then write a fact to replace the opinion. Possible responses shown.

1. In football, a touchdown scores 6 points. ~~It is easy to score points.~~

   Fact: The team with the most points wins. (3 points)

2. ~~Golf is the hardest sport.~~ Golfers use clubs to hit the ball.

   Fact: Golf is played outside. (3)

3. ~~Swimmers should wear red suits.~~ Many swimmers begin at a young age.

   Fact: Some swimmers do the backstroke. (3)

4. A baseball catcher wears a mask. ~~Everyone should have a turn to catch.~~

   Fact: A baseball is round. (3)

5. ~~All schools should have sports teams.~~ Many children play sports.

   Fact: Some children play T-ball. (3)

Read directions to students.
Writing
© Houghton Mifflin Harcourt Publishing Company. All rights reserved.

Assessment Tip: Total 15 points
Grade 3, Unit 6

Name _____ Date _____

Reader's Guide

Saving Buster

Pet Reporter

You are a reporter. You are going to write a newspaper article about Buster's accident and how the neighbors helped. Newspaper reporters ask questions to find facts for their stories. Use the questions below to find facts. Then write the newspaper article.

Read pages 66–67. What happened to Buster?
He got hit by a truck and broke two legs. (2 points)

Read page 68. What is the problem that Donovan wants to help solve? (2)
There is not enough money to pay Buster's vet bill. (2)

Read pages 70–71. What was Donovan's idea for solving the problem?
He wanted to have a potluck cooking contest to raise money. (2)

Read pages 72–73. Did Donovan's solution raise the $2,000 needed to pay for Buster's care?
The cooking contest raised over $1,000, and local businesses paid the rest of the vet bill. (2)

Read directions to students.
Independent Reading
208
Assessment Tip: 8 Points
Grade 3, Unit 6

Name _____ Date _____

Now you know the facts about Buster's accident and how the neighborhood helped solve the problem. It is time to write your article for the local paper. Remember to include a headline or title for your story and an illustration.

NEWS

(Accept all articles that tell the

main problem and the solution:

Buster got hurt and his owners

could not pay for surgery;

Donovan organized a cooking

contest to cover the costs.)   (10)

Read directions to students.
Independent Reading
209
Assessment Tip: 10 Points
Grade 3, Unit 6

Saving Buster
Spelling: Words that Begin with *a* or *be*

Spelling Words

Basic
1. below
2. about
3. belong
4. around
5. again
6. alone
7. because
8. above
9. between
10. alive
11. behind
12. begin
13. along
14. before

Challenge
awhile
beyond

Name _____ Date _____

Words that Begin with *a* or *be*

Basic: Write the Basic Word that completes each sentence.

1. I was walking __along (1 point)__ my street when I spotted a kitten.

2. When it ran __between (1)__ my legs, I fell over!

3. Dad guessed the kitten is __about (1)__ two months old.

4. Dad said I could bring the kitten inside __because (1)__ it was cold out.

5. Then the kitten hid in a dark place __behind (1)__ the couch.

6. __Before (1)__ I could get it out, I had to move furniture.

7. The kitten jumped up on a shelf __above (1)__ the fireplace.

8. It followed a toy __around (1)__ in a circle.

9. The kitten made me laugh over and over __again (1)__

10. Dad and I agree that the kitten and I __belong (1)__ together.

Challenge 11–12: Write two sentences about animals. Use both Challenge Words. Possible response shown. (2)

Let's sit awhile and watch the ducks.

The grazing sheep disappeared beyond the trees.

Read directions to students.
Spelling
210

Assessment Tip: Total 12 points
Grade 3, Unit 6

Saving Buster
Spelling: Words that begin with *a* or *be*

Spelling Words

Basic
1. below
2. about
3. belong
4. around
5. again
6. alone
7. because
8. above
9. between
10. alive
11. behind
12. begin
13. along
14. before

Challenge
awhile
beyond

Name _____ Date _____

Word Sort

Write each Basic Word next to the correct heading.

Second syllable has three letters	Basic Words: below, begin (2 points)
Second syllable has four letters	Basic Words: about, belong, again, alone, above, alive, behind, along, before (9) Challenge Word: beyond (1)
Second syllable has five letters	Basic Words: around, because, between (3) Challenge Word: awhile (1)

Challenge: Add the Challenge Words to your Word Sort.

Read directions to students.
Spelling
211

Assessment Tip: Total 16 points
Grade 3, Unit 6

Reader's Notebook

Name _____ Date _____

Using *I* and *Me*

Thinking Question
Is the pronoun the subject or the object of the sentence?

- Use the pronoun *I* only as the subject of a sentence. Always capitalize the word *I*.

    I am going to school.

- Use the pronoun *me* only as an object pronoun. When you talk about another person and yourself, it is polite to list yourself last.

    Julie handed the books to Lucy and **me**.

Activity: Write the pronoun *I* or *me* to complete each sentence.

1. I (1 point) _____ watched my dog chase the ball.

2. Dad and I (1) _____ entered a dish in the potluck contest.

3. Amy went to the vet with my dog Sparky and me (1) _____ .

4. My service dog helps me (1) _____ cross the street.

5. Can I (1) _____ help you plan the contest?

6. I (1) _____ liked the pasta salad the best.

7. The judge couldn't decide, so she gave the first prize to both Andy and me (1) _____ .

8. I (1) _____ own a black dog named Ruby.

9. Ruby has been with my sister and me (1) _____ since I was five years old.

10. Someday I (1) _____ would like to train puppies to be service dogs.

Read directions to students.
Grammar
© Houghton Mifflin Harcourt Publishing Company. All rights reserved.

Assessment Tip: Total 10 points
Grade 3, Unit 6

213

Name _____ Date _____

Proofreading for Spelling

Find the misspelled words and circle them. Write them correctly on the lines below. (2 points each)

Spelling Words

1. below
2. about
3. belong
4. around
5. again
6. alone
7. because
8. above
9. between
10. alive
11. behind
12. begin
13. along
14. before

Monday, July 9

This past weekend, our family took part in a barn raising. I'd never heard (abowt) these events (befoar) In a barn raising, a lot of people who (bilong) to a community get together to build a barn. No community member has to face the huge job of building a barn (aloan)

At first, I just walked (around) the barnyard. I didn't know where to (bigin) to help. Soon, a man called from a beam (abuve) me. "Son, could you please bring me some nails?" he asked. I leaped into action (becuze) I wanted to be part of the group. I set up a ladder (balow) the man and handed him the nails.

After that I worked hard all weekend, and that barn is done. It's a beauty! I would sure love to be part of a barn raising (agenn)

1. about
2. before
3. belong
4. alone
5. around
6. begin
7. above
8. because
9. below
10. again

Read directions to students.
Spelling
© Houghton Mifflin Harcourt Publishing Company. All rights reserved.

Assessment Tip: Total 20 points
Grade 3, Unit 6

212

Pronouns and Homophones

Homophones are words that sound alike but have different spellings and different meanings. Be sure to choose the correct homophone. Using the wrong homophone changes the meaning of the sentence.

> **Thinking Question**
> What are the clues in the sentence?

Homophone	Meaning	Example
its	belonging to it	The dog wagged **its** tail.
it's	it is	**It's** very cold outside.
your	belonging to you	I like **your** watch.
you're	you are	**You're** going to be late!
there	at or in that place	The book is over **there**.
their	belonging to them	**Their** dog can do tricks.
they're	they are	**They're** going to the store.

Activity: Read the sentences. Circle the correct homophones. (1 point each)

1. Dog training can be a fun activity for both you and (your / **you're**) dog.

2. **Its** (**It's**) important to work with your dog every day.

3. Dogs perform best when **their** (**they're**) praised for good behavior.

4. If **your** (**you're**) patient with your dog, you can teach him or her to roll over.

5. (**It's**) **Its** important to train a puppy.

6. You can buy a leash at a pet supply store. Ask a clerk to help you when you get (**there**) **they're**.

7. The best time to train **your** (**you're**) dog is when he or she is young.

8. Dogs can still be trained when **there** (**they're**) older, too.

Correct Pronouns

Read each pair of sentences. Fill in the circle next to the sentence that uses the correct pronoun. (2 points each)

1. Ⓐ Mom and I will make dinner.
   Ⓑ Mom and me will make dinner.

2. Ⓐ The dog brought the ball to Marisa and I.
   ⬤ The dog brought the ball to Marisa and me.

3. Ⓐ They're dog was trained to be a service dog.
   ⬤ Their dog was trained to be a service dog.

4. ⬤ It's fun to teach a dog to do tricks.
   Ⓑ Its fun to teach a dog to do tricks.

5. Ⓐ I saw your mom at the store.
   Ⓑ I saw you're mom at the store.

Making Comparisons

- **Adjectives** describe nouns. They can also show how people, places, and things are alike and different.

Comparing with Adjectives

compare two	add -*er*	taller
compare three or more	add -*est*	tallest

- **Adverbs** describe verbs. For adverbs that end in -*ly*, add *more* to compare two actions. Add *most* to compare three or more actions.

1–4. Write the correct form of the adjective in parentheses to complete each sentence.

1. Molly was the __smallest (1 point)__ of all the service dogs. (small)

2. The Smiths were __friendlier (1)__ than our other neighbors were. (friendly)

3. Of all of her classmates, Liz's voice is the __strongest (1)__ (strong)

4. Doug was the __youngest (1)__ member of the class. (young)

5–6. Rewrite the sentences, combining each pair of sentences.

5. Ralph is smarter than the cat. He is quicker too. __Ralph is smarter and quicker than the cat. (1)__

6. Of all the dogs in the park, Benny has the biggest feet. He also has the longest tail. __Of all the dogs in the park, Benny has the biggest feet and the longest tail. (1)__

Assessment Tip: Total 6 points
Grammar
216
Grade 3, Unit 6

Conventions

Sentence with incorrect use of *I* and *me*	Corrected sentence
Me and my mom did everything we could to help out.	My mom and I did everything we could to help out.

Sentence with incorrect homophone	Corrected sentence
Their cooking wonderful food for the dinner tonight.	They're cooking wonderful food for the dinner tonight.

Proofread each sentence. Check for the correct use of the pronouns *I* and *me* and the correct use of homophones. Write the corrected sentence on the line.

1. David and me think the cooking contest will be fun. (1 point)
   David and I think the cooking contest will be fun. (1 point)

2. They gave they're food to me and my mom.
   They gave their food to my mom and me. (1)

3. The dog left the bone over their.
   The dog left the bone over there. (1)

4. Its amazing how much money was raised.
   It's amazing how much money was raised. (1)

5. Me and my friends think it's important to help you're neighbors.
   My friends and I think it's important to help your neighbors. (1)

6. Its good when people help each other.
   It's good when people help each other. (1)

7. You can help them by watching there dog.
   You can help them by watching their dog. (1)

8. They're dog loves to play.
   Their dog loves to play. (1)

Grammar
217
Assessment Tip: Total 8 points
Grade 3, Unit 6

Focus Trait: Organization

Read each paragraph. Cross out the detail that does not tell about the main idea.
Then add a fact or a detail sentence that supports the main idea.
Possible responses shown.

1. Other animals pull vehicles. Oxen pulled pioneers' wagons in the 1800s. Locomotive trains can pull many cars. Some kinds of horses pull sleighs and carriages.
   Husky dogs pull dogsleds. (1 point)
   _____

2. Several types of animals carry people. For hundreds of years, people have ridden horses. Donkeys can carry people through rough terrain. Lots of kids ride bicycles to school. Some people also ride camels.
   Elephants give people rides at special events. (1)
   _____

3. In a beehive, different bees have different jobs. The queen lays eggs. Worker bees do a few jobs. They help make wax. They also feed other bees and help protect the hive. Some people are allergic to bees.
   Some worker bees hunt for nectar. (1)
   _____

4. Dogs do different kinds of work. Chihuahuas are a tiny kind of dog. There are herding dogs and police dogs. Some dogs are even actors!
   Service dogs help people who cannot see. (1)
   _____

Reading and Writing Glossary

Use this glossary to help you remember and use words that you are learning about reading and writing.

A

abstract noun A noun that names an idea, a feeling, or a quality. Abstract nouns are things that people cannot see, hear, taste, smell, or touch.

action verb A verb that tells what people or things do.

adjective A word that describes a noun. Adjectives may also be used to compare nouns.

adverb A word that describes a verb, adjective, or other adverb. Adverbs may tell how, when, or where an action takes place.

analogy A kind of comparison in which one pair of words is compared to another. Each pair relates by definition, meaning, or characteristics.

analyze To look at or study carefully.

antecedent The noun that a pronoun replaces.

antonym A word that has the opposite, or nearly the opposite, meaning than another word.

article A word, such as *a*, *an*, or *the*, that comes before a noun. Articles tell which noun.

author's purpose The reason an author has for writing.

B

base word A word to which endings, prefixes, and suffixes can be added.

biography A story about the events in a person's life told in time order.

C

caption Text that explains a photo or picture.

cause An event that makes something else happen.

character A person in a story.

chart A drawing that lists information in a way that makes it clear and easy to understand.

clarify To make clear.

comma Punctuation mark that tells a reader where to pause. A comma can also help to make a sentence's meaning more clear.

command A type of sentence that gives an order. A command may end with a period (.) or an exclamation mark (!).

common noun A noun that names any person, place, or thing.

compare To decide how people and things are alike.

complex sentence A sentence with two parts, a simple sentence and a dependent clause.

compound sentence A sentence made up of two simple sentences joined by a conjunction.

conclusion A good guess about something the author does not say directly.

conjunction Joining words such as *and, or, but,* and *so.* Conjunctions appear after a comma in a compound sentence.

context Sentences or details that help explain a particular word or phrase.

contrast To decide how people and things are different.

D

dependent clause A group of words that does not express a complete thought. A dependent clause may be found in a complex sentence.

detail Facts and examples that give more information about the main idea.

diagram An illustration that shows important details, such as how something works. A diagram may have labels or captions to tell what its parts show.

dictionary A reference book that contains an alphabetical list of words along with their meanings, pronunciations, parts of speech, and other information.

dictionary entry A word and its definition listed in a dictionary or glossary.

digital dictionary A reference source available online or on portable disks that provides meanings for words.

directions Text that tells how to do something step by step.

domain The subject a text is about.

domain-specific vocabulary Words related to a specific topic, such as science.

drama A story written to be acted out.

E

effect An event that happens because of an earlier action.

evaluate To form an opinion about something.

exclamation A sentence that shows a strong feeling and ends with an exclamation point (!).

expository nonfiction Text that gives facts about what something is, how something works, or why something is important.

F

fable A short story in which a character, usually an animal that behaves like a person, learns a lesson.

fact Something that can be proved true.

fairy tale A kind of traditional tale with magical characters and events.

fantasy An imaginative story with characters or events that are not real.

feelings A person's emotions about something or someone.

folktale A story that has been told for many years. A folktale often has a moral, or lesson.

formal language A serious and polite form of speaking or writing.

future tense Verb form which describes a future action.

G

glossary A text feature found at the end of a book that provides an alphabetical listing of specialized words, their meanings, and other information.

graphic features Artwork, such as pictures, diagrams, and charts, that gives readers more information about the text.

H

heading Tells the reader what a section of text is about.

historical fiction A story that is set in the past and tells about things that could happen in a real time and place.

homograph A word that has the same spelling as another word but has a different meaning and may be pronounced differently.

homophone A word that sounds the same as another word but is spelled differently and has a different meaning.

humorous fiction Story that has characters and events that are funny. The setting and characters may be unrealistic.

I

idiom An expression with a special meaning different from the usual meanings of the individual words.

illustration Artwork that helps show a story's events.

imagery The use of vivid descriptions that help readers form an image, or picture, in their minds.

informal language A more relaxed form of speaking or writing.

informational text Text that gives factual information about a topic.

informative writing Writing that gives facts about a topic.

L

legend An old story that people have told for many years. The events of the story may or may not be true.

literal meaning The exact meaning of a word or phrase.

M

main idea The most important idea in a text.

map A drawing of an area, such as a neighborhood, town, or state.

message A story's lesson or moral.

monitor To check one's understanding.

mood The overall feeling of a story.

moral A lesson that is usually taught through something that happens to a main character or through what the character learns.

motivation The reason a character acts a certain way.

myth A story that tells what a group of people believe about the world.

N

narrative nonfiction A selection that gives information about a topic but is told as a story.

narrative writing Writing that tells a story. A narrative tells about something that happened to a person or a character.

nonliteral meaning The symbolic or figurative meaning of a word.

noun Names a person, a place, or a thing.

O

object pronoun A word that takes the place of the object: *me, you, him, her, it, us, them.* An object pronoun follows action verbs and words such as *to, for, at, of,* and *with.*

opinion Something that tells someone's thought, feeling, or belief.

opinion writing Writing that tells what the writer believes and gives reasons.

P

part of speech The way a word is used in a sentence, for example, noun, verb, or adjective.

past tense Verb form which describes a past action.

photograph Shows true pictures of important text details.

play A story that can be performed for an audience.

plot The problem that characters face and the events of the story.

plural noun A noun that names more than one person, place, or thing.

poetry Uses the sound and rhythm of words to show images and express feelings.

point of view How one thinks or feels about a subject.

possessive noun Shows that a person or animal owns or has something.

possessive pronoun Takes the place of a possessive noun to show who or what owns or has something.

precise words Words that are descriptive and exact.

predicate The action part of the sentence that tells what the subject does or did.

prefix A word part added to the beginning of a base word. A prefix changes the meaning of the base word but cannot stand alone.

present tense Verb form which describes action that happens in the present.

pronoun A word that takes the place of one or more nouns in a sentence.

proper noun A noun that names a particular person, place, or thing. A proper noun begins with a capital letter.

Q

question A type of sentence that asks something and ends with a question mark (?).

question To ask yourself questions about a selection before, during, and after reading.

quotation marks Punctuation marks (" ") that indicate dialogue. Quotation marks show the exact words a person says.

R

realistic fiction Story that has characters and events that are like those in real life.

research report Writing that tells what a writer learned from doing research about a topic.

rhyme When words end with the same sound. Rhyme is often found in poems.

run-on An error in which a writer joins two simple sentences without using a comma or a conjunction.

S

scene A section division of a play, similar to chapters in a book.

sequence The order in which different steps or events happen.

series When you list three or more words together in a sentence. Commas separate the words in a series.

series books Books that tell different stories about the same character.

setting Where and when a story takes place.

shades of meaning Slight differences in meaning among words that are related, especially words that describe degrees of certainty.

signal word A word that indicates a cause and its effect.

simple sentence A group of words that tells a complete thought. A simple sentence has a subject and a predicate.

singular noun A noun that names only one person, place, or thing.

stage directions Instructions to actors on how to move and speak.

stanza A group of lines in a poem. Stanzas often follow a rhyming pattern.

statement A type of sentence that tells something and ends with a period (.).

steps in a procedure Directions that are written in sequence.

story structure The characters, setting, and plot of a story.

subject The naming part of a sentence that tells *who* or *what*.

subject pronoun A word that takes the place of a subject: *I, you, he, she, it, we, they*.

subordinating conjunction Joins a dependent clause to the main part of a sentence. Some subordinating conjunctions are *because, after, when,* and *if*.

suffix A word part that is added to the end of a base word. A suffix changes the meaning of the base word but cannot stand alone.

summarize To briefly tell the important parts of a text in your own words.

synonym A word that has the same, or nearly the same, meaning as another word.

T

text and graphic features Sidebars, diagrams, and photographs outside of the main body of the text.

text features Parts of text, such as special type, speech balloons, and labels, that help readers find information.

Grade 3

G8

Reading and Writing Glossary
© Houghton Mifflin Harcourt Publishing Company. All rights reserved.

Grade 3

G9

Reading and Writing Glossary
© Houghton Mifflin Harcourt Publishing Company. All rights reserved.

Reader's Notebook
© Houghton Mifflin Harcourt Publishing Company. All rights reserved.

229

Volume 2, p. G8–G9

theme An author's message about life to the reader.

thesaurus A book that provides a list of words, arranged in alphabetical order, and their synonyms.

timeline A line that shows the order in which events happened.

traditional tale A story that people have told for many years.

traits A person's qualities.

trickster tale An imaginative story in which one character tricks another.

V

verb The main word in the predicate.

visualize To create a mental picture.

W

word ending A word part, such as *-s, -ed,* or *-er,* added to the end of a base word.

word family A group of words with a common pattern, such as the same base word.

word root A word part from which other words are formed.